COMPLEX VARIABLES
AND
APPLICATIONS

COMPLEX VARIABLES
AND
APPLICATIONS

RUEL V. CHURCHILL

Professor of Mathematics
University of Michigan

SECOND EDITION

McGRAW-HILL BOOK COMPANY

New York   Toronto   London

1960

COMPLEX VARIABLES AND APPLICATIONS

Copyright © 1960 by McGraw-Hill, Inc.

11 12 13 14 – MP –9 8

10853

PREFACE

Theory of functions of a complex variable is a basic part of mathematical analysis. Its influence can be seen in almost every field of mathematics. In addition to its prominence in pure mathematics and its elegant logical structure, the theory represents one of the most powerful mathematical instruments of applied mathematicians, engineers, and physicists.

The first objective of this book is the presentation of a logical development of those parts of the classical theory which are most prominent in the applications of the subject. Except for some geometrical concepts that may be accepted intuitively, the presentation here is intended to be rigorous and self-contained. The selection of the methods of proof and the arrangement of topics were made on the basis of simplicity and brevity, sometimes at some sacrifice of elegance. If the theory of residues and conformal mapping are to be emphasized in a one-semester course, the time that can be devoted to the earlier theory is limited and the development of that part must be fairly concise.

The second objective is to give an introduction to applications, including the uses of the residue theory and contour integrals in evaluating real integrals, and applications of conformal mapping to problems in potentials, steady temperatures, and flow of fluids. The applications of conformal mapping present one of the classical methods of solving boundary value problems in partial differential equations, restricted to Laplace's equation with two independent variables. Thus the book serves as a companion volume to the author's books "Fourier Series and Boundary Value Problems" and "Operational Mathematics," where other classical methods of solving linear boundary value problems are treated. In the second book further applications of complex variables are presented in connection with Laplace transforms.

Most of the basic results are stated as theorems. Many examples and simple exercises are given to illustrate the theory and the applications. A table of conformal transformations is presented in Appendix 2.

The first nine chapters, with various substitutions from the rest of the book, have long served as the content of a three-hour course given each semester at the University of Michigan. The classes consist chiefly of graduate students and seniors majoring in engineering, mathematics, or physics. The students have first completed the equivalent of one semester of advanced calculus. Some of the material is not covered in the lectures because students are able to follow it without assistance from the instructor. As noted at the beginning of Chapter 5, Chapters 8 and 9 on conformal mapping and its applications can be introduced immediately after Chapter 4, in case that material is needed early in the semester.

The book is an extensive revision of the first edition, published in 1948. Most of the material has been rewritten with greater attention to sound logical procedures and clarity. Chapter 11, on integral formulas of the Poisson type, is entirely new. It is the first collection of such formulas, as far as the author knows. The number of exercises has been increased considerably, and answers are provided for most of them. More extensions of theory appear in the exercises.

In the course of developing the book through this edition the author has taken advantage of suggestions from many students and colleagues. Among his local colleagues, Prof. C. L. Dolph, B. Dushnik, T. H. Hildebrandt, W. Kaplan, and E. D. Rainville deserve special thanks. For helpful comments from colleagues elsewhere, including J. R. Britton, W. B. Curry, R. J. Duffin, W. L. Duren, T. J. Higgins, I. Marx, M. E. Shanks, and F. H. Steen, the author expresses his appreciation. The selection of some of the material or methods of proof was influenced by several of the books whose titles are included in Appendix 1.

Ruel V. Churchill

CONTENTS

COMPLEX VARIABLES
AND
APPLICATIONS

CHAPTER 1

COMPLEX NUMBERS

1. Definition. A complex number z can be defined as an ordered pair (x,y) of real numbers x and y,

$$(1) \qquad z = (x,y),$$

subject to rules and laws of operation to be specified below.

The pair $(x,0)$ is to be identified with the real number x:

$$(2) \qquad (x,0) = x.$$

This rule establishes the real numbers as a subset of the complex numbers.

It is convenient to have a name and symbol for the pair $(0,1)$. That pair is called the *imaginary unit i*:

$$(0,1) = i.$$

The real numbers x and y are called the *real* and *imaginary components* of (x,y), respectively, written

$$\mathcal{R}(z) = x, \qquad \mathcal{I}(z) = y.$$

A pair of type $(0,y)$ is a *pure imaginary* number.

Another rule to be imposed on such pairs is that two complex numbers are equal if and only if their real components are equal and their imaginary components are equal:

$$(3) \qquad (x_1,y_1) = (x_2,y_2) \qquad \text{if and only if } x_1 = x_2 \text{ and } y_1 = y_2.$$

In particular, since $0 = (0,0)$, then

$$z = (x,y) = 0 \qquad \text{if and only if } x = 0 \text{ and } y = 0.$$

Any two complex numbers $z_1 = (x_1,y_1)$ and $z_2 = (x_2,y_2)$ have a sum and a product, written $z_1 + z_2$ and $z_1 z_2$, defined as the complex numbers given by the equations

(4) $z_1 + z_2 = (x_1,y_1) + (x_2,y_2) = (x_1 + x_2, y_1 + y_2),$
(5) $z_1z_2 = (x_1,y_1)(x_2,y_2) = (x_1x_2 - y_1y_2, x_1y_2 + x_2y_1).$

In particular, then, $(x,0) + (0,y) = (x,y)$ and $(0,y) = (y,0)(0,1).$ Thus each complex number that is not itself real can be written as the sum of a real number and a pure imaginary number:

(6) $$z = (x,y) = x + yi.$$

The product zz is written z^2; z^3 means zz^2, etc. According to definition (5), $(0,1)^2 = (-1,0)$; that is,

$$i^2 = -1.$$

In view of equation (6), formula (5) can be written

$$(x_1 + y_1i)(x_2 + y_2i) = x_1x_2 - y_1y_2 + (x_1y_2 + x_2y_1)i.$$

The formal expansion of the product on the left, carried out as if the binomials were real, and the replacement of i^2 by -1, leads to this same result. Definition (5) justifies that formal procedure.

Ordered pairs (1) of real numbers that satisfy conditions (2) to (5) are *defined* as complex numbers.

2. Further Properties. Several other operations on complex numbers are to be defined. The operation of subtraction is the inverse of addition; that is, if the difference $z_1 - z_2$ is called z_3,

$$z_1 - z_2 = z_3,$$

then z_3 is the complex number that must be added to z_2 to produce z_1:

$$z_2 + z_3 = z_1 \qquad \text{or} \qquad (x_2,y_2) + (x_3,y_3) = (x_1,y_1).$$

In view of definition (4), Sec. 1, of addition, then

$$(x_2 + x_3, y_2 + y_3) = (x_1,y_1)$$

and, by identifying corresponding components here, we see that

$$x_2 + x_3 = x_1, \qquad y_2 + y_3 = y_1.$$

Solving for x_3 and y_3, we arrive at the law of subtraction:

(1) $z_1 - z_2 = (x_1 - x_2, y_1 - y_2) = x_1 - x_2 + (y_1 - y_2)i.$

Division is the inverse of multiplication; that is,

$$\frac{z_1}{z_2} = z_3 \quad \text{if } z_2 z_3 = z_1 \qquad (z_2 \neq 0),$$

or $(x_2 x_3 - y_2 y_3,\ x_2 y_3 + x_3 y_2) = (x_1, y_1).$

Here we can equate corresponding components and solve the resulting simultaneous equations for x_3 and y_3 to obtain the law of division:

$$(2) \qquad \frac{z_1}{z_2} = \frac{x_1 x_2 + y_1 y_2}{x_2{}^2 + y_2{}^2} + \frac{x_2 y_1 - x_1 y_2}{x_2{}^2 + y_2{}^2} i \qquad (z_2 \neq 0).$$

It is useful to note that this same formula arises in a purely manipulative manner when the numerator and denominator on the left are both multiplied by $x_2 - y_2 i$.

Division by zero is not defined.

From the formulas for the quotient and product it is easily shown that

$$(3) \qquad \frac{z_1}{z_2} = z_1 \left(\frac{1}{z_2}\right), \qquad \frac{1}{z_2 z_3} = \left(\frac{1}{z_2}\right)\left(\frac{1}{z_3}\right) \qquad (z_2 \neq 0,\ z_3 \neq 0).$$

The fundamental operations are illustrated in this example:

$$\frac{(-1 + 3i)(1 + 2i)}{2 - i} + 2i = \frac{-7 + i}{2 - i} + 2i = -\frac{15}{5} - \frac{5}{5} i + 2i$$
$$= -3 + i.$$

The commutative laws for addition and multiplication,

$$(4) \qquad z_1 + z_2 = z_2 + z_1, \qquad z_1 z_2 = z_2 z_1,$$

follow from the definition of complex numbers and from the fact that real numbers satisfy those laws. For example,

$$z_1 + z_2 = x_1 + x_2 + (y_1 + y_2)i = x_2 + x_1 + (y_2 + y_1)i$$
$$= z_2 + z_1.$$

The proof of the second of commutative laws (4) is left as an exercise. According to that law $yi = iy$, and henceforth we can write either

$$z = x + yi \qquad \text{or} \qquad z = x + iy.$$

The associative laws for addition and multiplication,

$$(5) \qquad z_1 + (z_2 + z_3) = (z_1 + z_2) + z_3,$$
$$(6) \qquad z_1(z_2 z_3) = (z_1 z_2) z_3,$$

and the distributive law of multiplication with respect to addition,

$$(7) \qquad z_1(z_2 + z_3) = z_1 z_2 + z_1 z_3,$$

are satisfied by complex numbers. Proofs that these laws follow from the definition and from corresponding laws for real numbers, as well as derivations of consequences of laws (4) to (7), are left to the exercises. Among the consequences we find, with the aid of formulas (3), that

$$(8) \qquad \frac{z_1 + z_2}{z_3} = \frac{z_1}{z_3} + \frac{z_2}{z_3}, \qquad \frac{z_1 z_2}{z_3 z_4} = \left(\frac{z_1}{z_3}\right)\left(\frac{z_2}{z_4}\right)$$
$$(z_3 \neq 0,\ z_4 \neq 0).$$

Note that the distributive law (7) is also a law for factoring.

Another property that follows from our definition is to be noted here. If the product of two complex numbers vanishes, then at least one of the factors must vanish; that is,

$$(9) \qquad z_1 z_2 = 0 \text{ implies } z_1 = 0 \text{ or } z_2 = 0.$$

From the definition of the product, it follows that, if $z_1 z_2 = 0$, then

$$(10) \qquad x_2 x_1 - y_2 y_1 = 0 \qquad \text{and} \qquad y_2 x_1 + x_2 y_1 = 0.$$

If x_1 and y_1 are not both zero, then the determinant of their coefficients in the homogeneous simultaneous equations (10) must vanish; that is,

$$x_2{}^2 + y_2{}^2 = 0,$$

and therefore $x_2 = y_2 = 0$. Hence either $z_1 = 0$ or $z_2 = 0$, or both.

3. Geometric Representation. It is natural to associate the ordered pair (x,y) that represents the complex number z with the rectangular cartesian coordinates of a point in the xy plane. Each complex number corresponds to just one point, and conversely. The number $-2 + i$, for instance, is represented by the point

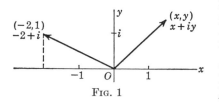

FIG. 1

$(-2,1)$ (Fig. 1). The origin represents the point $z = 0$. When used for the purpose of displaying complex numbers z geometrically, the xy plane is called the *complex plane* or the z plane.

Again, the number z can be thought of as the directed line segment, or vector, from the origin to the point (x,y); also as any vector obtained by translating that vector in the plane. Thus the vector from the point $(2,1)$ to the point $(3,3)$, which has an x component of 1 and a y component of 2, represents the number $1 + 2i$.   Both the vector representation and the point representation of complex numbers are very useful.

Hereafter we shall often refer to the complex number z as the point z or as the vector z.   Note, however, that the product z_1z_2

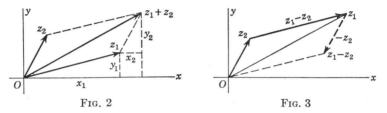

FIG. 2   FIG. 3

of two complex numbers is a complex number, a vector in the plane of the vectors z_1 and z_2.   Therefore this product is neither the scalar product nor the vector product used in vector analysis. Consequently our complex numbers z cannot be identified with the vectors of two-dimensional vector analysis.   The vectors in vector analysis, as well as matrices, are complex numbers of types other than those defined here; their algebras are different from the algebra for the numbers z.

According to the definition of the sum of two complex numbers, $z_1 + z_2$ corresponds to the point $(x_1 + x_2,\ y_1 + y_2)$.   It also corresponds to a vector with those coordinates as its components. Hence $z_1 + z_2$ is represented by the vector sum of the vectors z_1 and z_2, as shown in Fig. 2.

The difference $z_1 - z_2$ is represented by a vector from the point z_2 to the point z_1 (Fig. 3).

EXERCISES

1. Verify:

(a) $(\sqrt{2} - i) - i(1 - i\sqrt{2}) = -2i$;   (b) $(2,-3)(-2,1) = (-1,8)$;

(c) $(3,1)(3,-1)(\tfrac{1}{5}, \tfrac{1}{10}) = (2,1)$;   (d) $\dfrac{1 + 2i}{3 - 4i} + \dfrac{2 - i}{5i} = -\dfrac{2}{5}$;

(e) $\dfrac{5}{(1 - i)(2 - i)(3 - i)} = \dfrac{1}{2}i$;   (f) $(1 - i)^4 = -4$.

2. Exhibit the numbers z_1, z_2, $z_1 + z_2$, and $z_1 - z_2$ graphically, when

(a) $z_1 = 2i$, $z_2 = \frac{3}{2} - i$;   (b) $z_1 = (-\sqrt{3}, 1)$, $z_2 = (\sqrt{3}, 0)$;
(c) $z_1 = (-3, 1)$, $z_2 = (1, 4)$;   (d) $z_1 = x_1 + y_1 i$, $z_2 = x_1 - y_1 i$.

3. If $z \neq 0$ in parts (a) and (b) below, prove that

(a) $\dfrac{z}{z} = 1$;   (b) $\dfrac{1}{1/z} = z$;   (c) $\mathcal{I}(iz) = \mathcal{R}(z)$.

4. Show that each of the two numbers $z = 1 \pm i$ satisfies the equation $z^2 - 2z + 2 = 0$.

5. Establish formulas (3) of Sec. 2.

6. Prove the commutative law $z_1 z_2 = z_2 z_1$.

7. Prove the associative laws (5) and (6), Sec. 2.

8. Prove the distributive law (7), Sec. 2.

9. If k is a real number and $z = (x, y)$, show that $kz = (kx, ky)$ and hence that $-z = -x - yi$, where $-z$ denotes $(-1)z$.

10. Establish the first of formulas (8), Sec. 2.

11. Prove that $z(z_1 + z_2 + z_3) = zz_1 + zz_2 + zz_3$.

12. Show that the product of three numbers z_1, z_2, and z_3 does not depend on which two factors are multiplied together first, so that the product may be written $z_1 z_2 z_3$.

13. If $z_1 z_2 z_3 = 0$, prove that at least one of the three factors is zero.

14. Prove that $(z_1 z_2)(z_3 z_4) = (z_1 z_3)(z_2 z_4)$.

15. Establish the second of formulas (8), Sec. 2, and show that

$$\frac{zz_1}{zz_2} = \frac{z_1}{z_2} \qquad (z \neq 0,\ z_2 \neq 0).$$

16. Show that the point represented by $\frac{1}{2}(z_1 + z_2)$ is the mid-point of the line segment between points z_1 and z_2.

17. Prove that $(1 + z)^2 = 1 + 2z + z^2$.

18. Use induction to prove the binomial formula

$$(1 + z)^n = 1 + nz + \frac{n(n - 1)}{2!} z^2 + \cdots$$
$$+ \frac{n(n - 1) \cdots (n - k + 1)}{k!} z^k + \cdots + z^n,$$

where n and k are positive integers.

4. Complex Conjugates. The complex conjugate, or simply the conjugate, of a complex number $z = (x, y) = x + yi$ is the number

$$\bar{z} = (x, -y) = x - yi.$$

The point $\bar{z}$ is the reflection of point z in the x axis (Fig. 4).

If $z_1 = (x_1, y_1)$ and $z_2 = (x_2, y_2)$, then

$$\overline{z_1 + z_2} = x_1 + x_2 - (y_1 + y_2)i = (x_1 - y_1 i) + (x_2 - y_2 i);$$

that is, the conjugate of the sum is the sum of the conjugates:

(1) $$\overline{z_1 + z_2} = \bar{z}_1 + \bar{z}_2.$$

The reader can prove in like manner that the operation of taking conjugates is also distributive with respect to subtraction, multiplication, and division; that is,

(2) $$\overline{z_1 - z_2} = \bar{z}_1 - \bar{z}_2,$$

(3) $$\overline{z_1 z_2} = \bar{z}_1 \bar{z}_2,$$

(4) $$\overline{\left(\frac{z_1}{z_2}\right)} = \frac{\bar{z}_1}{\bar{z}_2} \qquad\qquad (z_2 \neq 0).$$

The conjugate of $z_1 - z_2$ is exhibited as a vector in Fig. 4.

Note that the conjugate of $\bar{z}$ is z.

The conjugate of a real number is the number itself. Also, it should be noted that the sum of a complex number and its conjugate is a real number; in fact

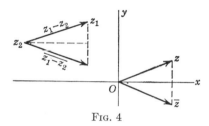

FIG. 4

(5) $$z + \bar{z} = 2x = 2\Re(z).$$

Also, the difference of a complex number and its conjugate is a pure imaginary number, namely,

(6) $$z - \bar{z} = 2yi = 2\Im(z)i.$$

5. Absolute Values. If x and y are real, the nonnegative real number $\sqrt{x^2 + y^2}$ is called the *absolute value* or *modulus* of the complex number $z = x + iy$; that is, by definition,

(1) $$|z| = |x + iy| = \sqrt{x^2 + y^2}.$$

Geometrically, the absolute value of z is the length of the vector z; it is the distance of the point z from the origin. Consequently, $|z_1 - z_2|$ *is the distance between the points z_1 and z_2.* This is also evident from the definition (1), since

(2) $$|z_1 - z_2| = |(x_1 - x_2) + i(y_1 - y_2)|$$
$$= \sqrt{(x_1 - x_2)^2 + (y_1 - y_2)^2}.$$

The condition $|z - i| = 3$, for instance, requires point z to lie on a circle of radius 3 with center at $(0,1)$.

The statement $|z_1| > |z_2|$ means that the point z_1 is farther from the origin than is the point z_2. The elementary notion of linear order, greater than or less than, applies to absolute values because they are real numbers. *Neither the statement $z_1 > z_2$ nor the condition $z_1 < z_2$ has meaning unless z_1 and z_2 are both real.*

Associated with each complex number z are three real numbers already defined, $|z|$, $\Re(z)$, and $\Im(z)$. They are related by the equation

$$|z|^2 = [\Re(z)]^2 + [\Im(z)]^2$$

and the conditions

(3) $|z| \geqq |\Re(z)| \geqq \Re(z),$ $|z| \geqq |\Im(z)| \geqq \Im(z).$

Since $\bar{z} = (x,-y)$ when $z = (x,y)$, it is clear that

(4) $$z\bar{z} = x^2 + y^2 = |z|^2,$$
(5) $$|\bar{z}| = |z|.$$

From the definitions of product, quotient, and absolute value we can show that absolute-value signs are distributive in products and quotients; that is,

(6) $$|z_1 z_2| = |z_1|\,|z_2|,$$
(7) $$\left|\frac{z_1}{z_2}\right| = \frac{|z_1|}{|z_2|} \qquad (z_2 \neq 0).$$

It is simpler, however, to establish those formulas with the aid of formula (4) and properties of conjugates. To prove formula (6), for instance, we can use an extension of the associative law (Exercise 14, Sec. 3) to write

$$|z_1 z_2|^2 = (z_1 z_2)(\overline{z_1 z_2}) = (z_1 z_2)(\bar{z}_1 \bar{z}_2) = (z_1 \bar{z}_1)(z_2 \bar{z}_2);$$
that is, $$|z_1 z_2|^2 - |z_1|^2 |z_2|^2 = 0.$$
Thus $$(|z_1 z_2| - |z_1|\,|z_2|)(|z_1 z_2| + |z_1|\,|z_2|) = 0.$$

If neither z_1 nor z_2 is zero, the second factor in parentheses has a positive value, so that the first factor must vanish, and formula (6) follows. When $z_1 = 0$ or $z_2 = 0$, formula (6) is clearly true.

The two *triangle inequalities*

(8) $$|z_1 + z_2| \leqq |z_1| + |z_2|,$$
(9) $$|z_1 - z_2| \geqq |\,|z_1| - |z_2|\,|$$

are statements that no side of a triangle is greater in length than the sum of the other two sides (Fig. 2), nor less than the difference of the lengths of the other two sides (Fig. 3). In view of inequality (9),

$$|z_1 - z_2| \geqq |z_1| - |z_2|,$$

but this condition is trivial unless $|z_1| > |z_2|$. Also note that, by replacing z_2 by $-z_2$ in conditions (8) and (9), we can write

$$|z_1 - z_2| \leqq |z_1| + |z_2|, \qquad |z_1 + z_2| \geqq | |z_1| - |z_2| |.$$

The triangle inequalities can be proved algebraically. For example, inequality (8) is established by first writing

$$|z_1 + z_2|^2 = (z_1 + z_2)(\bar{z}_1 + \bar{z}_2) = z_1\bar{z}_1 + z_2\bar{z}_2 + (z_1\bar{z}_2 + \bar{z}_1z_2).$$

Now $\bar{z}_1z_2$ is the conjugate of $z_1\bar{z}_2$. Therefore

$$z_1\bar{z}_2 + \bar{z}_1z_2 = 2\Re(z_1\bar{z}_2),$$

and $\quad |z_1 + z_2|^2 - (|z_1| + |z_2|)^2 = -2[|z_1|\,|z_2| - \Re(z_1\bar{z}_2)].$

According to conditions (3) and (5), $\Re(z_1\bar{z}_2) \leqq |z_1\bar{z}_2| = |z_1|\,|z_2|$. Hence

$$|z_1 + z_2|^2 - (|z_1| + |z_2|)^2 \leqq 0,$$

and when the member on the left is factored, condition (8) follows.

According to triangle inequality (8),

$$|z_1 + z_2 + z_3| \leqq |z_1 + z_2| + |z_3| \leqq |z_1| + |z_2| + |z_3|.$$

The property is easily extended, by induction, to the form

(10) $$\left| \sum_{k=1}^{n} z_k \right| \leqq \sum_{k=1}^{n} |z_k| \qquad (n = 1, 2, \ldots).$$

6. The Polar Form. Let r and θ be the polar coordinates of the point representing z (Fig. 5), where $r \geqq 0$. Then

(1) $$x = r \cos \theta, \qquad y = r \sin \theta,$$

and the complex number z can be written in the polar form

(2) $$z = r (\cos \theta + i \sin \theta) \qquad (r \geqq 0).$$

The radius vector r is $\sqrt{x^2 + y^2}$; that is,

(3) $$r = |z|.$$

The angle θ is called the *argument* of z, written arg z. When $z \neq 0$, the values of θ can be found from equations (1) or from the formula

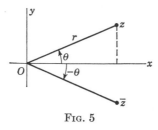

FIG. 5

$$(4) \qquad \tan \theta = \frac{y}{x}$$

and the quadrant in which the point z lies. But arg z is multiple-valued, because, in equations (1), sin θ and cos θ are periodic functions of θ with period 2π radians. If $z \neq 0$, there is just one value of θ in radians in the interval $\theta_0 \leq \theta < \theta_0 + 2\pi$, where θ_0 is any number. When $z = 0$, then $r = 0$, and θ is arbitrary.

As one example, we note that, if $z = 2 - 2i$, then $r = 2\sqrt{2}$ and arg $z = -\pi/4 \pm 2n\pi$ $(n = 0, 1, 2, \ldots)$; as another,

$$-i = \cos\frac{3\pi}{2} + i\sin\frac{3\pi}{2} = \cos\left(-\frac{\pi}{2}\right) + i\sin\left(-\frac{\pi}{2}\right).$$

When z has the form (2), the polar form of its conjugate is

$$(5) \qquad \bar{z} = r[\cos(-\theta) + i\sin(-\theta)].$$

Thus one of the values of arg $(\bar{z})$ is $-$ arg z.

It is often convenient to use the polar representation about some point z_0 other than the origin. The representation

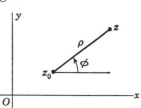

FIG. 6

$$(6) \qquad z - z_0 = \rho(\cos\phi + i\sin\phi)$$

of $z - z_0$ in polar form can be interpreted graphically as indicated in Fig. 6. That is, ρ is the distance between z and z_0, $\rho = |z - z_0|$, and ϕ is the angle of inclination of the vector $z - z_0$.

As an illustration, the equation

$$z + i = z - (-i) = 4(\cos\phi + i\sin\phi),$$

where ϕ assumes all values in the interval $0 \leq \phi < 2\pi$, represents all points z on the circle with center at $(0, -1)$ and radius 4.

7. Products, Powers, and Quotients. The product of the two numbers

$$z_1 = r_1(\cos\theta_1 + i\sin\theta_1), \qquad z_2 = r_2(\cos\theta_2 + i\sin\theta_2)$$

is

$$z_1 z_2 = r_1 r_2 [\cos \theta_1 \cos \theta_2 - \sin \theta_1 \sin \theta_2$$
$$+ i(\sin \theta_1 \cos \theta_2 + \cos \theta_1 \sin \theta_2)],$$

and this formula reduces to the polar form of the product,

(1) $$z_1 z_2 = r_1 r_2 [\cos (\theta_1 + \theta_2) + i \sin (\theta_1 + \theta_2)].$$

Thus one of the arguments of the product is the sum $\theta_1 + \theta_2$ of the arguments of the factors,

$$\arg (z_1 z_2) = \arg z_1 + \arg z_2.$$

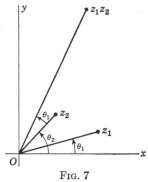

Fig. 7

Geometrically, the length of the vector $z_1 z_2$ is equal to the product of the lengths of z_1 and z_2. The angle of inclination of the vector $z_1 z_2$ is the sum of the angles θ_1 and θ_2 (Fig. 7). In particular, when a complex number z is multiplied by i, the resulting vector iz is the one obtained by rotating the vector z through a right angle in the positive (counterclockwise) direction, without changing the length of the vector, since

$$iz = \left(\cos \frac{\pi}{2} + i \sin \frac{\pi}{2} \right) r(\cos \theta + i \sin \theta)$$
$$= r \left[\cos \left(\theta + \frac{\pi}{2} \right) + i \sin \left(\theta + \frac{\pi}{2} \right) \right].$$

It follows from formula (1) that

$$z_1 z_2 \cdot \cdot \cdot z_n = r_1 r_2 \cdot \cdot \cdot r_n [\cos (\theta_1 + \theta_2 + \cdot \cdot \cdot + \theta_n)$$
$$+ i \sin (\theta_1 + \theta_2 + \cdot \cdot \cdot + \theta_n)].$$

Consequently, if $z = r(\cos \theta + i \sin \theta)$ and if n is a positive integer,

(2) $$z^n = r^n(\cos n\theta + i \sin n\theta).$$

When $r = 1$, this formula reduces to *De Moivre's theorem* for positive integral exponents,

(3) $$(\cos \theta + i \sin \theta)^n = \cos n\theta + i \sin n\theta$$

The quotient of two complex numbers is given in its polar form by the formula

(4) $$\frac{z_1}{z_2} = \frac{r_1}{r_2}[\cos{(\theta_1 - \theta_2)} + i\sin{(\theta_1 - \theta_2)}] \qquad (r_2 \neq 0).$$

Since division is the inverse of multiplication, this formula can be established easily from formula (1). It follows, as a special case, that

$$\frac{1}{z} = \frac{1}{r}[\cos{(-\theta)} + i\sin{(-\theta)}] = \frac{1}{r}(\cos{\theta} - i\sin{\theta}),$$

and, in view of equation (2), if z^{-n} is written for $1/z^n$,

(5) $$z^{-n} = \frac{1}{z^n} = \frac{1}{r^n}[\cos{(-n\theta)} + i\sin{(-n\theta)}] = \left(\frac{1}{z}\right)^n.$$

Thus the formula (2) and De Moivre's theorem (3) are valid when the exponent is any negative integer.

EXERCISES

1. Show that

(a) $\overline{\bar{z} + 3i} = z - 3i;$ (b) $\overline{iz} = -i\bar{z};$

(c) $\dfrac{(2+i)^2}{3-4i} = 1;$ (d) $|(2\bar{z} + 5)(\sqrt{2} - i)| = \sqrt{3}\,|2z + 5|.$

2. Find one value of arg z when

(a) $z = \dfrac{z_1}{z_2}$ $(z_2 \neq 0);$ (b) $z = z_1{}^n$ $(n = 1, 2, \ldots);$

(c) $z = \dfrac{-2}{1 + i\sqrt{3}};$ (d) $z = \dfrac{i}{-2 - 2i};$ (e) $z = (\sqrt{3} - i)^6.$

         Ans. (a) arg z_1 − arg $z_2;$ (b) n arg $z_1;$ (c) $2\pi/3;$ (e) π.

3. Use the polar form to show that

(a) $i(1 - i\sqrt{3})(\sqrt{3} + i) = 2 + 2i\sqrt{3};$ (b) $\dfrac{5i}{2+i} = 1 + 2i;$

(c) $(-1 + i)^7 = -8(1 + i);$

(d) $(1 + i\sqrt{3})^{-10} = 2^{-11}(-1 + i\sqrt{3}).$

4. Let z_0 be a fixed complex number and R a positive constant. Show why point z lies on a circle of radius R with center at $-z_0$ when z satisfies any one of the equations

$$(a)\ |z + z_0| = R; \quad (b)\ z + z_0 = R(\cos \phi + i \sin \phi),$$

where ϕ is real; (c) $z\bar{z} + \bar{z}_0 z + z_0 \bar{z} + z_0 \bar{z}_0 = R^2$.

5. Prove that (a) z is real if $\bar{z} = z$; (b) z is either real or pure imaginary if $z^2 = (\bar{z})^2$.

6. In Sec. 4, establish (a) formula (3); (b) formula (4).

7. Prove that (a) $\overline{z_1 z_2 z_3} = \bar{z}_1 \bar{z}_2 \bar{z}_3$; (b) $\overline{(z^4)} = (\bar{z})^4$.

8. Prove property (7), Sec. 5, on the absolute value of a quotient.

9. If $z_2 z_3 \neq 0$, show that

$$(a)\ \overline{\left(\frac{z_1}{z_2 z_3}\right)} = \frac{\bar{z}_1}{\bar{z}_2 \bar{z}_3}; \quad (b)\ \left|\frac{z_1}{z_2 z_3}\right| = \frac{|z_1|}{|z_2||z_3|}.$$

10. Give an algebraic proof of triangle inequality (9), Sec. 5.

11. If $|z_2| \neq |z_3|$, prove that

$$\left|\frac{z_1}{z_2 + z_3}\right| \leqq \frac{|z_1|}{|\,|z_2| - |z_3|\,|}.$$

12. Prove that $|z|\sqrt{2} \geqq |\Re(z)| + |\mathscr{I}(z)|$.

13. Given that $z_1 z_2 \neq 0$, use the polar form with arguments measured in radians to prove that

$$\Re(z_1 \bar{z}_2) = |z_1|\,|z_2|$$

if and only if arg $z_2 = $ arg $z_1 \pm 2n\pi$ $(n = 0, 1, 2, \ldots)$.

14. Given that $z_1 z_2 \neq 0$, use the result in Exercise 13 to prove that

$$|z_1 + z_2| = |z_1| + |z_2|$$

if and only if arg $z_2 = $ arg $z_1 \pm 2n\pi$. Also, note the geometric verification of this statement.

15. Given that $z_1 z_2 \neq 0$, use the result in Exercise 13 to prove that

$$|z_1 - z_2| = |\,|z_1| - |z_2|\,|$$

if and only if arg $z_2 = $ arg $z_1 \pm 2n\pi$. Also, note the geometric verification of this statement.

16. Establish the formula

$$1 + z + z^2 + \cdots + z^n = \frac{1 - z^{n+1}}{1 - z} \qquad (z \neq 1),$$

for the sum of a finite geometric series; then derive the formulas

(a) $1 + \cos \theta + \cos 2\theta + \cdots + \cos n\theta = \dfrac{1}{2} + \dfrac{\sin [(n + \frac{1}{2})\theta]}{2 \sin (\theta/2)}$,

(b) $\sin \theta + \sin 2\theta + \cdots + \sin n\theta = \dfrac{1}{2} \cot \dfrac{\theta}{2} - \dfrac{\cos [(n + \frac{1}{2})\theta]}{2 \sin (\theta/2)}$,

where $0 < \theta < 2\pi$.

8. Extraction of Roots. The problem of extracting the nth roots $z^{1/n}$ of a complex number z is that of solving the equation

$$(1) \qquad\qquad z_0{}^n = z$$

for z_0, when z and the positive integer n are given.

Let the polar form of z be

$$z = r(\cos \theta + i \sin \theta),$$

when $z \neq 0$, and write

$$z_0 = r_0(\cos \theta_0 + i \sin \theta_0),$$

where r_0 and θ_0 are as yet unknown.   Then equation (1) becomes

$$r_0{}^n(\cos n\theta_0 + i \sin n\theta_0) = r(\cos \theta + i \sin \theta).$$

Consequently, if the angles are measured in radians,

$$r_0{}^n = r, \qquad n\theta_0 = \theta \pm 2k\pi,$$

where k is either zero or any positive integer.   Since we have taken r and r_0 as positive numbers, it follows that r_0 is the real positive nth root of r.   Now

$$\theta_0 = \frac{\theta}{n} \pm \frac{2k\pi}{n};$$

but these values of θ_0 yield the same value of z_0 for any two integers k that differ by a multiple of n.   Therefore there are just n distinct solutions of equation (1) when $z \neq 0$, namely,

$$(2) \qquad z_0 = \sqrt[n]{r}\left(\cos \frac{\theta + 2\pi k}{n} + i \sin \frac{\theta + 2\pi k}{n}\right),$$

where $k = 0, 1, 2, \ldots, n - 1$.   These are the n values of $z^{1/n}$.

Geometrically, the length of each of the n vectors $z^{1/n}$ is the positive number $\sqrt[n]{r}$.   The argument of one of those vectors is the angle obtained by dividing θ by n, and the other arguments are obtained by adding multiples of $2\pi/n$ to θ/n.

When $z = 0$, equation (1) has only the solution $z_0 = 0$; hence $0^{1/n} = 0$.

Since $1 = \cos 0 + i \sin 0$, the nth roots of unity can be written

(3) $1^{1/n} = \cos \dfrac{2\pi k}{n} + i \sin \dfrac{2\pi k}{n}$ $(k = 0, 1, 2, \ldots, n - 1)$.

In particular, when $k = 1$, the root is a complex number denoted by ω:

(4) $\omega = \cos \dfrac{2\pi}{n} + i \sin \dfrac{2\pi}{n}.$

In view of De Moivre's theorem (Sec. 7), the roots (3) are

(5) $1, \omega, \omega^2, \ldots, \omega^{n-1}.$

In the complex plane the nth roots of unity are the vertices of a regular polygon of n sides inscribed in the circle $|z| = 1$,

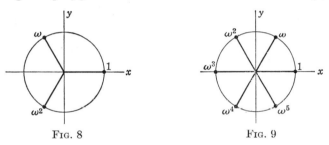

FIG. 8   FIG. 9

with one vertex at the point $z = 1$. See Fig. 8 for $n = 3$ and Fig. 9 for $n = 6$.

If z_1 is any particular nth root of z, then

(6) $z_1, z_1\omega, z_1\omega^2, \ldots, z_1\omega^k, \ldots, z_1\omega^{n-1}$

are the n nth roots of z, because multiplying z_1 by ω^k corresponds to increasing the argument of z_1 by the angle $2k\pi/n$.

Let m and n be positive integers with no common factor. According to equation (2) and expression (6),

(7) $(z^m)^{1/n} = \sqrt[n]{r^m} \left(\cos \dfrac{m\theta}{n} + i \sin \dfrac{m\theta}{n} \right) \omega^h$

$(h = 0, 1, \ldots, n - 1)$,

(8) $(z^{1/n})^m = (\sqrt[n]{r})^m \left[\left(\cos \dfrac{\theta}{n} + i \sin \dfrac{\theta}{n} \right) \omega^k \right]^m$

$= \sqrt[n]{r^m} \left(\cos \dfrac{m\theta}{n} + i \sin \dfrac{m\theta}{n} \right) \omega^{km}$

$(k = 0, 1, \ldots, n - 1)$.

These two sets of n numbers are the same if the sets ω^h and ω^{km} coincide when both h and k range through the values $0, 1, 2,$ $\ldots, n - 1$.

We first show that ω^{km} has n distinct values. If some two of its values, corresponding to two distinct values k' and k'' of k, are the same, then the two points $\omega^{k'm}$ and $\omega^{k''m}$ coincide and, in view of equation (4), there is a positive integer p such that

$$\frac{2\pi k'm}{n} = \frac{2\pi k''m}{n} \pm 2\pi p, \quad \text{or} \quad (k' - k'')\frac{m}{n} = \pm p.$$

Since m/n is not reducible, it follows that $k' - k''$ must be divisible by n; that is, a positive integer j exists such that $k' - k'' = \pm nj$. But this is impossible because $|k' - k''| < n$.

We now show that, for each fixed value of k, the number ω^{km} is one of the n distinct numbers ω^h, so that the two sets of n numbers are identical. Let qn be the greatest multiple of n that does not exceed km, q being either zero or some positive integer, so that

$$km = qn + h'$$

where h' has one of the values $0, 1, 2, \ldots, n - 1$. Then from equation (4) it follows that $\omega^{km} = \omega^{h'}$, and this is the number ω^h when $h = h'$.

This completes the proof that the two sets of numbers (7) and (8) are the same. Thus *the n numbers in either set can be written $z^{m/n}$*:

$$(9) \quad z^{m/n} = \sqrt[n]{r^m} \left\{ \cos\left[\frac{m}{n}(\theta + 2\pi k)\right] + i \sin\left[\frac{m}{n}(\theta + 2\pi k)\right] \right\},$$

where $k = 0, 1, 2, \ldots, n - 1$.

We shall define z^c, where c is any complex number, in Sec. 28. The number $1/z^c$ is written z^{-c}. Thus, if the exponent is rational, we write $z^{-m/n}$ for $1/z^{m/n}$. We can show from results already established that the set $z^{-m/n}$ may be written

$$(10) \qquad z^{-m/n} = (z^{1/n})^{-m} = (z^{-m})^{1/n}.$$

9. Regions in the Complex Plane. Definitions of some technical terms will be given at this time.

A *neighborhood* of a point z_0 is the set of all points z for which

$$(1) \qquad |z - z_0| < \epsilon,$$

where ϵ is some positive constant.   Thus a neighborhood consists of all points of a disk, or circular region, including the center z_0 but excluding the points on the boundary circle.   The term *neighborhood* will be used consistently in this sense.

A point z_0 is a *limit point* for a set of points in the z plane if every neighborhood of z_0 contains points, other than z_0, of the set.   Thus each point on the circle $|z| = c$ is a limit point for the set $|z| < c$, and those limit points do not belong to the set. Each point of that set $|z| < c$ is also a limit point of the set. As another example, the set of points $z = 1/n$ $(n = 1, 2, \ldots)$ has the limit point $z = 0$.

An *interior point* of a set S is a point of S such that some neighborhood of that point contains only points in S.   Thus interior points are always limit points.   If a limit point z_0 for a set S is not an interior point, that is, if each neighborhood of z_0 contains a point not in S as well as points in S, then z_0 is a *boundary point* for the set.   In particular, then, every limit point that does not belong to the set is a boundary point.   The origin $z = 0$, as well as each point on the unit circle $|z| = 1$, is a boundary point for either of the two sets

(2) $0 < |z| < 1$ or $0 < |z| \leqq 1.$

Set (1) and the first of sets (2) are examples of *open regions*, sets that contain only interior points.   A set consisting of all points of an open region and some of its boundary points, such as the second of sets (2), will be called simply a region.   If all its points are interior to a circle $|z| = c$ for some constant c, a region is *bounded*.   Thus regions (2) are bounded, and the open region $x > 0$ is unbounded.   A bounded region that includes all its limit points will be called a *closed region*.   The closure $\bar{R}$ of a bounded region R is the set consisting of all points of R and all its boundary points.   The closed region $|z| \leqq 1$, for instance, is the closure of each of regions (2).

A region is *connected* if each pair of its points can be joined by some continuous chain of a finite number of line segments all points of which lie in the region.   Thus the open region consisting of all points interior to the circle $|z| = 1$ and all points exterior to $|z| = 2$ is not connected.

A connected open region is called a *domain*.   The domain

(3) $0 < \arg z < 2\pi,$ $|z| > 0,$

for example, contains all points of the plane except the origin and points on the positive x axis.

EXERCISES

1. Find all values of each of the following roots.   Check graphically.

(a) $(2i)^{\frac{1}{2}}$;   (b) $(-i)^{\frac{1}{3}}$;   (c) $(-1)^{\frac{1}{3}}$;   (d) $8^{\frac{1}{6}}$.

Ans. (a) $\pm(1+i)$;   (b) $i, (\pm \sqrt{3} - i)/2$;
(d) $\pm \sqrt{2}, (\pm 1 \pm i \sqrt{3})/\sqrt{2}$.

2. Find all values of

(a) $(-1 + i \sqrt{3})^{\frac{3}{2}}$;   (b) $(-1)^{-\frac{3}{4}}$.   Ans. (a) $\pm 2 \sqrt{2}$.

3. Find the four roots of the equation $z^4 + 4 = 0$ and use them to factor $z^4 + 4$ into quadratic factors with real coefficients.

Ans. $(z^2 + 2z + 2)(z^2 - 2z + 2)$.

4. From the formula for the sum of a finite geometric series (Exercise 16, Sec. 7) show that, if w is any imaginary nth root of unity, then

$$1 + w + w^2 + \cdots + w^{n-1} = 0$$

5. Prove that the usual quadratic formula solves the quadratic equation $az^2 + bz + c = 0$ when the coefficients a, b, and c are complex numbers.

6. If m and n are positive integers, show (a) that

$$(z_1 z_2)^m = z_1{}^m z_2{}^m;$$

(b) that the two sets of numbers $(z_1 z_2)^{1/n}$ and $z_1{}^{1/n} z_2{}^{1/n}$ are the same; and hence (c) that the two sets $(z_1 z_2)^{m/n}$ and $z_1{}^{m/n} z_2{}^{m/n}$ are the same.

7. Describe geometrically the region determined by each of the following conditions.   Also, classify the region with the aid of the terms defined in Sec. 9.

(a) $|\Re(z)| < 2$;   (b) $|z - 4| > 3$;   (c) $|z - 1 + 3i| \leqq 1$;
(d) $|\mathfrak{I}(z)| > 1$;   (e) $\Re(z) > 0$;   (f) $0 \leqq \arg z \leqq \pi/4, z \neq 0$.

Ans. (a), (b), (e) unbounded domain; (c) closed region, the closure of a bounded domain; (d) unbounded open region, not connected.

8. Describe each of these regions geometrically:

(a) $-\pi < \arg z < \pi, |z| > 2$;   (b) $1 < |z - 2i| < 2$;
(c) $|2z + 3| > 4$;   (d) $\mathfrak{I}(z^2) > 0$;

(e) $\Re\left(\dfrac{1}{z}\right) < \dfrac{1}{2}$;   (f) $|z - 4| > |z|$.

CHAPTER 2

ANALYTIC FUNCTIONS

10. Functions of a Complex Variable. When z denotes any one of the numbers of a set S of complex numbers, we call z a complex variable. If for each value of z in S the value of a second complex variable w is prescribed, then w is a *function* of the complex variable z on the set S:

$$w = f(z).$$

The set S is usually some domain. Then it is called a *domain of definition* of the function w. The totality of values $f(z)$ corresponding to all z in S constitute another set R of complex numbers, known as the *range* of the function w.

A function is single-valued on a set S if it has just one value corresponding to each value of z in S. Let us agree that the term *function signifies a single-valued function* unless the contrary is clearly indicated. Most of our work with multiple-valued functions, such as $z^{\frac{1}{2}}$, can be carried out conveniently by dealing with single-valued functions, each of which takes on just one of the multiple values for each value of z in a specified domain.

The domain of definition of each of the functions

$$f_1(z) = z^3 + 2iz - 3, \qquad f_2(z) = |z|, \qquad f_3(z) = \frac{1}{z^2 + 1}$$

is the entire complex plane, except that f_3 is undefined at the two points $z = \pm i$. Note that f_2 is a real-valued function of the complex variable z; in fact its range is the nonnegative half of the real axis.

The functions $x = \Re(z)$ and $y = \Im(z)$ are also real-valued. If u and v are any two real-valued functions of the two real variables x and y, then $u + iv$ is a function of z. On the other hand, each given function $f(z)$ has specific real and imaginary

19

components that are real-valued functions of x and y. If u and v denote those components, then

$$f(z) = u(x,y) + iv(x,y).$$

For example, if

$$f(z) = z^2 = (x + iy)^2,$$
then $\qquad u = x^2 - y^2 \qquad \text{and} \qquad v = 2xy.$

As further examples, the function

$$f_4(z) = x^2 + i(2x + y)$$

is defined over the entire z plane. But the domain of definition of the function

$$f_5(z) = y \int_0^\infty e^{-xt}\, dt + i \sum_{n=0}^\infty y^n$$

is the semi-infinite strip $x > 0$, $-1 < y < 1$, since the improper integral exists and the infinite series converges only when x and y are so restricted.

If n is zero or a positive integer and if $a_0, a_1, \ldots, a_n$ are complex constants, the function

$$P(z) = a_0 + a_1 z + a_2 z^2 + \cdots + a_n z^n \qquad (a_n \neq 0)$$

is a *polynomial* in z, of degree n. Note that the sum here has a *finite* number of terms. The domain of definition of every polynomial is the entire plane. The function f_1 above is a polynomial of degree 3. Quotients of polynomials, $P(z)/Q(z)$, also called rational fractional functions, are defined for all z except those for which $Q(z) = 0$. The function f_3 above is an example. Polynomials and their quotients constitute two elementary, but important, classes of functions of a complex variable.

11. Mapping. Properties of a real-valued function $f(x)$ of a real variable x are exhibited geometrically by the graph of the function. The equation $y = f(x)$ establishes a correspondence between points x on the x axis and points y on the y axis; that is, it maps points x into points y. But the graphical description is improved by mapping each point x into a point (x,y) of the xy plane at a directed distance y above or below point x. The curve so obtained is the graph of $f(x)$. In a similar way, we use a surface to exhibit graphically a real-valued function $f(x,y)$ of the real variables x and y.

But when $w = f(z)$ and the variables w and z are complex, no such convenient graphical representation of the function f is available, because a plane is needed for the representation of each of the variables. Some information about the function can be displayed graphically, however, by showing sets of corresponding points z and w. It is generally simpler to draw separate complex planes for the two variables z and w. Then, corresponding to each point (x,y) in the z plane, in a domain of definition of f, there is a point (u,v) in the w plane, where $w = u + iv$.

The correspondence between points in the two planes is called a *mapping* or a *transformation* of points in the z plane into points of the w plane by the function f. Corresponding points, or corresponding sets of points, are called *images* of each other.

In order to use such graphic terms as *translation*, *rotation*, and *reflection*, it is sometimes convenient to consider the mapping as a transformation in just one plane. The function $z + 2$, for instance, can be thought of as a translation of each point z to a position $w = z + 2$ two units to the right of z. The function $w = \bar{z}$ maps each point z into the reflection $\bar{z}$ of that point in the real axis.

The mapping of curves and regions usually displays more information about the function than the mapping of individual points. As an illustration, the function

$$w = \sqrt{x^2 + y^2} - iy$$

maps all points on each circle $x^2 + y^2 = c^2$, where $c \geq 0$, into some points of the line $u = c$ in the w plane, since $u = \sqrt{x^2 + y^2}$. But for all points z on the circle, y assumes all values from $-c$ to c and, since $v = -y$, the values of v range between c and $-c$. The circle's image, $u = c$, $-c \leq v \leq c$, is the segment of the line $u = c$ included between the lines $v = u$ and $v = -u$ (Fig. 10). Since the two points $z = x + iy$ and $z = -x + iy$ have the same image w, each point of the line segment, except the end points, is the image of two points on the circle. The domain D of definition of the function w is the entire z plane. Each point of D lies on one of those circles, since c is any nonnegative constant, and the image of that circle is the line segment described

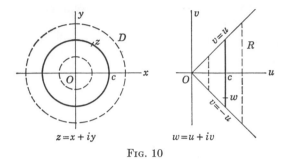

$z = x + iy$ $w = u + iv$

FIG. 10

above.   Conversely, every such line segment is an image of
one of the circles.   Hence the image of D, or the range R of the
function w, is the quadrant

$$u \geqq 0, \; -u \leqq v \leqq u.$$

12. Limits.   Let a function f be defined at all points in some
neighborhood of a point z_0, except possibly at the point z_0 itself.
The statement that the limit of that function, as z approaches z_0,
is a number w_0,

$$(1) \qquad\qquad \lim_{z \to z_0} f(z) = w_0,$$

means that the value $f(z)$ of the function is arbitrarily close to
the value w_0 for all points z in a neighborhood of z_0, except
possibly when $z = z_0$, when that neighborhood is made sufficiently small.   Let us express the definition in a precise and
usable form.

Given a function f and two complex numbers z_0 and w_0, the
statement (1) means that, corresponding to each positive number ϵ there exists a positive number δ such that

$$(2) \qquad |f(z) - w_0| < \epsilon \qquad \text{whenever } |z - z_0| < \delta \quad (z \neq z_0).$$

Graphically, the definition (2) requires that for each positive
number ϵ some positive number δ exist such that all points z,
except z_0, interior to the circle $|z - z_0| = \delta$ in the z plane have
image points $w = f(z)$ that are confined to the interior of the
circle $|w - w_0| = \epsilon$ in the w plane (Fig. 11).   Note that all image
points are required to belong to the neighborhood $|w - w_0| < \epsilon$;
they need not constitute the entire neighborhood.   When $f(z)$

is a constant w_0, for instance, w is just the center w_0 of that neighborhood. The points z, however, constitute the entire domain $0 < |z - z_0| < \delta$. The symbol $z \to z_0$ therefore implies that z approaches z_0 in an arbitrary manner, not from some particular direction.

The limit is established when some formula is found for δ as a function of ϵ. Any such formula $\delta = \phi(\epsilon)$ is not a unique one, however, because condition (2) is also satisfied when δ is replaced

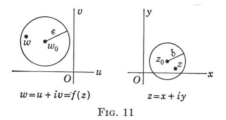

$$w = u + iv = f(z) \qquad\qquad z = x + iy$$

Fig. 11

by any smaller positive number; $\delta = \frac{1}{2}\phi(\epsilon)$, for instance, is another formula.

The definition provides a means of testing whether w_0 is the limit of f. It does not give directly a method of determining the limit w_0. Theorems on limits, derived from the definition, enable us to find limits of many functions.

Let us apply the definition to prove that

$$(3) \qquad\qquad \lim_{z \to 1} \frac{z^2 - 1}{z - 1} = 2.$$

The value of the function $f(z) = (z^2 - 1)/(z - 1)$ is not defined when $z = 1$; but when $z \neq 1$, then $f(z) = z + 1$. Thus

$$|f(z) - 2| = |z + 1 - 2| = |z - 1| \qquad (z \neq 1),$$

and hence

$$|f(z) - 2| < \epsilon \qquad \text{whenever } 0 < |z - 1| < \epsilon;$$

that is, condition (2) is satisfied for every positive number ϵ if $\delta = \epsilon$. This proves statement (3).

As another example, let us show that

$$(4) \qquad\qquad \lim_{z \to 2i} (2x + iy^2) = 4i \qquad\qquad (z = x + iy).$$

For each positive number ϵ we shall exhibit a number δ such that

$$(5) \qquad\qquad |2x + iy^2 - 4i| < \epsilon$$

whenever $|z - 2i| < \delta$. To simplify our problem, we write

$$|2x + iy^2 - 4i| \leq 2|x| + |y^2 - 4| = 2|x| + |y - 2|\,|y + 2|$$

and look for a value of δ such that

(6) $2\,|x| < \dfrac{\epsilon}{2}$ and $|y - 2|\,|y + 2| < \dfrac{\epsilon}{2}.$

But if $|z - 2i|$ is small, then the value of y is close to 2, and $y + 2$ has a value near 4. The second of inequalities (6) may therefore be satisfied if $|y - 2| < \epsilon/10$, that is, if

$$-\frac{\epsilon}{10} < y - 2 < \frac{\epsilon}{10} \quad \text{or} \quad 4 - \frac{\epsilon}{10} < y + 2 < 4 + \frac{\epsilon}{10}.$$

Then $|y + 2| < 4 + \epsilon/10 < 5$, provided that $\epsilon < 10$, and therefore $|y - 2|\,|y + 2| < \epsilon/2$. If $\epsilon \geq 10$ in the inequality (5), then that inequality is certainly satisfied when $|2x + iy^2 - 4i| < 5$, and we can safely use the value of δ that corresponds to the case $\epsilon = 5$.

We have now shown that condition (5) is satisfied whenever the point z lies in the rectangular domain (Fig. 12)

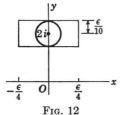

FIG. 12

$$|x| < \frac{\epsilon}{4}, \quad |y - 2| < \frac{\epsilon}{10} \quad (0 < \epsilon < 10).$$

The neighborhood $|z - 2i| < \epsilon/10$ is interior to that domain. Our formula for δ that establishes the limit (4) can therefore be written

(7) $\delta = \begin{cases} \dfrac{\epsilon}{10} & \text{when } 0 < \epsilon < 10, \\[2mm] \dfrac{1}{2} & \text{when } \epsilon \geq 10. \end{cases}$

When the limit of a function f exists at z_0, that limit has a unique value. For suppose that it could have two distinct values w_0 and w_1. Then for every positive number ϵ, however small, a number δ would exist such that

$$|f(z) - w_0| < \epsilon \quad \text{and} \quad |f(z) - w_1| < \epsilon$$
$$\text{when } 0 < |z - z_0| < \delta.$$

It would follow that

$$|[f(z) - w_0] - [f(z) - w_1]| \leq |f(z) - w_0| + |f(z) - w_1| < 2\epsilon;$$

that is, $|w_1 - w_0| < 2\epsilon$. But w_0 and w_1 are distinct constants, and hence $|w_1 - w_0|$ cannot be made arbitrarily small. The uniqueness of the limit is therefore proved.

13. Theorems on Limits. We can expedite our treatment of limits by establishing the connection between the limit of a function of a complex variable and the limits of real functions of two real variables. Limits of the latter type are treated in advanced calculus. We shall use their definition and properties freely.

Theorem 1. *Let us write*

$$f(z) = u(x,y) + iv(x,y), \quad z = x + iy, \quad and \quad z_0 = x_0 + iy_0.$$

Then the condition that the limit of f exists at z_0,

$$(1) \qquad\qquad \lim_{z \to z_0} f(z) = u_0 + iv_0,$$

is satisfied if and only if

$$(2) \qquad \lim_{\substack{x \to x_0 \\ y \to y_0}} u(x,y) = u_0 \quad and \quad \lim_{\substack{x \to x_0 \\ y \to y_0}} v(x,y) = v_0.$$

To establish the necessity of conditions (2), we assume that statement (1) is true. Then for each positive number ϵ a number δ exists such that

$$(3) \qquad\qquad |u - u_0 + i(v - v_0)| < \epsilon$$
$$\text{whenever } 0 < |x - x_0 + i(y - y_0)| < \delta.$$

Since
$$|u - u_0| \leqq |u - u_0 + i(v - v_0)|$$
and
$$|v - v_0| \leqq |u - u_0 + i(v - v_0)|,$$

it follows that

$$(4) \qquad |u - u_0| < \epsilon \quad and \quad |v - v_0| < \epsilon$$
$$\text{whenever } 0 < (x - x_0)^2 + (y - y_0)^2 < \delta^2.$$

Thus there is a neighborhood of the point (x_0, y_0) throughout which, except possibly at the point itself, $|u(x,y) - u_0| < \epsilon$ and $|v(x,y) - v_0| < \epsilon$. A square region interior to the circular neighborhood will also answer the purpose. According to the definition of a limit of a real-valued function of two real variables, the limits of u and v exist and have the values shown in conditions (2).

Conversely, if conditions (2) are satisfied, then corresponding to each positive number ϵ, two numbers δ_1 and δ_2 exist such that

$$|u - u_0| < \frac{\epsilon}{2} \qquad \text{whenever } 0 < (x - x_0)^2 + (y - y_0)^2 < \delta_1{}^2$$

and

$$|v - v_0| < \frac{\epsilon}{2} \qquad \text{whenever } 0 < (x - x_0)^2 + (y - y_0)^2 < \delta_2{}^2.$$

Let δ denote the smaller of the two numbers δ_1 and δ_2. Then, since

$$|u - u_0 + i(v - v_0)| \leq |u - u_0| + |v - v_0|,$$

condition (3) follows. Thus statement (1) is a consequence of statements (2), and the proof of the theorem is complete.

Theorem 2. *Let f and F be functions whose limits exist at z_0:*

$$(5) \qquad \lim_{z \to z_0} f(z) = w_0, \qquad \lim_{z \to z_0} F(z) = W_0.$$

Then

$$(6) \qquad \lim_{z \to z_0} [f(z) + F(z)] = w_0 + W_0,$$

$$(7) \qquad \lim_{z \to z_0} [f(z)F(z)] = w_0 W_0,$$

and, if $W_0 \neq 0$,

$$(8) \qquad \lim_{z \to z_0} \frac{f(z)}{F(z)} = \frac{w_0}{W_0}.$$

This fundamental theorem can be established directly from the definition (Sec. 12) of the limit of a function of a complex variable. But with the aid of Theorem 1 it follows almost immediately from theorems on limits of real-valued functions of two real variables.

Consider the proof of property (7), for example. We write

$$f(z) = u(x,y) + iv(x,y), \qquad F(z) = U(x,y) + iV(x,y),$$
$$z_0 = x_0 + iy_0, \qquad w_0 = u_0 + iv_0, \qquad W_0 = U_0 + iV_0.$$

Then, according to our hypotheses (5) and Theorem 1, the limits, as (x,y) approaches (x_0,y_0), of u, v, U, and V exist and have the values u_0, v_0, U_0, and V_0, respectively. The real and imaginary components of the function

$$f(z)F(z) = uU - vV + i(uV + vU)$$

therefore have the limits $(u_0 U_0 - v_0 V_0)$ and $(u_0 V_0 + v_0 U_0)$, according to theorems on limits of sums and products of functions.

Therefore $f(z)F(z)$ has the limit

$$u_0 U_0 - v_0 V_0 + i(u_0 V_0 + v_0 U_0),$$

which is equal to $w_0 W_0$, and statement (7) follows.

Corresponding proofs of conclusions (6) and (8) can be written.

In order to prove (8) directly from the definition of the limit of a function of a complex variable, a useful auxiliary result, concerning a function F whose limit W_0 is not zero, should be noted. It is convenient to define $F(z_0)$ to be W_0. Then there is a neighborhood of z_0 such that $|F(z)|$ is *bounded away from zero;* that is, $|F(z)|$ exceeds some positive constant, for all z in that neighborhood. This can be seen by writing δ_0 for a value of δ that corresponds to the value $\frac{1}{2}|W_0|$ for ϵ. Then

$$(9) \qquad |F(z) - W_0| < \tfrac{1}{2}|W_0| \qquad \text{whenever } |z - z_0| < \delta_0.$$

It is left to the exercises to show that, as a consequence,

$$(10) \qquad |F(z)| > \tfrac{1}{2}|W_0| \qquad \text{whenever } |z - z_0| < \delta_0.$$

In particular, $F(z) \neq 0$ for any value of z in that neighborhood of z_0.

From the definition of the limit we can see that

$$\lim_{z \to z_0} z = z_0,$$

since we can write $\delta = \epsilon$ when $f(z) = z$. It follows from statement (7) on the limit of a product, and by induction, that

$$(11) \qquad \lim_{z \to z_0} z^n = z_0{}^n \qquad\qquad (n = 1, 2, \ldots),$$

where z_0 is any complex number. Also, the limit of a constant is that constant. In view of Theorem 2, then, the limit of a polynomial

$$P(z) = a_0 + a_1 z + a_2 z^2 + \cdots + a_n z^n$$

is the value of that polynomial at z_0, for every number z_0:

$$(12) \qquad \lim_{z \to z_0} P(z) = P(z_0).$$

EXERCISES

1. Describe the domain of definition of the function

$$g(z) = \frac{y}{x} + \frac{1}{1 - y} i.$$

For all z in the domain of definition of the function f_5 described in Sec. 10, show that $g(z) = f_5(z)$.

2. Let b, c, and z_0 denote complex constants. Use the definition of the limit (Sec. 12) to prove that

(a) $\lim\limits_{z \to z_0} c = c$;   (b) $\lim\limits_{z \to z_0} (bz + c) = bz_0 + c$;

(c) $\lim\limits_{z \to z_0} (z^2 + c) = z_0^2 + c$;   (d) $\lim\limits_{z \to z_0} \Re(z) = \Re(z_0)$;

(e) $\lim\limits_{z \to z_0} \bar{z} = \bar{z}_0$;   (f) $\lim\limits_{z \to 1-i} [x + i(2x + y)] = 1 + i$.

3. Prove statement (6) in Theorem 2, (a) by using Theorem 1 and properties of limits of real-valued functions; (b) directly from the definition (Sec. 12) of the limit of a function.

4. Prove that condition (10) follows from condition (9).

5. If n is a positive integer and P and Q are polynomials and if $Q(z_0) \neq 0$, use Theorem 2 and established limits to find

(a) $\lim\limits_{z \to z_0} \dfrac{1}{z^n}$ $(z_0 \neq 0)$;   (b) $\lim\limits_{z \to i} \dfrac{iz^3 - 1}{z + i}$;   (c) $\lim\limits_{z \to z_0} \dfrac{P(z)}{Q(z)}$.

$Ans.$ (a) $1/z_0^n$; (b) 0; (c) $P(z_0)/Q(z_0)$.

14. Continuity. A function f is *continuous* at a point z_0 if and only if all three of the following conditions are satisfied:

(1) $f(z_0)$ exists,

(2) $\lim\limits_{z \to z_0} f(z)$ exists,

(3) $\lim\limits_{z \to z_0} f(z) = f(z_0)$.

Those conditions imply that $f(z)$ is defined throughout some neighborhood of the point z_0. A natural modification of this definition is needed in order to define the continuity of a function at a point on the boundary of a region in which the function is defined. Suppose that $f(z)$ is defined throughout a region extending up to and including a curve C, but not extending across C. Then f is continuous at a point z_0 on C if and only if the conditions (2) and (3) are satisfied, where, in this case, the limit is the limit from the interior of the region; that is, the neighborhood $|z - z_0| < \delta$ used in defining the limit is to be replaced by that part of the neighborhood which lies in the given region.

As a result of the theorems on limits, if any two functions are **continuous**, their sum and their product are also continuous, and their quotient is continuous except for those values of z for which the denominator vanishes.

Every polynomial in z is continuous at each point, according to formula (12), Sec. 13. The quotient of two polynomials is continuous for each value of z for which the denominator is different from zero.

From Theorem 1, Sec. 13, it follows that

(4) $f = u + iv$ *is continuous*
          if and only if u and v are continuous.

Properties of continuous functions of z may thus be deduced from properties of continuous functions u and v of x and y. For instance, when f is a continuous function of z at every point in a closed region R, then u and v are continuous in R, and therefore bounded in R; consequently f is *bounded* in R; that is, for some constant M,

$$|f(z)| < M \qquad \text{for all } z \text{ in } R.$$

According to statement (4), $xy^2 + i(2x - y)$ is a continuous function of z everywhere, because polynomials xy^2 and $2x - y$ in x and y are everywhere continuous functions of the two variables x and y. Likewise, $e^x + i \sin (xy)$ is continuous for all z because of the continuity of the exponential and sine functions and the function xy.

Condition (3) can be written as follows. Corresponding to each positive number ϵ, a number δ exists such that

(5) $|f(z) - f(z_0)| < \epsilon \qquad \text{whenever } |z - z_0| < \delta.$

The number δ that corresponds to a given ϵ may depend on z_0. However, if f is continuous at every point of a *closed* region R, then f is *uniformly continuous* there; that is, for each given ϵ, a number δ, independent of z_0, exists such that condition (5) is satisfied simultaneously for every point z_0 in R. This follows from statement (4) and the corresponding property for real-valued functions u and v.

Let D be a domain of definition of a function f. For all z in some neighborhood N of a point z_0 let the range of a function g be included in D. Then $f[g(z)]$ is defined when z is in N. If g is continuous at z_0 and f is continuous at the point $g(z_0)$, then the *composite function* of z, $f(g)$, is continuous at z_0. In brief, a *continuous function of a continuous function is continuous.* This follows from the statement (5) of the definition of continuity. For each ϵ there is a number δ' such that

$$|f[g(z)] - f[g(z_0)]| < \epsilon \qquad \text{whenever } |g(z) - g(z_0)| < \delta';$$

but corresponding to δ' there is a number δ such that the latter inequality is satisfied whenever $|z - z_0| < \delta$.

Since f and g here are each functions of a single complex variable, we remark that the composite function $f(g)$ does not include sums, products, or quotients of two functions. Conditions for the continuity of those combinations of functions were given at the beginning of this section.

15. The Derivative. Let z denote any point of some neighborhood of a fixed point z_0, where that neighborhood is within the domain of definition of a function f. We write $\Delta z = z - z_0$ and consider Δz as our complex variable. The derivative f', or df/dz, of f at z_0 is then defined by the equation

$$(1) \qquad f'(z_0) = \lim_{\Delta z \to 0} \frac{f(z_0 + \Delta z) - f(z_0)}{\Delta z},$$

if the limit exists. That is, if the complex number $f'(z_0)$, the derivative, exists, then to every positive number ϵ there corresponds a number δ such that

$$(2) \qquad \left| \frac{f(z_0 + \Delta z) - f(z_0)}{\Delta z} - f'(z_0) \right| < \epsilon$$

$$\text{whenever } 0 < |\Delta z| < \delta.$$

If $f(z) = z^2$, for example, then $f'(z_0) = 2z_0$ at any point z_0 because

$$\lim_{\Delta z \to 0} \frac{(z_0 + \Delta z)^2 - z_0^2}{\Delta z} = \lim_{\Delta z \to 0} (2z_0 + \Delta z) = 2z_0,$$

since $2z_0 + \Delta z$ is a polynomial in Δz.

In view of equation (1), whenever $f'(z_0)$ exists, then

$$\lim_{\Delta z \to 0} [f(z_0 + \Delta z) - f(z_0)] = \lim_{\Delta z \to 0} \frac{f(z_0 + \Delta z) - f(z_0)}{\Delta z} \lim_{\Delta z \to 0} \Delta z = 0;$$

that is,

$$(3) \qquad \lim_{z \to z_0} f(z) = f(z_0).$$

Thus f *is necessarily continuous at any point* z_0 *where its derivative exists.* But continuity of a function does not imply differentiability, as the following example shows.

The function $w = |z|^2$ is continuous at every point. We shall show that its derivative exists only at the point $z = 0$. For this function the difference quotient can be written

$$(4) \quad \frac{\Delta w}{\Delta z} = \frac{|z_0 + \Delta z|^2 - |z_0|^2}{\Delta z} = \frac{(z_0 + \Delta z)(\bar{z}_0 + \overline{\Delta z}) - z_0 \bar{z}_0}{\Delta z}$$

$$= \bar{z}_0 + \overline{\Delta z} + z_0 \frac{\overline{\Delta z}}{\Delta z}.$$

When $z_0 = 0$, $\Delta w/\Delta z = \overline{\Delta z}$ and its limit is zero; that is,

$$\frac{d}{dz} |z|^2 = 0 \qquad\qquad \text{at } z = 0.$$

Suppose $z_0 \neq 0$. If w' exists, then $\Delta w/\Delta z$ has the unique limit w' as Δz approaches zero in any manner. In particular, if Δz is real, $\Delta z = \Delta x$ in Fig. 13; then $\overline{\Delta z} = \Delta z$ and, according to equation (4), the limit must be $\bar{z}_0 + z_0$. But if Δz is confined to the vertical diameter of the region $0 < |\Delta z| < \delta$, $\Delta z = i \Delta y$; then $\overline{\Delta z} = -\Delta z$, and the limit must be $\bar{z}_0 - z_0$. Since $z_0 \neq 0$, the limit cannot exist; hence $|z|^2$ has no derivative at z_0.

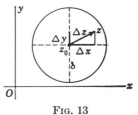

FIG. 13

16. Differentiation Formulas. The definition of the derivative $f'(z)$ is identical in form to that of the derivative of a real-valued function of a real variable x. But a significant difference between the definitions is this: the limit involved in the definition of $f'(z)$ is a two-dimensional one. Many results from the calculus of real variables do not carry over to the calculus of complex variables. As a minor illustration, we note that the function $|x|^2$ has the derivative $2x$ for every real x; but we have shown above that the derivative of $|z|^2$ exists only at the point $z = 0$.

The basic differentiation formulas given below can be derived from the definition of the derivative and theorems on limits by the same steps used in the case of real variables. Let c be a complex constant, and let w denote a function whose derivative

$w'(z)$ exists; then

(1) $$\frac{d}{dz}(c) = 0, \qquad \frac{d}{dz}(z) = 1,$$

(2) $$\frac{d}{dz}(cw) = c\frac{dw}{dz}.$$

If the derivatives $w_1'(z)$ and $w_2'(z)$ of two functions w_1 and w_2 exist, then

(3) $$\frac{d}{dz}(w_1 + w_2) = w_1'(z) + w_2'(z),$$

(4) $$\frac{d}{dz}(w_1 w_2) = w_1(z)w_2'(z) + w_2(z)w_1'(z),$$

and, if $w_2(z) \neq 0$,

(5) $$\frac{d}{dz}\frac{w_1}{w_2} = \frac{w_2(z)w_1'(z) - w_1(z)w_2'(z)}{[w_2(z)]^2}.$$

For the composite function $w_1(w_2)$, where $w_1'(t)$ exists at the point $t = w_2(z)$ and $w_2'(z)$ exists,

(6) $$\frac{d}{dz}[w_1(w_2)] = \frac{dw_1}{dw_2}\frac{dw_2}{dz}.$$

If n is a positive integer, then at every point z,

(7) $$\frac{d}{dz}(z^n) = nz^{n-1},$$

and this formula is true if $z \neq 0$ when n is a negative integer.

As an example, if $w_1 = z^5$ and $w_2 = 2z + 1$ in formula (6), then

$$\frac{d}{dz}(2z+1)^5 = \frac{d}{dz}(w_2{}^5) = 5w_2{}^4\frac{dw_2}{dz} = 10(2z+1)^4.$$

If we write

$$\Delta w_1 = w_1(z + \Delta z) - w_1(z), \qquad \Delta w_2 = w_2(z + \Delta z) - w_2(z),$$

and $f(z) = w_1(z)w_2(z)$, the difference quotient for formula (4) reduces to the form

(8) $$\frac{\Delta f}{\Delta z} = w_1\frac{\Delta w_2}{\Delta z} + w_2\frac{\Delta w_1}{\Delta z} + \Delta w_2\frac{\Delta w_1}{\Delta z}.$$

Since $w_1'(z)$ and $w_2'(z)$ exist, then w_2 is continuous at the point z, and therefore $\lim \Delta w_2 = 0$ as $\Delta z \to 0$. The proof of formula

(4) is completed by applying the limit theorems for sums and products to the expression (8) for $\Delta f/\Delta z$.

A sound derivation of formula (6), for the derivative of a function w_1 of a function w_2, is not so simple. If the function w_2 is a constant, the formula becomes the first of formulas (1). Suppose w_2 is not a constant. In place of z we now write z_0 for the point where w_2' is assumed to exist, and we write t_0 for the complex number $w_2(z_0)$. Then $w_1'(t_0)$ is also assumed to exist; thus $w_1(t)$ is defined at all points in some neighborhood N of t_0, say, $|t - t_0| < \delta_1$. Since w_2 must be continuous at z_0, a number δ_2 exists such that

$$(9) \qquad |\Delta w_2| < \delta_1, \qquad \text{whenever } |\Delta z| < \delta_2,$$

where $\Delta w_2 = w_2(z_0 + \Delta z) - t_0$; that is, the points $w_2(z_0 + \Delta z)$ lie in the neighborhood N when $|\Delta z| < \delta_2$.

Every neighborhood of z_0 contains points $z_0 + \Delta z$ where $\Delta w_2 \neq 0$, since w_2 is not a constant. For all those values of Δz such that $\Delta w_2 \neq 0$ we write

$$(10) \qquad \frac{\Delta w_1}{\Delta z} = \frac{\Delta w_1}{\Delta w_2} \frac{\Delta w_2}{\Delta z},$$

where $\Delta w_1 = w_1[w_2(z_0 + \Delta z)] - w_1(t_0)$. The limit, as $\Delta z \to 0$, of the product on the right in equation (10) exists if $\Delta w_1/\Delta w_2$ has a limit as $\Delta z \to 0$, because the limit of the second factor is $w_2'(z_0)$. Since $w_1'(t_0)$ exists as a unique limit, it follows that for each positive number ϵ there is a number δ_3 such that

$$(11) \qquad \left| \frac{\Delta w_1}{\Delta w_2} - w_1'(t_0) \right| < \epsilon$$

whenever $|\Delta w_2| < \delta_3$. But, according to the continuity condition (9), a number δ ($\delta < \delta_2$) exists such that $|\Delta w_2| < \delta_3$ whenever $|\Delta z| < \delta$. Thus condition (11) is satisfied whenever $|\Delta z| < \delta$, so that $\Delta w_1/\Delta w_2$ has the limit $w_1'(t_0)$ as $\Delta z \to 0$. It follows from equation (10) that $dw_1/dz = w_1'(t_0)w_2'(z_0)$; this is an alternate form of formula (6).

EXERCISES

1. From the conditions and conclusions of this section show that the derivative of a polynomial

$$P(z) = a_0 + a_1z + a_2z^2 + \cdots + a_nz^n \qquad (n = 1, 2, \ldots)$$

exists everywhere and that $P'(z) = a_1 + 2a_2 z + \cdots + n a_n z^{n-1}$.

2. Show that the quotient $P(z)/Q(z)$ of two polynomials has a derivative at every point z where $Q(z) \neq 0$ (see Exercise 1).

3. Use the results of this section to find $f'(z)$ when

(a) $f(z) = 3z^2 - 2z + 4$;   (b) $f(z) = (1 - 4z^2)^3$;

(c) $f(z) = \dfrac{z-1}{2z+1}$ $\left(z \neq -\dfrac{1}{2} \right)$;   (d) $f(z) = z^2 (1 + z^{-2})^4$ $(z \neq 0)$.

4. Derive formula (5) of this section.

5. Use either induction or the binomial formula (Exercise 18, Sec. 3) to derive formula (7) when n is a positive integer.

6. Derive formula (7) when n is a negative integer and $z \neq 0$.

7. Apply the definition of the derivative directly to prove that $f'(z_0) = -1/z_0^2$ when $f(z) = 1/z$ and $z_0 \neq 0$.

8. Apply the definition of the derivative to show that, if $f(z) = \Re(z)$, then $f'(z)$ does not exist anywhere.

9. Show that the function $\bar{z}$ is nowhere differentiable.

10. Determine whether the function $\Im(z)$ has a derivative anywhere.

17. The Cauchy-Riemann Conditions.   Suppose that a function f has a derivative at z_0.   We write $z_0 = x_0 + i y_0$,

$$
\begin{aligned}
(1) \qquad & f(z) = u(x,y) + iv(x,y), \qquad f'(z_0) = a + ib, \\
& \Delta f = f(z_0 + \Delta z) - f(z_0), \\
& \Delta u = u(x_0 + \Delta x,\, y_0 + \Delta y) - u(x_0, y_0),
\end{aligned}
$$

and Δv for the corresponding change in $v(x,y)$.   Then

$$
\lim_{\Delta z \to 0} \frac{\Delta f}{\Delta z} = \lim_{\Delta z \to 0} \frac{\Delta u + i\,\Delta v}{\Delta x + i\,\Delta y} = a + ib,
$$

and, in view of Theorem 1, Sec. 13, it follows that

$$
(2) \qquad \lim_{\substack{\Delta x \to 0 \\ \Delta y \to 0}} \Re\left(\frac{\Delta u + i\,\Delta v}{\Delta x + i\,\Delta y} \right) = a, \qquad \lim_{\substack{\Delta x \to 0 \\ \Delta y \to 0}} \Im\left(\frac{\Delta u + i\,\Delta v}{\Delta x + i\,\Delta y} \right) = b.
$$

In particular, when $\Delta y = 0$, that is, when $\Delta z = \Delta x$ (Fig. 13), these limits reduce to limits of functions of a single variable Δx and it follows that

$$
\lim_{\Delta x \to 0} \frac{u(x_0 + \Delta x,\, y_0) - u(x_0, y_0)}{\Delta x} = a,
$$

$$
\lim_{\Delta x \to 0} \frac{v(x_0 + \Delta x,\, y_0) - v(x_0, y_0)}{\Delta x} = b;
$$

that is, $\partial u / \partial x$ and $\partial v / \partial x$ exist at the point (x_0, y_0) and

$$(3) \qquad \frac{\partial u}{\partial x} = a, \qquad \frac{\partial v}{\partial x} = b \qquad \text{at } (x_0, y_0).$$

Similarly, when $\Delta x = 0$ $(\Delta z = i \, \Delta y)$, we find from equations (2) that

$$\lim_{\Delta y \to 0} \frac{v(x_0, \, y_0 + \Delta y) - v(x_0, y_0)}{\Delta y} = a,$$

$$\lim_{\Delta y \to 0} \frac{u(x_0, \, y_0 + \Delta y) - u(x_0, y_0)}{-\Delta y} = b;$$

thus the partial derivatives with respect to y exist, and

$$(4) \qquad \frac{\partial v}{\partial y} = a, \qquad \frac{\partial u}{\partial y} = -b \qquad \text{at } (x_0, y_0).$$

According to equations (3) and (4) then, at the point z_0

$$(5) \qquad \frac{\partial u}{\partial x} = \frac{\partial v}{\partial y} \qquad \text{and} \qquad \frac{\partial u}{\partial y} = -\frac{\partial v}{\partial x}.$$

These equations are the *Cauchy-Riemann* conditions, so named in honor of the French mathematician A. L. Cauchy[1] (1789–1857), who discovered and used them, and in honor of the German mathematician G. F. B. Riemann (1826–1866), who made them fundamental in his development of the theory of analytic functions.

Since $f'(z_0) = a + ib$, equations (3) and (4) furnish two useful expressions for the derivative of f, namely,

$$(6) \qquad f'(z) = \frac{\partial u}{\partial x} + i \frac{\partial v}{\partial x} = \frac{\partial v}{\partial y} - i \frac{\partial u}{\partial y}$$

at the point $z = z_0$. The following theorem is now established.

Theorem. *If the derivative $f'(z)$ of a function $f = u + iv$ exists at a point z, then the partial derivatives of the first order, with respect to x and y, of each of the components u and v must exist at that point and satisfy the Cauchy-Riemann conditions (5). Also, $f'(z)$ is given in terms of those partial derivatives by formula (6).*

As an illustration, we cite the function

$$f(z) = z^2 = x^2 - y^2 + 2xyi.$$

---

[1] Pronounced *ko-she*.

We proved earlier that its derivative exists everywhere, in fact that $f'(z) = 2z$. Hence the Cauchy-Riemann conditions must be satisfied everywhere. To verify this, we note that $u = x^2 - y^2$ and $v = 2xy$ and therefore

$$\frac{\partial u}{\partial x} = 2x = \frac{\partial v}{\partial y}, \qquad \frac{\partial u}{\partial y} = -2y = -\frac{\partial v}{\partial x}.$$

Also, according to formula (6),

$$f'(z) = \frac{\partial u}{\partial x} + i\frac{\partial v}{\partial x} = 2x + 2yi = 2z.$$

The above theorem presents *necessary* conditions for the existence of $f'(z)$. It shows, for instance, that at each point z where $z \neq 0$ the function $|z|^2$ cannot have a derivative. In this case $u = x^2 + y^2$ and $v = 0$. Although the partial derivatives exist everywhere, $\partial u/\partial x = 2x$ and $\partial v/\partial y = 0$, while $\partial u/\partial y = 2y$ and $\partial v/\partial x = 0$, the Cauchy-Riemann conditions are not satisfied unless $x = y = 0$. Note that the theorem does not ensure the existence of the derivative of $|z|^2$ at $z = 0$; but Theorem 1 in the following section does so.

18. Sufficient Conditions. Conditions on u and v that ensure the existence of the derivative $f'(z)$ are given here.

Theorem 1. *Let u and v be real- and single-valued functions of x and y which, together with their partial derivatives of the first order, are continuous at a point (x_0, y_0). If those partial derivatives satisfy the Cauchy-Riemann conditions at that point, then the derivative $f'(z_0)$ of the function $f = u + iv$ exists, where $z = x + iy$ and $z_0 = x_0 + iy_0$.*

Since u and its partial derivatives of the first order are continuous at (x_0, y_0), those functions are defined throughout some neighborhood of that point. When $(x_0 + \Delta x, \ y_0 + \Delta y)$ is a point in the neighborhood, we can write

$$\Delta u = u(x_0 + \Delta x, \ y_0 + \Delta y) - u(x_0, y_0)$$
$$= \frac{\partial u}{\partial x}\Delta x + \frac{\partial u}{\partial y}\Delta y + \epsilon_1 \Delta x + \epsilon_2 \Delta y,$$

where $\partial u/\partial x$ and $\partial u/\partial y$ are the values of the partial derivatives at the point (x_0, y_0) and where ϵ_1 and ϵ_2 approach zero as both Δx and Δy approach zero. The above formula for Δu is established in advanced calculus in connection with the definition of the differential of the function u.

A similar formula may be written for Δv.   Therefore,

$$\Delta f = f(z_0 + \Delta z) - f(z_0) = \Delta u + i\,\Delta v$$
$$= \frac{\partial u}{\partial x}\,\Delta x + \frac{\partial u}{\partial y}\,\Delta y + \epsilon_1\,\Delta x + \epsilon_2\,\Delta y$$
$$+ i\left(\frac{\partial v}{\partial x}\,\Delta x + \frac{\partial v}{\partial y}\,\Delta y + \epsilon_3\,\Delta x + \epsilon_4\,\Delta y\right).$$

Assuming now that the Cauchy-Riemann conditions are satisfied at the point (x_0, y_0), we can replace $\partial u/\partial y$ by $-\partial v/\partial x$ and $\partial v/\partial y$ by $\partial u/\partial x$ and write the last equation in the form

$$\Delta f = \frac{\partial u}{\partial x}\,(\Delta x + i\,\Delta y) + i\frac{\partial v}{\partial x}\,(\Delta x + i\,\Delta y) + \delta_1\,\Delta x + \delta_2\,\Delta y,$$

where δ_1 and δ_2 approach zero as Δz approaches zero ($\Delta z = \Delta x + i\,\Delta y$).   It follows that

$$(1) \qquad \frac{\Delta f}{\Delta z} = \frac{\partial u}{\partial x} + i\frac{\partial v}{\partial x} + \delta_1\frac{\Delta x}{\Delta z} + \delta_2\frac{\Delta y}{\Delta z}.$$

Since $|\Delta x| \leqq |\Delta z|$ and $|\Delta y| \leqq |\Delta z|$, then

$$\left|\frac{\Delta x}{\Delta z}\right| \leqq 1, \qquad \left|\frac{\Delta y}{\Delta z}\right| \leqq 1,$$

so that the last two terms on the right of equation (1) tend to zero with Δz.   Therefore, at the point z_0,

$$(2) \qquad f'(z) = \lim_{\Delta z \to 0}\frac{\Delta f}{\Delta z} = \frac{\partial u}{\partial x} + i\frac{\partial v}{\partial x};$$

that is, the derivative $f'(z_0)$ exists, and the theorem is proved.

As an illustration of Theorem 1, the functions $u = e^x \cos y$ and $v = e^x \sin y$ are continuous functions of the two variables x and y at all points, as are their partial derivatives of the first order.   It is easily seen that the partial derivatives satisfy the Cauchy-Riemann conditions everywhere.   Consequently the derivative $f'(z)$ of the function

$$(3) \qquad f(z) = e^x \cos y + i\,e^x \sin y$$

exists everywhere.   Since $\partial u/\partial x = u$ and $\partial v/\partial x = v$, it follows from equation (2) that

$$(4) \qquad f'(z) = f(z).$$

Again, let u and v satisfy all the hypotheses stated in Theorem 1; but now we assume that $z_0 \neq 0$. Under the coordinate transformation

$$(5) \qquad x = r \cos \theta, \qquad y = r \sin \theta$$

we can show by the chain rule for differentiation that, since the Cauchy-Riemann conditions (5), Sec. 17, are satisfied at z_0, then the conditions

$$(6) \qquad \frac{\partial u}{\partial r} = \frac{1}{r} \frac{\partial v}{\partial \theta}, \qquad \frac{1}{r} \frac{\partial u}{\partial \theta} = -\frac{\partial v}{\partial r} \qquad (r \neq 0)$$

are satisfied at that point. Here θ is measured in radians. Conversely, conditions (6) imply conditions (5), Sec. 17. Details are left to Exercise 7, below.

Equations (6) are the *Cauchy-Riemann conditions in polar coordinates*. They are useful in connection with the following alternate form of Theorem 1.

Theorem 2. *Let $u(r,\theta)$ and $v(r,\theta)$ each have a single real value at each point z in some neighborhood of a point (r_0,θ_0), and let u, v, and their partial derivatives of the first order with respect to r and θ be continuous functions of z at (r_0,θ_0) and satisfy the Cauchy-Riemann conditions (6) in polar coordinates, at that point, where $r_0 \neq 0$. Then the derivative $f'(z_0)$ of the function $f = u + iv$ exists, where $z_0 = r_0(\cos \theta_0 + i \sin \theta_0)$ and $z = r(\cos \theta + i \sin \theta)$; moreover, at the point $z = z_0$,*

$$(7) \qquad f'(z) = (\cos \theta - i \sin \theta) \left(\frac{\partial u}{\partial r} + i \frac{\partial v}{\partial r} \right).$$

The method used above to prove Theorem 1 can be used again here. The details are not so simple in this case, because of the nature of the formula for Δz in terms of Δr and $\Delta \theta$. The proof is outlined in Exercises 8 to 10 below.

EXERCISES

1. From the theorem in Sec. 17 show that $f'(z)$ does not exist at any point if $f(z)$ is

(*a*) $\bar{z}$;   (*b*) $z - \bar{z}$;   (*c*) $2x + xy^2 i$;   (*d*) $e^x(\cos y - i \sin y)$.

2. Use Theorem 1 to show that $f'(z)$ and its derivative $f''(z)$ exist everywhere, and use formula (2) to find $f'(z)$ and $f''(z)$, when

(a) $f(z) = iz + 2$;   (b) $f(z) = e^{-z}(\cos y - i \sin y)$;
(c) $f(z) = z^3$;   (d) $f(z) = \cos x \cosh y - i \sin x \sinh y$.
          Ans. (b) $f'(z) = -f(z)$, $f''(z) = f(z)$; (d) $f''(z) = -f(z)$.

3. From the results given in Secs. 17 and 18 determine where $f'(z)$ exists and find its value there, when

(a) $f(z) = \dfrac{1}{z}$;   (b) $f(z) = x^2 + iy^2$;   (c) $f(z) = z \, \mathcal{s}(z)$.

   Ans. (a) $f'(z) = -\dfrac{1}{z^2}$ $(z \neq 0)$; (b) $f'(x + ix) = 2x$; (c) $f'(0) = 0$.

4. If $f(z) = z^{\frac{1}{2}}$ where

$$z^{\frac{1}{2}} = \sqrt{r} \left(\cos \frac{\theta}{2} + i \sin \frac{\theta}{2} \right) \quad (r > 0, 0 < \theta < 2\pi),$$

use Theorem 2 to show that $f'(z)$ exists everywhere except along the positive real axis and at the origin and that $f'(z) = 1/[2f(z)]$.

5. If $f(z) = x^3 - i(y - 1)^3$, then $\partial u/\partial x + i \, \partial v/\partial x = 3x^2$.   Why does $3x^2$ represent $f'(z)$ only at the point $z = i$?

6. The hypothesis in Sec. 17, that $f'(z_0) = a + ib$, can be stated as the condition that for each positive number ϵ there is a number δ such that

$$\left| \frac{\Delta f}{\Delta z} - a - ib \right| < \epsilon \quad \text{whenever } 0 < |\Delta z| < \delta.$$

Use that condition to derive equations (3) and (4), Sec. 17.

7. Under the coordinate transformations (5) and the continuity conditions stated in Theorem 1, obtain the partial derivatives of u and v with respect to r and θ in terms of derivatives with respect to x and y; then prove that, at the point z_0 $(z_0 \neq 0)$, conditions (6) are satisfied when conditions (5), Sec. 17, are satisfied, and conversely.

8. To simplify the formulas here, write $E(\theta) = \cos \theta + i \sin \theta$; then the polar form of z is $z = rE(\theta)$. If $\Delta z = (r_0 + \Delta r)E(\theta_0 + \Delta\theta) - r_0 E(\theta_0)$, where $r_0 > 0$, derive the formulas

$$\Delta z = E(\theta_0 + \Delta\theta)[\Delta r + ir_0 \sin \Delta\theta + r_0(1 - \cos \Delta\theta)]$$
$$= E(\theta_0 + \Delta\theta)[\Delta r + ir_0 \, \Delta\theta + r_0 \, \Delta\theta \, h(\Delta\theta)],$$

where $h(\Delta\theta) = \dfrac{1 - \cos \Delta\theta}{\Delta\theta} - i \dfrac{\Delta\theta - \sin \Delta\theta}{\Delta\theta}$ and $\lim\limits_{\Delta\theta \to 0} h(\Delta\theta) = 0.$

9. When $r_0 > 0$ in Exercise 8, prove that $|\Delta\theta/\Delta z|$ is bounded for all Δr and $\Delta\theta$ when $|\Delta\theta|$ is sufficiently small; also, write $|\Delta z|^2$ in terms of Δr and $\Delta\theta$ and prove that $|\Delta r/\Delta z|$ is bounded when $|\Delta r| < r_0$.

10. Prove Theorem 2 by first deriving, with the aid of conditions (6) and results found in Exercises 8 and 9, these formulas:

$$\Delta f = \left(\frac{\partial u}{\partial r} + i\frac{\partial v}{\partial r}\right)(\Delta r + ir_0\,\Delta\theta) + \sigma_1\,\Delta r + \sigma_2\,\Delta\theta$$

$$= E(-\theta_0 - \Delta\theta)\left(\frac{\partial u}{\partial r} + i\frac{\partial v}{\partial r}\right)\Delta z + \sigma_1\,\Delta r + \sigma_3\,\Delta\theta,$$

where $\partial u/\partial r$ and $\partial v/\partial r$ are evaluated at z_0 and where

$$\sigma_n \to 0 \qquad \text{as } \Delta z \to 0 \qquad\qquad (n = 1, 2, 3).$$

19. Analytic Functions. A function f of the complex variable z is *analytic at a point* z_0 if its derivative $f'(z)$ exists not only at z_0 but at every point z in some neighborhood of z_0. It is *analytic in a domain* of the z plane if it is analytic at every point in that domain. The terms "regular" and "holomorphic" are sometimes introduced to denote analyticity in domains of certain classes.

The function $|z|^2$, for instance, is not analytic at any point, since its derivative exists only at the point $z = 0$, not throughout any neighborhood.

An *entire* function is one that is analytic at every point of the z plane, that is, throughout the entire plane. We have shown (Exercise 1, Sec. 16) that the derivative of every polynomial in z exists at every point; hence *every polynomial*

$$P(z) = a_0 + a_1 z + a_2 z^2 + \cdots + a_n z^n \qquad (n = 0, 1, 2, \ldots)$$

is an entire function.

If a function is analytic at some point in every neighborhood of a point z_0 except at z_0 itself, then z_0 is called a *singular point*, or a *singularity*, of the function.

For example, we have seen that, if

$$f(z) = \frac{1}{z}, \qquad \text{then} \qquad f'(z) = -\frac{1}{z^2} \qquad (z \neq 0).$$

Thus f is analytic at every point except the point $z = 0$, where it is not continuous, so that $f'(0)$ cannot exist. The point $z = 0$ is a singular point. On the other hand, our definition assigns no singular points at all to the function $|z|^2$, since the function is nowhere analytic.

A necessary, but by no means sufficient, condition for a function to be analytic in a domain D is clearly that the function be continuous throughout D. The Cauchy-Riemann conditions are also necessary, but not sufficient. Two sets of sufficient conditions for analyticity in D are given by Theorems 1 and 2, Sec. 18, if the hypotheses stated in those theorems are satisfied at every point of D. But other useful sets of sufficient conditions arise in the following way from the conditions of validity of the differentiation formulas (Sec. 16).

The derivatives of the sum and product of two functions exist wherever the functions themselves have derivatives. Thus, *if two functions are analytic in a domain D, their sum and their product are both analytic in D.* Similarly, *their quotient is analytic in D* provided that the function in the denominator does not vanish at any point of D. In particular, the quotient P/Q of two polynomials is analytic in any domain throughout which $Q(z) \neq 0$.

Let g be an analytic function of z in a domain D_1, and let R denote the range of $g(z)$ for all z in D_1. Then, if f is analytic in a domain D_2 that contains R, it follows from the conditions of validity of differentiation formula (6), Sec. 16, that the composite function $f[g(z)]$ is analytic in D_1. In brief, *an analytic function of an analytic function is analytic.*

As an illustration, the function $g(z) = 1 + z^2$ is entire. According to Exercise 4, Sec. 18, the function

$$f(z) = z^{\frac{1}{2}} = \sqrt{r}\left(\cos\frac{\theta}{2} + i \sin\frac{\theta}{2}\right) \qquad (r > 0, 0 < \theta < 2\pi)$$

is analytic in its domain of definition. In particular, it is analytic in the upper half plane $\mathcal{I}(z) > 0$, an example of the domain called D_2 in the preceding paragraph. Since $\mathcal{I}[g(z)] = 2xy$, the range of g is confined to that half plane if $xy > 0$. Thus the composite function

$$f[g(z)] = (1 + z^2)^{\frac{1}{2}} \qquad (x > 0, y > 0)$$

is analytic in the domain D_1 consisting of the quadrant $x > 0$, $y > 0$ of the z plane.

We note also that *an entire function of an entire function is again entire.*

20. Harmonic Functions. Let the function $f = u + iv$ be analytic in some domain of the z plane. Then at every point of the domain

$$(1) \qquad \frac{\partial u}{\partial x} = \frac{\partial v}{\partial y}, \qquad \frac{\partial u}{\partial y} = -\frac{\partial v}{\partial x},$$

and therefore

$$(2) \qquad \frac{\partial^2 u}{\partial x^2} = \frac{\partial^2 v}{\partial x \, \partial y}, \qquad \frac{\partial^2 u}{\partial y^2} = -\frac{\partial^2 v}{\partial y \, \partial x},$$

provided these second derivatives exist. We shall show in Chap. 5 (Sec. 52) that, when f is analytic, the partial derivatives of u and v of all orders exist and are continuous functions of x and y. Granting this for the present, it follows that the two cross derivatives in equations (2) are equal and therefore that

$$(3) \qquad \frac{\partial^2 u}{\partial x^2} + \frac{\partial^2 u}{\partial y^2} = 0$$

throughout the domain.

Equation (3) is *Laplace's* partial differential equation in two independent variables x and y. Any function that has continuous partial derivatives of the second order and that satisfies Laplace's equation is called a *harmonic function*.

The function v, as well as u, is harmonic when the function $f = u + iv$ is an analytic function. This can be shown by differentiating the first of equations (1) with respect to y, the second with respect to x, and subtracting to get the equation

$$(4) \qquad \frac{\partial^2 v}{\partial x^2} + \frac{\partial^2 v}{\partial y^2} = 0.$$

If the function $f = u + iv$ is analytic, then u and v are called *conjugate harmonic functions*. This is a different use of the word *conjugate* from that employed in defining $\bar{z}$.

Given one of two conjugate harmonic functions, the Cauchy-Riemann equations (1) can be used to find the other. We shall now illustrate one method of obtaining the conjugate harmonic of a given harmonic function.

The function

$$u = y^3 - 3x^2 y$$

is readily seen, by direct substitution into Laplace's equation, to be a harmonic function. In order to find its harmonic conjugate v, we note that

$$\frac{\partial u}{\partial x} = -6xy,$$

from which, by using one of the Cauchy-Riemann equations, we may conclude that

$$\frac{\partial v}{\partial y} = -6xy.$$

Integrating this equation with respect to y with x held fixed, we find that

$$v = -3xy^2 + \phi(x),$$

where $\phi(x)$ is at present an arbitrary function of x.   But since $\partial v/\partial x = -\partial u/\partial y$, it follows that

$$-3y^2 + \phi'(x) = -3y^2 + 3x^2;$$

therefore $\phi'(x) = 3x^2$ and $\phi(x) = x^3 + c$, where c is an arbitrary constant.   Hence the harmonic conjugate of the function $u = y^3 - 3x^2y$ is

$$v = -3xy^2 + x^3 + c.$$

The corresponding function $f = u + iv$ is

(5) $$f(z) = y^3 - 3x^2y + i(x^3 - 3xy^2) + ic.$$

It is easily verified that

$$f(z) = i(z^3 + c).$$

This form is suggested by noting that when $y = 0$, equation (5) becomes

$$f(x) = i(x^3 + c).$$

Later on (Sec. 78) we shall show that, corresponding to each harmonic function u, a conjugate harmonic function v exists. We shall use a line integral to write an explicit formula for v in terms of u.

EXERCISES

1. Prove that each of these functions is entire:

(a) $f(z) = 3x + y + i(3y - x)$;
(b) $f(z) = \sin x \cosh y + i \cos x \sinh y$;
(c) $f(z) = e^{-y}(\cos x + i \sin x)$;
(d) $f(z) = (z^2 - 2)e^{-x}(\cos y - i \sin y)$.

2. Show why each of these functions is nowhere analytic:

(a) $f(z) = xy + iy$;   (b) $f(z) = e^y(\cos x + i \sin x)$.

3. Determine the singular points of each of these functions and state why the function is analytic everywhere except at those points:

(a) $\dfrac{2z+1}{z(z^2+1)}$;   (b) $\dfrac{z^3+i}{z^2-3z+2}$;   (c) $(z+2)^{-1}(z^2+2z+2)^{-1}$.

Ans. (a) $z = 0$, $\pm i$; (c) $z = -2$, $-1 \pm i$.

4. If $z = r(\cos\theta + i\sin\theta)$, prove that the function

$$F(z) = \log r + i\theta \qquad \left(r > 0, -\frac{\pi}{2} < \theta < \frac{\pi}{2}\right)$$

is analytic in the domain of definition indicated and that $F'(z) = 1/z$ there.   Then show why the composite function $F(2z + i - 2)$ is an analytic function of z in the domain $x > 1$.

5. If $u + iv$ is analytic, state why $-v + iu$ is also analytic.   Consequently, show that, if u and v are conjugate harmonic functions, then u and $-v$ are also conjugate harmonic functions.   In the example given in Sec. 20, therefore, $3xy^2 - x^3 + C$ is another harmonic conjugate to the function $y^3 - 3x^2y$.

6. Show that u is harmonic in some domain and find a harmonic conjugate v, when

(a) $u = 2x(1 - y)$;   (b) $u = 2x - x^3 + 3xy^2$;
(c) $u = \sinh x \sin y$;   (d) $u = y(x^2 + y^2)^{-1}$.

Ans. (a) $v = x^2 - y^2 + 2y$; (c) $v = -\cosh x \cos y$.

7. Let u and v be conjugate harmonic functions.   Their contour curves or level lines are the families of curves $u = c_1$ and $v = c_2$.   Prove that these families of curves are orthogonal.   More precisely, show that at any point (x_0,y_0) that is common to a curve $u = c_1$ and a curve $v = c_2$, the tangents (or normals) to the two curves are perpendicular, provided $\partial u/\partial x$ and $\partial u/\partial y$ do not both vanish at the point, that is, provided $f'(z_0) \neq 0$ where $f = u + iv$.

8. Show that when

$$f(z) = u + iv = z^2,$$

the families of curves $u = c_1$ and $v = c_2$ are those shown in Fig. 14. Note the orthogonality of these curves as proved in Exercise 7.   The curves $u = 0$ and $v = 0$ intersect at the origin and are not orthogonal to each other.   Why is this fact in agreement with the result of Exercise 7?

9. Sketch the families of curves $u = c_1$ and $v = c_2$ when $f(z) = 1/z$ and note the orthogonality proved in Exercise 7.

10. Sketch the families of curves $u = c_1$ and $v = c_2$ when

$$f(z) = \frac{z-1}{z+1},$$

and note how the results of Exercise 7 are illustrated here.

11. Solve Exercise 9 using polar coordinates.

12. Let a function f be analytic in a domain D that does not include the point $z = 0$. If $f(z) = u(r,\theta) + iv(r,\theta)$, use the Cauchy-Riemann

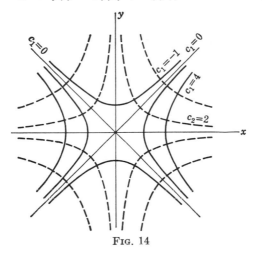

FIG. 14

conditions in polar coordinates to show that, in D, both u and v satisfy Laplace's equation in polar coordinates,

$$r^2 \frac{\partial^2 u}{\partial r^2} + r \frac{\partial u}{\partial r} + \frac{\partial^2 u}{\partial \theta^2} = 0 \qquad (\theta \text{ in radians}),$$

given that all partial derivatives of u and v up to the second order are continuous.

13. In the domain $r > 0$, $0 < \theta < 2\pi$, show that the function $u = \log r$ is harmonic (Exercise 12) and find its harmonic conjugate.

Ans. $v = \theta + c$.

14. If in some domain a function $f = u + iv$ and its complex conjugate $\bar{f} = u - iv$ are both analytic, prove that f is a constant.

15. If f is analytic in some domain, prove that its absolute value $|f|$ cannot be a constant there unless f is a constant.

16. Point out why the final statement in Sec. 19, that the composition $f(g)$ of two entire functions is an entire function, is true without qualification. Also, state why a *linear combination* $bf + cg$, where b and c are complex constants, of entire functions f and g is again entire.

CHAPTER 3

ELEMENTARY FUNCTIONS

21. The Exponential Function. We *define* the exponential function, exp, in terms of real-valued functions by the equation

(1) $$\exp z = e^x(\cos y + i \sin y),$$

where $z = x + iy$ and the number y is used as the *radian* measure of the angle in defining the numbers $\cos y$ and $\sin y$. The symbol e^z is also used to denote exp z; but at present that symbol cannot represent a zth power of the base e of natural logarithms, because only real exponents have been introduced. Note that exp z is *single-valued* for each z.

As to reasons for choosing the definition (1), we note first that, in case $y = 0$, the definition reduces to that of the real exponential function, exp $x = e^x$. In case $x = 0$, equation (1) becomes

(2) $$\exp (iy) = \cos y + i \sin y.$$

This definition of exp (iy), or e^{iy}, is a natural one if we are to expect the Maclaurin series representation of e^t (t real) to apply when t is replaced by iy, for then the series can be written, formally,

(3) $$\sum_{n=0}^{\infty} \frac{(iy)^n}{n!} = \sum_{n=0}^{\infty} \frac{i^{2n}y^{2n}}{(2n)!} + \sum_{n=0}^{\infty} \frac{i^{2n+1}y^{2n+1}}{(2n+1)!}$$

$$= \sum_{n=0}^{\infty} (-1)^n \frac{y^{2n}}{(2n)!} + i \sum_{n=0}^{\infty} (-1)^n \frac{y^{2n+1}}{(2n+1)!},$$

where $0! = 1$. The last two series here are the Maclaurin series for $\cos y$ and $\sin y$, respectively.

Actually, exp z is often defined as the sum of a power series in z that reduces to series (3) when $x = 0$. But then infinite

46

series in powers of z (Chap. 6) must be introduced before exponential functions.

The exponential function (1) *is an entire function.*   This follows from Theorem 1, Sec. 18, since the components

$$(4) \qquad u = e^x \cos y, \qquad v = e^x \sin y$$

and their partial derivatives are everywhere continuous and satisfy the Cauchy-Riemann conditions.   Moreover,

$$\frac{\partial u}{\partial x} + i \frac{\partial v}{\partial x} = u + iv;$$

that is,

$$(5) \qquad \frac{d}{dz} \exp z = \exp z.$$

The two functions (4) are conjugate harmonic functions of x and y everywhere, because they are the components of an entire function (Sec. 20).

If w is an analytic function of z in a domain D, then the composite function exp w is an analytic function of z in D, because the exponential function is entire.   According to formula (6), Sec. 16, for the derivative of a function of a function, when z is in D,

$$(6) \qquad \frac{d}{dz} \exp w = \frac{dw}{dz} \exp w.$$

22. Other Properties of exp z.   Since $e^x > 0$ for each real number x, for each number z our definition

$$(1) \qquad \exp z = e^x(\cos y + i \sin y)$$

represents the complex number exp z in polar form

$$(2) \qquad \exp z = \rho(\cos \phi + i \sin \phi), \qquad \text{where } \rho = e^x, \phi = y;$$

that is, $|\exp z| = e^x$, while y is a value of the argument in radians:

$$(3) \qquad |e^z| = e^x, \qquad \arg e^z = y.$$

Thus $|e^z| > 0$ for every value of z, which means that

$$(4) \qquad e^z \neq 0 \qquad\qquad \text{for any number } z.$$

According to the representation (2), corresponding to each positive value of ρ there is a value of x ($x = \log \rho$) and, independently, to each angle ϕ there corresponds a value y $(y = \phi)$. Consequently, *the range of the exponential function is the entire complex plane except for the origin* $\rho = 0$.

Values of z must exist, for instance, such that $\exp z = -1$. Since -1 has the polar form (2) where $\rho = 1$ and $\phi = \pi \pm 2n\pi$ $(n = 0, 1, 2, \ldots)$, it follows that $x = 0$ and $y = \pi \pm 2n\pi$, or $z = (1 \pm 2n)\pi i$.

Laws of exponents for the function follow from the representation (2) of $\exp z$ in polar form and our formulas (Secs. 7 and 8) for products, quotients, powers, and roots of complex numbers in polar form.   We write $z_1 = x_1 + iy$, $z_2 = x_2 + iy_2$,

$$\exp z_1 = \rho_1(\cos \phi_1 + i \sin \phi_1) \quad \text{where } \rho_1 = e^{x_1}, \phi_1 = y_1,$$
$$\exp z_2 = \rho_2(\cos \phi_2 + i \sin \phi_2) \quad \text{where } \rho_2 = e^{x_2}, \phi_2 = y_2.$$

Then

$$(\exp z_1)(\exp z_2) = \rho_1\rho_2[\cos (\phi_1 + \phi_2) + i \sin (\phi_1 + \phi_2)]$$
$$= e^{x_1}e^{x_2}[\cos (y_1 + y_2) + i \sin (y_1 + y_2)].$$

But $e^{x_1}e^{x_2} = e^{x_1+x_2}$ and $x_1 + x_2 + i(y_1 + y_2) = z_1 + z_2$; hence

$$(5) \qquad (\exp z_1)(\exp z_2) = \exp (z_1 + z_2).$$

In like manner we find that

$$(6) \qquad \frac{\exp z_1}{\exp z_2} = \exp (z_1 - z_2);$$

in particular, $1/\exp z = \exp (-z)$.   Also, if m and n are positive integers,

$$(7) \qquad (\exp z)^n = \exp (nz),$$

$$(8) \qquad (\exp z)^{m/n} = \exp \left[\frac{m}{n} (z + 2\pi ki) \right]$$
$$(k = 0, 1, 2, \ldots, n - 1).$$

Since $\exp (z + 2\pi i) = \exp z \exp (2\pi i)$ and $\exp (2\pi i) = 1$, *the exponential function is periodic* with period $2\pi i$; that is,

$$(9) \qquad \exp (z + 2\pi i) = \exp z.$$

From the definition (1) we can see that

$$(10) \qquad \exp \bar{z} = \overline{\exp z}.$$

In terms of the exponential function, the polar form of a complex number, $z = r(\cos \theta + i \sin \theta)$, has the convenient representations

$$(11) \qquad z = r \exp (i\theta) = re^{i\theta}.$$

Also, formulas for operations on numbers in polar form take simpler forms; for instance, $\bar{z} = r \exp (-i\theta)$, and

$$(12) \quad z_1 z_2 = r_1 r_2 \exp [i(\theta_1 + \theta_2)], \qquad \frac{z_1}{z_2} = \frac{r_1}{r_2} \exp [i(\theta_1 - \theta_2)]$$

$$(r_2 \neq 0).$$

EXERCISES

1. Show that

(a) $\exp 0 = 1$;   (b) $\exp (2 \pm 3\pi i) = -e^2$;

(c) $\exp \left(\frac{\pi}{2} i\right) = i$;   (d) $\exp \frac{2 + \pi i}{4} = \sqrt{e}\, \frac{1 + i}{\sqrt{2}}$.

2. Show that

(a) $\exp (z + \pi i) = -\exp z$;

(b) $\exp (-nz) = \dfrac{1}{(\exp z)^n}$ $(n = 1, 2, \ldots)$.

3. When z has the polar representation $z = r \exp (i\theta)$, show that

(a) $\bar{z} = r \exp (-i\theta)$;   (b) $\exp (\log r + i\theta) = z$.

4. Find all values of z such that

(a) $\exp z = -2$;   (b) $\exp z = 1 + i \sqrt{3}$;   (c) $\exp (2z - 1) = 1$.
Ans. (a) $z = \log 2 \pm (2n + 1)\pi i$;   (c) $z = \frac{1}{2} \pm n\pi i$
$$(n = 0, 1, 2, \ldots).$$

5. Derive the exponential laws (6) and (7), with the aid of formulas in Sec. 7.

6. Derive the exponential law (8), with the aid of formulas in Sec. 8.

7. Show that $\exp (i\bar{z}) \neq \overline{\exp (iz)}$ unless $z = \pm n\pi$, where $n = 0, 1, 2, \ldots$.

8. Simplify $|\exp (2z + i)|$ and $|\exp (iz^2)|$ and show that

$$|\exp (2z + i) + \exp (iz^2)| \leq e^{2x} + e^{-2xy}.$$

9. Prove that $|\exp (-2z)| < 1$ whenever the point z lies in the half plane $x > 0$, and only for such values of z.

10. (a) If exp z is real, show that $\mathcal{I}(z) = \pm n\pi$ $(n = 0, 1, 2, \ldots)$.
(b) For what set of values of z does exp z have pure imaginary values?

11. Examine the behavior (a) of exp $(x + iy)$ as $x \to -\infty$; (b) of exp $(2 + iy)$ as $y \to \infty$.

12. State why the function $2z^2 - 3 - ze^z + e^{-z}$ is entire.

13. Prove that exp $\bar{z}$ is nowhere an analytic function of z.

14. Show in two ways that the function exp (z^2) is entire. What is its derivative?   *Ans.* $2z$ exp (z^2).

15. Simplify $\mathfrak{R}[\exp (1/z)]$.   Why must this be a harmonic function of x and y in every domain that does not contain the origin?

16. If $u + iv$ is an analytic function of z in a domain D, show that the functions U and V, where

$$U(x,y) = \exp [u(x,y)] \cos [v(x,y)],$$
$$V(x,y) = \exp [u(x,y)] \sin [v(x,y)],$$

must be harmonic in D, in fact, that they are conjugate harmonic functions.

23. The Trigonometric Functions.   From the formulas

$$e^{iy} = \cos y + i \sin y, \qquad e^{-iy} = \cos y - i \sin y,$$

it follows that, for every real number y,

(1) $$\frac{e^{iy} + e^{-iy}}{2} = \cos y, \qquad \frac{e^{iy} - e^{-iy}}{2i} = \sin y.$$

It is therefore natural to *define* the cosine and sine functions of a complex variable z by the equations

(2) $$\cos z = \frac{e^{iz} + e^{-iz}}{2}, \qquad \sin z = \frac{e^{iz} - e^{-iz}}{2i}.$$

Both sin z and cos z are entire functions, according to equations (2), because they are linear combinations (Exercise 16, Sec. 20) of the entire functions exp (iz) and exp $(-iz)$.

Knowing the derivatives of the exponential functions in equations (2), we find the differentiation formulas

(3) $$\frac{d}{dz} \sin z = \cos z, \qquad \frac{d}{dz} \cos z = - \sin z.$$

The other four trigonometric functions are defined in terms of the sine and cosine functions by the usual relations

(4)
$$\tan z = \frac{\sin z}{\cos z}, \qquad \cot z = \frac{\cos z}{\sin z},$$
$$\sec z = \frac{1}{\cos z}, \qquad \csc z = \frac{1}{\sin z}.$$

Thus $\tan z$ and $\sec z$ are analytic in any domain where $\cos z \neq 0$. and $\cot z$ and $\csc z$ are analytic in any domain where $\sin z \neq 0$. By differentiating the right-hand members of equations (4), we find that

(5)
$$\frac{d}{dz}\tan z = \sec^2 z, \qquad \frac{d}{dz}\cot z = -\csc^2 z,$$
$$\frac{d}{dz}\sec z = \sec z \tan z, \qquad \frac{d}{dz}\csc z = -\csc z \cot z.$$

From the definition of $\cos z$ it follows that

$$\cos z = \cos (x + iy) = \tfrac{1}{2}(e^{ix-y} + e^{-ix+y})$$
$$= \tfrac{1}{2}e^{-y}(\cos x + i \sin x) + \tfrac{1}{2}e^{y}(\cos x - i \sin x)$$
$$= \frac{e^{y} + e^{-y}}{2} \cos x - i\,\frac{e^{y} - e^{-y}}{2} \sin x.$$

Thus the real and imaginary parts of $\cos z$ are displayed as follows:

(6) $\quad \cos z = \cos (x + iy) = \cos x \cosh y - i \sin x \sinh y.$

In the same manner we find that

(7) $\quad \sin z = \sin (x + iy) = \sin x \cosh y + i \cos x \sinh y.$

It is evident from these two formulas that

(8) $\qquad \sin (iy) = i \sinh y, \qquad \cos (iy) = \cosh y;$

also that $\sin \bar{z}$ and $\cos \bar{z}$ are the complex conjugates of $\sin z$ and $\cos z$, respectively.

These properties on the periodic character of the functions follow readily from formulas (6) and (7) and the definition of $\tan z$:

(9)
$$\cos (z + \pi) = -\cos z, \qquad \sin (z + \pi) = -\sin z,$$
$$\tan (z + \pi) = \tan z;$$
(10) $\qquad \cos (z + 2\pi) = \cos z, \qquad \sin (z + 2\pi) = \sin z.$

24. Further Properties of Trigonometric Functions. By using either formulas (1) and (2) or formulas (7) and (6) of the preceding section, the reader can show that

$$(1) \qquad\qquad |\sin z|^2 = \sin^2 x + \sinh^2 y,$$
$$(2) \qquad\qquad |\cos z|^2 = \cos^2 x + \sinh^2 y.$$

It is clear from these two formulas that the complex functions $\sin z$ and $\cos z$ are not bounded in absolute value, whereas in real variables the absolute values of the sine and cosine functions are never greater than unity.

The expected trigonometric identities are still valid in complex variables; thus

$$(3) \qquad\qquad \sin^2 z + \cos^2 z = 1,$$
$$(4) \qquad \sin (z_1 + z_2) = \sin z_1 \cos z_2 + \cos z_1 \sin z_2,$$
$$(5) \qquad \cos (z_1 + z_2) = \cos z_1 \cos z_2 - \sin z_1 \sin z_2,$$
$$(6) \qquad \sin (-z) = - \sin z, \qquad \cos (-z) = \cos z,$$
$$(7) \qquad\qquad \sin \left(\frac{\pi}{2} - z \right) = \cos z,$$
$$(8) \qquad \sin 2z = 2 \sin z \cos z, \qquad \cos 2z = \cos^2 z - \sin^2 z,$$

etc. Proofs may be based entirely upon the properties of the exponential function. They are left as exercises.

A value of z for which $f(z) = 0$ is called a *zero* of the function f.

The real zeros of sin z and cos z are their only zeros. To prove this for the sine function, we write $\sin z = 0$; then, according to equation (7), Sec. 23, x and y must satisfy the simultaneous equations

$$\sin x \cosh y = 0, \qquad \cos x \sinh y = 0.$$

Since x and y are real, $\cosh y \geq 1$, so that it cannot vanish, and $\sin x = 0$ only when $x = 0, \pm\pi, \pm 2\pi, \ldots$. But for those values of x, $\cos x$ does not vanish. Hence $\sinh y = 0$; that is, $y = 0$. Therefore

$$(9) \quad \sin z = 0 \text{ implies } z = 0 \text{ or } z = \pm n\pi \qquad (n = 1, 2, \ldots).$$

This statement also applies to $\tan z$. In like manner we find that

$$(10) \qquad \cos z = 0 \text{ implies } z = \pm \frac{(2n - 1)\pi}{2} \qquad (n = 1, 2, \ldots).$$

In view of statement (10), the singular points of $\tan z$ consist of the points $z = \pm (2n - 1)\pi/2$; the tangent function is analytic at all other points.

EXERCISES

1. Establish the differentiation formulas (5), Sec. 23.

2. Derive formulas (7) and (8) in Sec. 23.

3. Derive formula (1) above; then show that

$$|\sinh y| \leq |\sin z| \leq \cosh y.$$

4. Derive formula (2); then show that $|\sinh y| \leq |\cos z| \leq \cosh y$.

5. Show that $|\sin z| \geq |\sin x|$ and $|\cos z| \geq |\cos x|$.

6. Establish identities (3) and (4) of this section.

7. Prove that (a) $1 + \tan^2 z = \sec^2 z$; (b) $1 + \cot^2 z = \csc^2 z$.

8. Establish the identities

(a) $2 \sin (z_1 + z_2) \sin (z_1 - z_2) = \cos 2z_2 - \cos 2z_1$;

(b) $2 \cos (z_1 + z_2) \sin (z_1 - z_2) = \sin 2z_1 - \sin 2z_2$.

9. Show that $\cos (i\bar{z}) = \overline{\cos (iz)}$ for all z, and that $\sin (i\bar{z}) \neq \overline{\sin (iz)}$ unless $z = \pm n\pi i$, where $n = 0, 1, 2, \ldots$.

10. Prove statement (10) of this section.

11. With the aid of the identities in Exercise 8 show that (a) if $\cos z_1 = \cos z_2$, then $z_2 = \pm z_1 \pm 2n\pi$; (b) if $\sin z_1 = \sin z_2$, then either $z_2 = z_1 \pm 2n\pi$ or $z_2 = -z_1 \pm (2n + 1)\pi$, where $n = 0, 1, 2, \ldots$.

12. Find all roots of the equation $\cos z = 2$.

Ans. $z = \pm 2n\pi + i \cosh^{-1} 2 = \pm 2n\pi \pm i \log (2 + \sqrt{3})$
$$(n = 0, 1, 2, \ldots).$$

13. Find all roots of the equation $\sin z = \cosh 4$.

Ans. $z = (\pm 2n + \tfrac{1}{2})\pi \pm 4i$ $(n = 0, 1, 2, \ldots)$.

14. Show in two ways that each of these functions is everywhere harmonic:

(a) $\sin x \sinh y$; (b) $\cos 2x \sinh 2y$.

15. If w is an analytic function of z in some domain, state why $\sin w$ and $\cos w$ are analytic functions of z in that domain, with derivatives $\cos w \, dw/dz$ and $- \sin w \, dw/dz$, respectively.

16. Show that neither (a) $\sin \bar{z}$ nor (b) $\cos \bar{z}$ is an analytic function of z anywhere.

25. Hyperbolic Functions. The hyperbolic sine and cosine of a complex argument are defined as they were with real arguments; that is,

$$(1) \qquad \sinh z = \frac{e^z - e^{-z}}{2}, \qquad \cosh z = \frac{e^z + e^{-z}}{2}.$$

The hyperbolic tangent of z is defined by the equation

$$\tanh z = \frac{\sinh z}{\cosh z},$$

and then coth z, sech z, and csch z are defined as the reciprocals of tanh z, cosh z, and sinh z, respectively.

Since exp z and exp $(-z)$ are entire, it follows from definitions (1) that sinh z and cosh z are entire functions. The function tanh z is analytic in every domain that contains no zeros of cosh z.

The calculus and algebra of those hyperbolic functions can be derived readily from the definitions above. The formulas are the same as those established for the corresponding functions of real variables; thus

(2) $\dfrac{d}{dz} \sinh z = \cosh z, \qquad \dfrac{d}{dz} \cosh z = \sinh z,$

(3) $\dfrac{d}{dz} \tanh z = \operatorname{sech}^2 z, \qquad \dfrac{d}{dz} \coth z = - \operatorname{csch}^2 z,$

(4)
$$\dfrac{d}{dz} \operatorname{sech} z = - \operatorname{sech} z \tanh z,$$
$$\dfrac{d}{dz} \operatorname{csch} z = - \operatorname{csch} z \coth z.$$

Some of the most frequently used identities are

(5) $\cosh^2 z - \sinh^2 z = 1,$
(6) $\sinh (z_1 + z_2) = \sinh z_1 \cosh z_2 + \cosh z_1 \sinh z_2,$
(7) $\cosh (z_1 + z_2) = \cosh z_1 \cosh z_2 + \sinh z_1 \sinh z_2,$
(8) $\sinh 2z = 2 \sinh z \cosh z,$
(9) $\sinh (-z) = - \sinh z, \qquad \cosh (-z) = \cosh z.$

The relations between the hyperbolic and circular functions also follow from the definitions of those functions in terms of the exponential functions; thus

(10) $\sinh (iz) = i \sin z, \qquad \cosh (iz) = \cos z,$
(11) $\sin (iz) = i \sinh z, \qquad \cos (iz) = \cosh z.$

The real and imaginary components of the first two hyperbolic functions are shown in the formulas

(12) $\sinh (x + iy) = \sinh x \cos y + i \cosh x \sin y,$
(13) $\cosh (x + iy) = \cosh x \cos y + i \sinh x \sin y.$

The reader can show in various ways that

(14) $|\sinh z|^2 = \sinh^2 x + \sin^2 y,$

(15) $|\cosh z|^2 = \sinh^2 x + \cos^2 y.$

The functions sinh z and cosh z are periodic with period $2\pi i$; but their ratio tanh z is also periodic with period πi. The zeros of sinh z are the numbers $\pm n\pi i$, and the zeros of cosh z are $\pm (n + \frac{1}{2})\pi i$, where $n = 0, 1, 2, \ldots$. Consequently the latter set of numbers, $z = \pm (n + \frac{1}{2})\pi i$, is the set of singular points of the function tanh z.

EXERCISES

1. Derive the differentiation formulas (2) and (4).

2. Prove the identities (5) and (7).

3. Show how formulas (12) and (13) follow from identities (6), (7), and (10).

4. Derive formula (15); then show that sinh $|x| \leqq |\cosh z| \leqq \cosh x$.

5. Show that sinh $(z + \pi i) = -$ sinh z and cosh $(z + \pi i) = -$ cosh z, and hence that tanh $(z + \pi i) =$ tanh z.

6. Find all the zeros of (a) sinh z; (b) cosh z.

7. Find all the roots of the equations

(a) $\cosh z = \frac{1}{2}$; (b) $\sinh z = i$; (c) $\cosh z = -2$.

        Ans. (a) $(\pm \frac{1}{3} \pm 2n)\pi i$; (b) $(\frac{1}{2} \pm 2n)\pi i$ $(n = 0, 1, 2, \ldots)$.

8. Why is the function sinh (e^z) entire? Write its real component as a function of x and y and state why that component must be a harmonic function everywhere.

26. The Logarithmic Function. Branches. Henceforth let us write either Log r or ln r, instead of log r, for the real natural logarithm of a positive number r. We now *define* the function log of a complex variable z, where $z = r \exp (i\theta)$ and the argument θ is measured in *radians*, by the equation

(1) $\log z = \log (re^{i\theta}) = \text{Log } r + i\theta$ if $r > 0$.

The definition is a natural one in the sense that it is written by formally using properties of real logarithms.

Corresponding to the particular argument Θ of z such that

$$-\pi < \Theta \leqq \pi,$$

we may write $z = r \exp [i(\Theta \pm 2n\pi)]$, where $n = 0, 1, 2, \ldots$

Thus formula (1) can be written

$$(2) \qquad \log z = \operatorname{Log} r + i(\Theta \pm 2n\pi) \qquad (n = 0, 1, 2, \ldots);$$

that is, the function $\log z$ is multiple-valued with infinitely many values. We shall call the *principal value* of $\log z$ the number defined by formula (2) when $n = 0$, and write this as $\operatorname{Log} z$; thus

$$(3) \qquad \operatorname{Log} z = \operatorname{Log} r + i\Theta \qquad (r > 0, -\pi < \Theta \leqq \pi).$$

Note that, if z is real and positive, then $z = r$, so that the symbol $\operatorname{Log} r$ represents the principal value of $\log r$.

Consider the behavior of the single-valued function $\operatorname{Log} z$ defined by equation (3), at each point $z = x_0$ $(x_0 < 0)$ of the negative real axis. At that point $r = -x_0$ and $\Theta = \pi$. But the imaginary component Θ of $\operatorname{Log} z$ is not a continuous function of z at x_0, because its value there is π while its value throughout the lower half of each small neighborhood of x_0 is near $-\pi$. Therefore $\operatorname{Log} z$ is not continuous at the point $z = x_0$, and so its derivative cannot exist there.

The single-valued function

$$(4) \qquad \operatorname{Log} z = \operatorname{Log} r + i\Theta \qquad (r > 0, -\pi < \Theta < \pi),$$

defined at all points $z = r \exp (i\Theta)$ except for the origin and points on the negative real axis, does have continuous components

$$u = \operatorname{Log} r, \qquad v = \Theta$$

throughout its domain of definition. Moreover, the derivatives

$$\frac{\partial u}{\partial r} = \frac{1}{r}, \qquad \frac{\partial u}{\partial \Theta} = 0, \qquad \frac{\partial v}{\partial r} = 0, \qquad \frac{\partial v}{\partial \Theta} = 1$$

are all continuous functions of the point z in that domain, and they satisfy the Cauchy-Riemann conditions in polar coordinates. It follows from Theorem 2, Sec. 18, that *the function $\operatorname{Log} z$ defined by equation (4) is analytic in its domain of definition $r > 0$, $-\pi < \Theta < \pi$.* Furthermore,

$$\frac{d}{dz} \operatorname{Log} z = \exp (-i\Theta) \left(\frac{\partial u}{\partial r} + i \frac{\partial v}{\partial r} \right) = \frac{1}{r \exp(i\Theta)};$$

that is, the formula for the derivative of that function becomes

$$(5) \qquad \frac{d}{dz} \operatorname{Log} z = \frac{1}{z} \qquad (z \neq 0, -\pi < \arg z < \pi).$$

The function log z defined by equation (1) can be made single-valued and continuous by limiting r and θ so that $r > 0$ and $\theta_0 < \theta < \theta_0 + 2\pi$, where θ_0 is any fixed angle in radians. Then we can write

$$(6) \qquad \log z = \operatorname{Log} r + i\theta \qquad (r > 0, \theta_0 < \theta < \theta_0 + 2\pi).$$

Throughout the domain of definition of this function, $\log r$ and θ and their partial derivatives with respect to r and θ are continuous functions of z, and the partial derivatives satisfy the Cauchy-Riemann conditions in polar coordinates. Hence $\log z$ is analytic in the domain $r > 0$, $\theta_0 < \theta < \theta_0 + 2\pi$, and

$$(7) \qquad \frac{d}{dz} \log z = \frac{1}{z} \qquad (r > 0, \theta_0 < \arg z < \theta_0 + 2\pi).$$

A *branch* F of a multiple-valued function f is any single-valued function that is analytic in some domain at each point of which the value $F(z)$ is one of the values $f(z)$. The requirement of analyticity prevents F from taking on a random selection of the values of the function f.

In view of this definition, the principal values of the logarithm described by equation (4) represent a branch $\operatorname{Log} z$, the *principal branch*, of the multiple-valued function $\log z$. But for each fixed θ_0 the function defined by equation (6) is also a branch of that multiple-valued function.

Each point of the negative real axis $\Theta = \pi$, as well as the origin, is a singular point of the principal branch $\operatorname{Log} z$, according to our definition (Sec. 19) of a singular point. The ray $\Theta = \pi$ is called the *branch cut* for the principal branch, a line or curve of singular points introduced in defining a branch of a multiple-valued function. The ray $\theta = \theta_0$ is a branch cut for the branch (6) of the logarithmic function. The singular point $z = 0$, common to all branch cuts for the multiple-valued function $\log z$, is called a *branch point*.

27. Properties of Logarithms. If $w = \log z$, then, regardless of which value is used for $\log z$, we can write the inverse relation

$$e^w = \exp (\operatorname{Log} r + i\theta) = \exp (\operatorname{Log} r) \exp (i\theta) = re^{i\theta} = z;$$

that is, for *each* of the many values $\log z$,

$$(1) \qquad\qquad \exp (\log z) = z \qquad\qquad (z \neq 0).$$

Conversely, if $e^z = w$ and $z = x + iy$, then

$$\log w = \log (e^x e^{iy}) = \text{Log } e^x + i(y \pm 2p\pi) = x + iy \pm 2p\pi i$$

where $p = 0, 1, 2, \ldots$. For the value $\log w$ that corresponds to the value $p = 0$, it follows that

$$(2) \qquad\qquad \log w = z \text{ when } e^z = w;$$

that is, *for the appropriate choice of the logarithm,*

$$(3) \qquad\qquad \log (\exp z) = z.$$

The functions exp and log are therefore *inverses* of each other.

Let z_1 and z_2 denote two complex numbers, where

$$z_1 = r_1 \exp (i\theta_1), \qquad z_2 = r_2 \exp (i\theta_2) \qquad (r_1 > 0, r_2 > 0).$$

Since $\text{Log } r_1 + \text{Log } r_2 = \text{Log } (r_1 r_2)$, we can write

$$\log z_1 + \log z_2 = \text{Log } (r_1 r_2) + i(\theta_1 + \theta_2),$$

where the values chosen for θ_1 and θ_2 depend on the values selected for $\log z_1$ and $\log z_2$. But the number on the right is then one particular logarithm of $r_1 r_2 \exp [i(\theta_1 + \theta_2)]$; thus

$$(4) \qquad\qquad \log z_1 + \log z_2 = \log (z_1 z_2),$$

provided we choose the appropriate value of the logarithm on the right.

Similarly, for each choice of $\log z_1$ and $\log z_2$ there is a value of $\log (z_1/z_2)$ such that

$$(5) \qquad\qquad \log z_1 - \log z_2 = \log \frac{z_1}{z_2}.$$

As an illustration of formula (4), suppose that

$$z_1 = z_2 = e^{\pi i} = -1 \qquad \text{and} \qquad \log z_1 = \log z_2 = \pi i.$$

Then $\log z_1 + \log z_2 = 2\pi i$ and $z_1 z_2 = 1$. Formula (4) is satisfied when we write $\log 1 = 2\pi i$; it is not satisfied when any other value of $\log 1$, such as the principal value $\text{Log } 1 = 0$, is chosen.

Now let m and n denote two fixed positive integers and write

$$z = r \exp (i\theta) \qquad (r > 0, -\pi < \theta \leq \pi).$$

When p and p' take the successive values $0, 1, 2, \ldots$, all numbers of the two sets $m \log z$ and $\log z^m$ are given by the equations

(6) $m \log z = m[\text{Log } r + i(\theta \pm 2\pi p)]$

$$= \text{Log } r^m + i(m\theta \pm 2\pi m p),$$

(7) $\log z^m = \text{Log } r^m + i(m\theta \pm 2\pi p').$

The second set of numbers contains the first set; in fact

(8) $\log z^m = m \log z$ when $p' = mp$.

On the other hand, the set of numbers $(1/n) \log z$ and the set $\log (z^{1/n})$, where $z^{1/n}$ itself is a set of n numbers, are the same. For when $q = 0, 1, 2, \ldots, n - 1$,

$$n \log (z^{1/n}) = n \log \left[r^{1/n} \exp \left(i \frac{\theta + 2\pi q}{n} \right) \right]$$

$$= \text{Log } r + i[\theta + 2\pi(q \pm pn)]$$

and $\pm pn + q$ represents the same set of integers as the set $\pm p$ $(p = 0, 1, 2, \ldots)$. Thus $n \log (z^{1/n}) = \log z$, or

(9) $\log (z^{1/n}) = \dfrac{1}{n} \log z.$

Since the exponential function is periodic with period $2\pi i$, we see from equations (6) and (7) that

$$\exp (m \log z) = \exp (\log z^m),$$

where the choice of values of the logarithms is arbitrary. When $\log z$ takes on its successive values, then, according to equation (9),

$$\exp \left(\frac{m}{n} \log z \right) = \exp [m \log (z^{1/n})] = \exp [\log (z^{m/n})].$$

But in view of formula (1), each of the n numbers $z^{m/n}$ can be written $\exp [\log (z^{m/n})]$, and therefore

(10) $z^{m/n} = \exp \left(\dfrac{m}{n} \log z \right).$

Thus for the various values of $\log z$ the right-hand member takes on just n distinct values, the numbers $z^{m/n}$.

EXERCISES

1. When $n = 0, 1, 2, \ldots$, show that

(a) $\log 1 = \pm 2n\pi i;$ (b) $\log (-1) = \pm (2n+1)\pi i;$
(c) $\log i = \frac{1}{2}\pi i \pm 2n\pi i;$ (d) $\log (i^{\frac{1}{2}}) = \frac{1}{4}\pi i \pm n\pi i.$

2. Show that

(a) Log $(-ei) = 1 - \frac{1}{2}\pi i$;   (b) Log $(1 - i) = \frac{1}{2}$ Log $2 - \frac{1}{4}\pi i$.

3. Find all roots of the equation log $z = \frac{1}{2}\pi i$.   *Ans. z = i.*

4. Find all roots of the equation $e^z = -3$.

Ans. z = Log 3 $\pm (2n + 1)\pi i$.

5. Establish formula (5) of this section.

6. For all points z in the right half plane $x > 0$ show that

$$\text{Log } z = \frac{1}{2} \text{ Log } (x^2 + y^2) + i \arctan \frac{y}{x},$$

where the inverse tangent has the principal value used in calculus, that is, $-\pi/2 < \arctan t < \pi/2$. Use this representation together with Theorem 1, Sec. 18, to give another proof that the principal branch Log z is analytic in the domain $x > 0$ and that formula (5), Sec. 26, is true there. But note that some complications arise with the inverse tangent and its differentiation in the remaining part of the full domain of analyticity, $r > 0$, $-\pi < \arg z < \pi$, of Log z, especially on the line $x = 0$.

7. Show in two ways that the function Log $(x^2 + y^2)$ is harmonic in every domain that does not contain the origin.

8. Write $z = r \exp (i\theta)$ and $z - 1 = \rho \exp (i\phi)$ and show that

$$\Re[\log (z - 1)] = \frac{1}{2} \text{ Log } (1 + r^2 - 2r \cos \theta)   (z \neq 1)$$

Why must this function satisfy Laplace's equation when $z \neq 1$?

28. Complex Exponents. When the exponent k is a real rational number, $k = m/n$, formula (10) of the preceding section presented the n values of z^k in the form

(1) $$z^k = \exp (k \log z)   \left(k = \frac{m}{n}, z \neq 0\right).$$

Earlier we defined z^{-k} as $1/z^k$.

We now *define z^c, where the exponent c is any complex number,* by replacing k by c in equation (1); that is,

(2) $$z^c = \exp (c \log z)   (z, c \text{ complex}, z \neq 0).$$

The definition identifies the two sets of numbers z^{-c} and $1/z^c$:

$$z^{-c} = \frac{1}{z^c}.$$

It includes formula (1) as a special case, but it also defines the multiple-valued function z^c when c is real and irrational and when c is not real. For example,

$$i^{-2i} = \exp (-2i \log i) = \exp [-2i(\tfrac{1}{2}\pi \pm 2n\pi)i]$$
$$= \exp (\pi \pm 4n\pi)$$
$$(n = 0, 1, 2, \ldots).$$

If $z = r \exp (i\theta)$ and θ_0 is a real constant, the function

(3)　　　　$\log z = \text{Log } r + i\theta$　　　$(r > 0, \theta_0 < \theta < \theta_0 + 2\pi)$

is single-valued and analytic in the domain indicated, as is the composite function $\exp (c \log z)$. Thus the function z^c defined by equation (2), in which $\log z$ is given by equation (3), is single-valued and analytic in the domain $r > 0$, $\theta_0 < \theta < \theta_0 + 2\pi$. The derivative of that branch of the multiple-valued power function (2) can be written, in terms of the logarithm defined by equation (3),

(4)　　$\dfrac{d}{dz} z^c = \exp (c \log z)\dfrac{c}{z} = c\,\dfrac{\exp (c \log z)}{\exp (\log z)}$
$$= c \exp [(c - 1) \log z].$$

The final member is the single-valued function cz^{c-1}; thus

(5)　　　　　$\dfrac{d}{dz} z^c = c\,\dfrac{z^c}{z} = cz^{c-1}$　　　$(r > 0, \theta_0 < \theta < \theta_0 + 2\pi).$

In particular, when $\theta_0 = -\pi$, so that $-\pi < \theta < \pi$, the function

(6)　　　　　　　$z^c = \exp (c \text{ Log } z)$　　　　　　　$(z \neq 0)$

is called the *principal branch* of the multiple-valued power function (2). It is single-valued and analytic in the domain $r > 0$, $-\pi < \theta < \pi$. The *principal value* of e^z as a power of e is therefore $\exp (z \text{ Log } e) = \exp z$.

As an example, we write the principal value of $(-i)^i$:

$$\exp [i \text{ Log } (-i)] = \exp \left[i \left(-i\frac{\pi}{2} \right) \right] = \exp \frac{\pi}{2}.$$

As another example, the principal branch of $z^{\frac{2}{3}}$,

$$z^{\frac{2}{3}} = \exp (\tfrac{2}{3} \text{ Log } z) = \exp (\tfrac{2}{3} \text{ Log } r + \tfrac{2}{3}i\theta) = \sqrt[3]{r^2} \exp (\tfrac{2}{3}\theta i),$$

is analytic in the domain $r > 0$, $-\pi < \theta < \pi$, as we can see also from Theorem 2, Sec. 18.

According to the definition (2), the *exponential function with base c*, where c is any complex constant other than zero, can be written

$$(7) \qquad\qquad c^z = \exp\,(z\,\log\,c) \qquad\qquad (c \neq 0).$$

When the number $\log c$ is specified, c^z is an entire function of z, and its differentiation formula is easily seen to be

$$(8) \qquad\qquad \frac{d}{dz}\,c^z = c^z\,\log\,c \qquad\qquad (c \neq 0).$$

29. Inverse Trigonometric Functions.   Inverses of the trigonometric and hyperbolic functions can be described in terms of logarithms.

We define the function $w = \sin^{-1} z$ as the inverse of the sine function; thus

$$z = \sin w = \frac{e^{iw} - e^{-iw}}{2i}.$$

Then we may obtain e^{iw} by solving the equation

$$e^{2iw} - 2ize^{iw} - 1 = 0,$$

which is quadratic in e^{iw}.   We find that

$$e^{iw} = iz + (1 - z^2)^{\frac{1}{2}},$$

where $(1 - z^2)^{\frac{1}{2}}$ is, as we know, a double-valued function of z. Finally we may write

$$(1) \qquad\qquad w = \sin^{-1} z = -i\,\log\,[iz + (1 - z^2)^{\frac{1}{2}}],$$

which is a multiple-valued function with infinitely many values. When specific branches of the square root and the logarithm are used, the function (1) becomes single-valued and analytic because it is a composition of analytic functions.

Similarly, the inverses of the functions $\cos w$ and $\tan w$ are found to be

$$(2) \qquad\qquad \cos^{-1} z = -i\,\log\,[z + (z^2 - 1)^{\frac{1}{2}}],$$

$$(3) \qquad\qquad \tan^{-1} z = \frac{i}{2}\,\log\,\frac{1 - iz}{1 + iz} = \frac{i}{2}\,\log\,\frac{i + z}{i - z}.$$

The derivatives of these three functions can be written from the above formulas.   The derivative of the last one,

$$(4) \qquad\qquad \frac{d}{dz}\,(\tan^{-1} z) = \frac{1}{1 + z^2},$$

does not depend on the manner in which the function is made single-valued.   The derivatives of the first two do depend on the values chosen for square roots; for instance,

$$(5) \qquad \frac{d}{dz}(\sin^{-1} z) = \frac{1}{(1 - z^2)^{\frac{1}{2}}}.$$

The inverses of the hyperbolic functions can be written in the corresponding manner.   It turns out that

$$(6) \qquad \sinh^{-1} z = \log [z + (z^2 + 1)^{\frac{1}{2}}],$$
$$(7) \qquad \cosh^{-1} z = \log [z + (z^2 - 1)^{\frac{1}{2}}],$$
$$(8) \qquad \tanh^{-1} z = \frac{1}{2} \log \frac{1 + z}{1 - z}.$$

EXERCISES

1. When $n = 0, 1, 2, \ldots$, show that

(a) $(1 + i)^i = \exp(-\frac{1}{4}\pi \pm 2n\pi) \exp(\frac{1}{2}i \operatorname{Log} 2)$;
(b) $(-1)^{1/\pi} = \exp[\pm(2n + 1)i]$.

2. Find the principal value of

(a) i^i;   (b) $[\frac{1}{2}e(-1 - i\sqrt{3})]^{3\pi i}$;   (c) $(1 - i)^{4i}$.
$\qquad\qquad\qquad$ *Ans.* (a) $\exp(-\frac{1}{2}\pi)$; (b) $-\exp(2\pi^2)$.

3. Show that, if $z \neq 0$,

(a) $z^0 = 1$;
(b) $|z^k| = \exp(k \operatorname{Log}|z|) = |z|^k$ $\qquad\qquad$ when k is real.

4. Let b, c, and z denote complex numbers, where $z \neq 0$.   If all powers here are principal values, prove that

(a) $z^{-c} = \dfrac{1}{z^c}$;

(b) $(z^c)^n = z^{nc}$ $\qquad\qquad\qquad\qquad\qquad$ $(n = 1, 2, \ldots)$;

(c) $z^b z^c = z^{b+c}$;   (d) $\dfrac{z^b}{z^c} = z^{b-c}$.

5. Use the principal values of z^i to write the conjugate harmonic functions $u(r,\theta)$ and $v(r,\theta)$ when $z^i = u + iv$.
6. Derive formula (8), Sec. 28; also, the formula for the derivative with respect to z of c^w, where $w'(z)$ exists.
7. Find the values of

(a) $\tan^{-1}(2i)$;   (b) $\tan^{-1}(1 + i)$;   (c) $\cosh^{-1}(-1)$;   (d) $\tanh^{-1} 0$.
$\qquad$ *Ans.* (a) $\pm(n + \frac{1}{2})\pi + \frac{1}{2}i \operatorname{Log} 3$; (d) $\pm n\pi i$ $(n = 0, 1, 2, \ldots)$.

8. Solve the equation $\sin z = 2$ for z (a) by identifying real and imaginary components of its members; (b) by using formula (1).

$Ans.$ $z = \frac{1}{2}\pi(1 \pm 4n) \pm i \operatorname{Log} (2 + \sqrt{3})$ $(n = 0, 1, 2, \ldots)$.

9. Solve the equation $\cos z = \sqrt{2}$ for z.

10. Derive formulas (2) and (5) of this section.

11. Derive formulas (3) and (4) of this section.

12. Derive formulas (6) and (8) of this section.

CHAPTER 4

MAPPING BY ELEMENTARY FUNCTIONS

The concept of mapping, or transformation of points, by a function f of a complex variable z was introduced in Sec. 11. Actually, functions were defined as point transformations. We pointed out that the nature of the function may be displayed graphically, to some extent, by the manner in which the function maps regions and curves from one complex plane to another. Furthermore, we shall show that the problem of finding a function of x and y that is harmonic in a region and satisfies prescribed conditions at the boundary of the region can often be solved by means of mapping by *analytic* functions. Such boundary value problems in Laplace's differential equation are prominent in physics and engineering (Chaps. 9, 10). As preparation for solving them, we should see how various regions are transformed by elementary analytic functions.

30. Linear Functions. The mapping by means of the function

$$(1) \qquad\qquad w = z + C,$$

where C is a complex constant, is the translation of every point z through the vector representing C. That is, if

$$z = x + iy, \qquad w = u + iv, \qquad C = C_1 + iC_2,$$

then the image of any point (x,y) in the z plane is the point

$$(x + C_1,\, y + C_2)$$

in the w plane. Since every point in any region of the z plane is mapped upon the w plane in this same manner, the image of the region is simply a translation of the given region. The two regions have the same shape, size, and orientation.

Let B be a complex constant whose polar form is $B = b \exp (i\beta)$. Then, if $z = r \exp (i\theta)$, the function

$$(2) \qquad\qquad w = Bz = bre^{i(\theta+\beta)}$$

maps the point (r,θ) in the z plane into that point in the w plane whose polar coordinates are br, $\theta + \beta$. That is, the mapping consists of a rotation of the radius vector of the point z about the origin through the angle $\beta = \arg B$ and an expansion or contraction of the radius vector by the factor $b = |B|$. Every region in the z plane is transformed by this rotation and expansion into a geometrically similar region in the w plane.

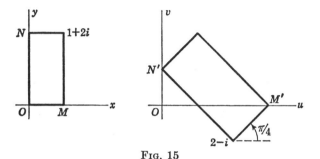

Fig. 15

By applying the transformation (1) to the variable w in equation (2), we see that the mapping by the general linear function

$$(3) \qquad w = Bz + C$$

consists of a rotation through the angle $\arg B$ and a magnification by the factor $|B|$, followed by a translation through the vector C.

As an illustration, the function

$$w = (1 + i)z + 2 - i$$

transforms the rectangular region shown in the z plane of Fig. 15 into the rectangular region shown in the w plane. This is evident geometrically, since $\arg (1 + i) = \pi/4$ and $|1 + i| = \sqrt{2}$.

As another illustration, let us note the image of the region $0 < x < 1$, the infinite strip between the lines $x = 0$ and $x = 1$, under the transformation

$$w = iz.$$

Since $i = \exp (i\pi/2)$, the transformation is a rotation through the angle $\pi/2$. Hence the image of the given strip is the strip $0 < v < 1$. This is also seen by noting that, since $w = iz$, then $u = -y$ and $v = x$. When $0 < x < 1$ and y is unrestricted, it follows that $0 < v < 1$, and u is unrestricted.

31. The Functions z^n.   First let us consider the function

$$w = z^2.$$

This transformation can be described easily in terms of polar coordinates, for if $z = r \exp(i\theta)$ and $w = \rho \exp(i\phi)$, then

$$\rho e^{i\phi} = r^2 e^{2i\theta}.$$

Thus the image of any point (r,θ) is that point in the w plane whose polar coordinates are $\rho = r^2$, $\phi = 2\theta$.

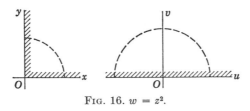

FIG. 16. $w = z^2$.

In particular, the function z^2 maps the entire first quadrant of the z plane, $0 \leq \theta \leq \pi/2$, $r \geq 0$, upon the entire upper half of the w plane (Fig. 16).

Circles about the origin, $r - r_0$, are transformed into circles $\rho = r_0^2$ in the w plane.   The semicircular region $r \leq r_0$, $0 \leq \theta < \pi$ is mapped onto the circular region $\rho \leq r_0^2$, and the first quadrant of that semicircular region is mapped onto the upper half of the circular region, as indicated by the broken lines in Fig. 16.

In each of the above mappings of regions by the transformation $w = z^2$, there is just one point in the transformed region corresponding to a given point in the original region, and conversely; that is, there is a unique or one to one correspondence between points in the two regions.   This uniqueness does not exist, however, for the circular region

$$r \leq r_0, \qquad 0 \leq \theta < 2\pi$$

and its image $\rho \leq r_0^2$, since each point w of the latter region is the image of two points z and $-z$ of the former.

In rectangular coordinates the transformation $w = z^2$ becomes

$$u + iv = x^2 - y^2 + 2xyi.$$

Whenever $2xy = c_2$, then $v = c_2$, and conversely, where c_2 is a real constant.   That is, every point on the hyperbola $2xy = c_2$ has some image point on the horizontal line $v = c_2$, and every point on the line has some image point on the hyperbola. Thus the image of the entire hyperbola is the entire line; but two points z and $-z$ of the hyperbola correspond to each point w of the line. Points of the upper branch ($y > 0$) of the hyperbola have a one to one correspondence with points on the line, because, as we noted above, there is a one to one correspondence between points of the upper half of the z plane and points of the w plane. The lower branch of the hyperbola also maps in that unique manner onto the line.

Likewise, the image of the line $u = c_1$ is the hyperbola $x^2 - y^2 = c_1$; but the pointwise correspondence is one to one for either of the two branches of the hyperbola. The mapping of lines $u = c_1$ and $v = c_2$ was shown in Chap. 2 (Fig. 14).

The domain $x > 0$, $y > 0$, $xy < 1$ consists of all points of the first quadrant that lie below the hyperbola $xy = 1$, or all points of the upper branches of all hyperbolas of the family $xy = c$ ($0 < c < 1$). The image of the domain therefore consists of all points of all the lines $v = 2c$; that is, the image of the domain is the horizontal strip $0 < v < 2$.

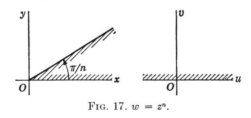

Fig. 17. $w = z^n$.

When n is a positive integer, the transformation

$$w = z^n, \qquad \text{or} \qquad \rho e^{i\phi} = r^n e^{in\theta},$$

maps the angular region $r \geq 0$, $0 \leq \theta \leq \pi/n$ onto the upper half ($\rho \geq 0$, $0 \leq \phi \leq \pi$) of the w plane (Fig. 17), since $\rho = r^n$ and $\phi = n\theta$. It transforms a circular arc

$$r = r_0 \qquad \left(\theta_0 \leq \theta < \theta_0 + \frac{2\pi}{n} \right)$$

into the circle $\rho = r_0^n$. Both mappings are one to one.

32. The Function $1/z$. The transformation

$$w = \frac{1}{z} \qquad \text{or} \qquad z = \frac{1}{w}$$

sets up a one to one correspondence between points in the z plane and points in the w plane, except for the points $z = 0$ and $w = 0$, which have no images.

In polar coordinates the transformation becomes

$$\rho e^{i\phi} = \frac{1}{r} e^{-i\theta}.$$

This can be described by means of the consecutive transformations

$$z' = \frac{1}{r} e^{i\theta}, \qquad w = \overline{z'}.$$

The first is an *inversion* with respect to the unit circle $r = 1$; that is, the point z' lies on the radius drawn through the point z, and its distance from the center is such that $|z'|\,|z| = 1$. The inversion is followed by a reflection $w = \overline{z'}$ in the real axis (Fig. 18). Thus points outside the unit circle are mapped into points inside the circle, and conversely. Points on the circle are reflected in the real axis.

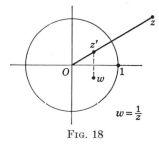

Fig. 18

When cartesian coordinates are used, the equation

$$w = u + iv = \frac{1}{x + iy}$$

gives the relations

$$u = \frac{x}{x^2 + y^2}, \qquad v = -\frac{y}{x^2 + y^2}$$

and

$$x = \frac{u}{u^2 + v^2}, \qquad y = -\frac{v}{u^2 + v^2}.$$

If a, b, c, d represent real numbers, the equation

(1) $$a(x^2 + y^2) + bx + cy + d = 0$$

represents any circle or line, depending on whether $a \neq 0$ or $a = 0$. Under the transformation $w = 1/z$, equation (1) becomes

(2) $$d(u^2 + v^2) + bu - cv + a = 0.$$

Also, whenever u and v satisfy equation (2), then x and y satisfy equation (1). Hence, if a and d are different from zero, both the curve and its image are circles; that is, circles not passing through the point $z = 0$ transform into other circles not passing through the point $w = 0$.

Similarly, equations (1) and (2) show that every circle through the origin $z = 0$ transforms into a straight line in the w plane. Lines in the z plane transform into circles through the origin

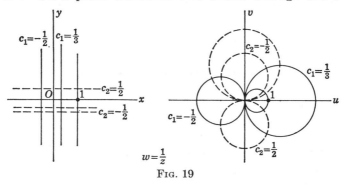

$$w = \frac{1}{z}$$

FIG. 19

$w = 0$, unless the line passes through $z = 0$, in which case the image is a line through the origin $w = 0$.

If we consider lines as limiting cases of circles, we can say that the transformation always carries circles into circles. In particular, the lines $x = c_1$ transform into the circles

$$(3) \qquad u^2 + v^2 - \frac{u}{c_1} = 0$$

tangent to the v axis at the origin, and the lines $y = c_2$ into the circles

$$(4) \qquad u^2 + v^2 + \frac{v}{c_2} = 0$$

if $c_1 \neq 0$ and $c_2 \neq 0$, as illustrated in Fig. 19.

The half plane $x > c_1$ has for its image the region

$$(5) \qquad \frac{u}{u^2 + v^2} > c_1.$$

When $c_1 > 0$, it follows that

$$(6) \qquad \left(u - \frac{1}{2c_1}\right)^2 + v^2 < \left(\frac{1}{2c_1}\right)^2;$$

that is, the point w is inside a circle tangent to the v axis at the origin.   Conversely, whenever u and v satisfy the inequality (6) and $c_1 > 0$, then the inequality (5) follows, and therefore $x > c_1$. Consequently, every point inside the circle is the image of some point in the half plane; thus the image of the half plane is the entire circular region (6).

33. The Point at Infinity.   Under the transformation $w = 1/z$, or

$$\rho e^{i\phi} = \frac{1}{r} e^{-i\theta},$$

the points z exterior to the circle $r = R$ map into points w interior to the circle $\rho = 1/R$.   The point $w = 0$ is not the image of any point in the finite z plane.   However, by making the radius R sufficiently large, the images of all points z outside the large circle $r = R$ are made to fall within an arbitrarily small neighborhood of the point $w = 0$.

It is sometimes convenient to use the concept of the point at infinity, or the infinite point, $z = \infty$.   Formally, this point is the image of the point $w = 0$ under the transformation $w = 1/z$. That is, whenever a statement is made about the behavior of a function at $z = \infty$, we mean precisely the behavior of the function at $z' = 0$, where $z' = 1/z$.

We may say, for example, that the function

$$w = \frac{4z^2}{(1 - z)^2}$$

maps the point $z = \infty$ into the point $w = 4$.   This means that, if we write $z = 1/z'$, so that

$$w = \frac{4/z'^2}{(1 - 1/z')^2} = \frac{4}{(z' - 1)^2},$$

then $w = 4$ when $z' = 0$.   Again, we may say that $w = \infty$ when $z = 1$; for if we write $w = 1/w'$, then

$$w' = \frac{(1 - z)^2}{4z^2},$$

and $w' = 0$ when $z = 1$.

The notion of the infinite point is an abbreviation for a limiting process, and in case of doubt we should rely on the direct use of limits.   Except when the contrary is stated, we shall continue to use the words *point* and *complex number* to signify points with finite coordinates and the complex numbers represented by such points.

EXERCISES

1. Under the transformation $w = iz + i$ show that the half plane $x > 0$ maps onto the half plane $v > 1$.

2. Find the region onto which the half plane $y > 0$ is mapped by the function $w = (1 + i)z$ (a) by using polar coordinates, (b) by using rectangular coordinates. Show the regions graphically.

Ans. The half plane $v > u$.

3. Find the image of the region $y > 1$ under the transformation $w = (1 - i)z$.

4. Find the image of the semi-infinite strip $x > 0$, $0 < y < 2$ under the transformation $w = iz + 1$. Show the regions graphically.

Ans. $-1 < u < 1$, $v > 0$.

5. If B and C are complex constants, give a geometrical description of the transformation $w = B(z + C)$.

6. Describe the region onto which the circular sector $0 < \theta < \pi/4$, $r < 1$ is mapped by the function (a) $w = z^2$; (b) $w = z^3$; (c) $w = z^4$.

7. What is the image in the z plane of the rectangular region bounded by the lines $u = 1$, $u = 2$, $v = 1$, $v = 2$, under the transformation $w = z^2$?

8. Show that the function $w = z^2$ maps the lines $y = c$ onto parabolas with common foci at the point $w = 0$. What is the image of the line $y = 0$?

9. Find the image of the infinite strip $0 < y < 1/(2c)$ under the transformation $w = 1/z$. Show the regions graphically.

Ans. $u^2 + (v + c)^2 > c^2$, $v < 0$.

10. Show that the image of the half plane $y > c$, under the transformation $w = 1/z$, is the interior of a circle, provided $c > 0$. What is the image when $c = 0$? When $c < 0$?

11. Find the image of the quadrant $x > 1$, $y > 0$ under the transformation $w = 1/z$. *Ans.* $|w - \frac{1}{2}| < \frac{1}{2}$, $v < 0$.

12. Find the image of the hyperbola $x^2 - y^2 = 1$ under the transformation $z = 1/w$. *Ans.* $\rho^2 = \cos 2\phi$.

13. Describe geometrically the transformation $w = 1/(z - 1)$.

14. Describe geometrically the transformation $w = i/z$; also show that it maps circles and lines onto circles and lines.

15. Find the image of the semi-infinite strip $x \geq 0$, $0 \leq y \leq 1$ under the transformation $w = i/z$. Show the regions graphically.

Ans. $0 \leq \phi \leq \pi/2$, $\rho \geq \cos \phi$.

16. When an actual circle is subjected to the transformation $w = 1/z$, prove that its center is not transformed into the center of the image circle.

34. The Linear Fractional Transformation. The transformation T:

$$(1) \qquad\qquad w = \frac{az + b}{cz + d} \qquad\qquad (ad - bc \neq 0),$$

where *a*, *b*, *c*, and *d* are complex constants, is called the *linear fractional transformation*. We abbreviate it as $w = T(z)$. If $ad - bc = 0$, the right-hand member of equation (1) is either a constant or meaningless.

The inverse T^{-1} of that transformation,

$$(2) \qquad\qquad z = \frac{-dw + b}{cw - a},$$

or $z = T^{-1}(w)$, is also a linear fractional transformation.

The transformation T assigns to each point of the z plane, except the point $z = -d/c$ when $c \neq 0$, a unique point of the w plane. According to the form (2) of equation (1), each point of the w plane, except the point $w = a/c$ when $c \neq 0$, has a unique image in the z plane. Those exceptional points for T and T^{-1} map into the points $w = \infty$ and $z = \infty$, respectively. The *extended* complex plane, or the *closure* of the plane, consists of all finite complex numbers plus the infinite point. Thus the transformation T sets up a one to one correspondence between all points of the extended z plane and the extended w plane.

Successive linear fractional transformations are also linear fractional. That is, if z in equation (1) undergoes a transformation T':

$$z = \frac{a'z' + b'}{c'z' + d'},$$

we find by direct substitution the constants α, β, γ, and δ such that

$$(3) \qquad\qquad w = \frac{\alpha z' + \beta}{\gamma z' + \delta}.$$

The linear fractional transformation (3) is denoted by TT', or $w = T[T'(z')]$. If T'' is a third linear fractional transformation, we find by direct substitutions that the successive transformations $(TT')T''$ and $T(T'T'')$ are the same; that is, compositions of linear fractional transformations satisfy the associative law

$$(4) \qquad T(T'T'') = (TT')T''.$$

The particular linear fractional transformation $w = z$ is the identity transformation T_0, such that $TT_0 = T$. We have now shown that, in the language of algebra, the set of all linear fractional transformations forms a *group* (Exercises 16 and 18, Sec. 35).

The linear fractional transformation always transforms circles and lines into circles and lines. We show this by writing T as a succession of transformations that have the property.

When $c \neq 0$, equation (1) can be written

$$w = \frac{a(z + d/c) + b - ad/c}{c(z + d/c)} = \frac{a}{c} + \frac{b - ad/c}{cz + d}.$$

Now let us write

$$(5) \qquad z' = cz + d, \qquad z'' = \frac{1}{z'};$$

then it follows that

$$(6) \qquad w = \frac{a}{c} + \frac{bc - ad}{c} z''.$$

Equations (5) and (6) represent three successive transformations that result in the transformation $w = T(z)$. The first and third are of the type

$$(7) \qquad w = Bz + C$$

discussed in Sec. 30. The second is a transformation of type $w = 1/z$ (Sec. 32). We noted that the linear transformation (7) does not change the shape of a curve and that the transformation $w = 1/z$ maps circles and lines onto circles and lines; thus T has the latter property.

If $c = 0$, the transformation (1) is of the type (7).

When cleared of fractions, equation (1) has the form

$$(8) \qquad Azw + Bz + Cw + D = 0,$$

an equation that is linear in z and linear in w, or *bilinear* in z and w. Hence an alternate name for the linear fractional transformation is the *bilinear transformation*.

There is just one bilinear transformation that maps three given distinct points z_1, z_2, and z_3 into three specified distinct points w_1, w_2, and w_3, respectively. The proof is left to the exercises. But we can verify that the transformation is given by the equation

(9)
$$\frac{(w - w_1)(w_2 - w_3)}{(w - w_3)(w_2 - w_1)} = \frac{(z - z_1)(z_2 - z_3)}{(z - z_3)(z_2 - z_1)},$$

which can be written in the bilinear form (8) by expanding products in the equation

(10) $(z - z_3)(w - w_1)(z_2 - z_1)(w_2 - w_3)$
$$= (z - z_1)(w - w_3)(z_2 - z_3)(w_2 - w_1).$$

For if $z = z_1$, the right-hand member of this last equation vanishes, and consequently $w = w_1$; similarly, if $z = z_3$, then $w = w_3$. If $z = z_2$, two factors are common to both sides of equation (10), and the equation reduces to

$$(w - w_1)(w_2 - w_3) = (w - w_3)(w_2 - w_1);$$

the solution of this linear equation in w is clearly $w = w_2$.

In equation (9), the infinite point can be introduced as one of the prescribed points in the w plane or in the z plane. For example, suppose $z_1 = 1$, $z_2 = 0$, $z_3 = -1$ and $w_1 = i$, $w_2 = 1$, $w_3 = \infty$. Setting $w_3 = 1/w_3'$, we can write the transformation in the form

$$\frac{(w - w_1)(w_3'w_2 - 1)}{(w_3'w - 1)(w_2 - w_1)} = \frac{(z - z_1)(z_2 - z_3)}{(z - z_3)(z_2 - z_1)}.$$

When $w_3' = 0$ and the values of the remaining constants are inserted here, the equation becomes

$$\frac{w - i}{1 - i} = \frac{z - 1}{(z + 1)(-1)}, \quad \text{or} \quad w = \frac{(-1 + 2i)z + 1}{z + 1}$$

Using either of these two forms, the reader can verify that the three given points map into the points specified and, in particular, that w becomes infinite as z approaches -1.

A *fixed point* z of a transformation is one whose image w represents the same number, $w = z$. The bilinear transformation has at most two fixed points, represented by the roots of the equation in z obtained by writing $w = z$ in either equation (1) or equation (8).

35. Special Linear Fractional Transformations. Let us determine all linear fractional transformations that map the upper half of the z plane $y \geq 0$ onto the unit disk $|w| \leq 1$.

The boundary $y = 0$ of the half plane must have the boundary $|w| = 1$ of the unit disk as its image, for the transformation

$$(1) \qquad\qquad w = \frac{az + b}{cz + d}$$

maps lines onto circles or lines. In this case, the line $y = 0$ must map onto a circle because the region in the w plane is of finite extent. Suppose that this circle is interior to the circle $|w| = 1$. Since w is a continuous function of z, points just below the x axis would map into points near that circle, interior to the circle $|w| = 1$, contrary to the required conditions.

If we make three specific points on the line $y = 0$ map into points on the circle $|w| = 1$, then the whole line will map onto this circle, since the three image points determine the image circle. Every mapping of the line onto the circle must carry those three prescribed points into some three points on the circle.

According to equation (1), the requirement that $|w| = 1$ for each of the three points $z = 0$, $z = 1$, and $z = \infty$ leads to the equations

$$(2) \qquad\qquad\qquad\qquad |b| = |d|,$$
$$(3) \qquad\qquad\qquad |a + b| = |c + d|,$$
$$(4) \qquad\qquad\qquad\qquad |a| = |c|.$$

It follows from the last equation that $a \neq 0$ and $c \neq 0$, because both of those coefficients vanish when either one does, and then the transformation (1) maps the entire z plane into a single point. Therefore we may write

$$w = \frac{a}{c} \frac{z + b/a}{z + d/c}$$

or, since $|a/c| = 1$,

$$(5) \qquad\qquad\qquad w = \exp{(i\theta_0)} \frac{z - z_1}{z - z_2},$$

where θ_0 is any real constant. Also, $|b/a| = |d/c|$, according to equations (2) and (4); therefore $|z_1| = |z_2|$.

We have as yet made no use of condition (3). Let us impose the corresponding condition, that $|w| = 1$ when $z = 1$, upon equation (5).   Then

$$|1 - z_1| = |1 - z_2|,$$

or $\qquad (1 - z_1)(1 - \bar{z}_1) = (1 - z_2)(1 - \bar{z}_2).$

But $z_1\bar{z}_1 = z_2\bar{z}_2$, since $|z_1| = |z_2|$, and the above relation reduces to

$$z_1 + \bar{z}_1 = z_2 + \bar{z}_2,$$

or $\mathfrak{R}(z_1) = \mathfrak{R}(z_2)$. Therefore either $z_2 = z_1$ or $z_2 = \bar{z}_1$. The condition $z_2 = z_1$ leads to the transformation $w = \exp(i\theta_0)$ of the z plane into a single point; hence $z_2 = \bar{z}_1$.

The required transformation must therefore have the form

$$(6) \qquad\qquad w = e^{i\theta_0} \frac{z - z_1}{z - \bar{z}_1}$$

where it is evident that the point $w = 0$ is the image of the point $z = z_1$, so that if the upper half plane is to map onto the interior of the circle $|w| = 1$, it follows that z_1 must be in the upper half plane; that is,

$$(7) \qquad\qquad y_1 = \mathcal{I}(z_1) > 0.$$

We verify that the transformation (6) does map the half plane onto the unit disk by interpreting the equation

$$|w| = \frac{|z - z_1|}{|z - \bar{z}_1|}$$

geometrically (Fig. 20).   Since points z and z_1 are in the upper half plane, they lie on the same side of the perpendicular bisector of the line segment from z_1 to $\bar{z}_1$.

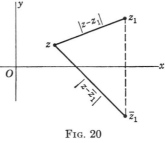

Fig. 20

Hence the distance $|z - z_1|$ does not exceed the distance $|z - \bar{z}_1|$; that is, $|w| \leqq 1$.   The transformation (6) is therefore the one sought.

The identity transformation $w = z$ is not the only one that can map a region onto itself.   In fact, all the transformations

$$(8) \qquad\qquad w = e^{i\theta_1} \frac{z - z_0}{\bar{z}_0 z - 1}$$

where θ_1 is real and $|z_0| < 1$ map the unit disk $|z| \leqq 1$ onto the unit disk $|w| \leqq 1$.   The proof is left for the exercises.

Two transformations, each of which maps a region R_1 onto a region R_2, need not be the same.   This is illustrated by the transformations (6) with different sets of values of the constants θ_0 and z_1.

EXERCISES

1. Find the linear fractional transformation that maps the points $z_1 = 2$, $z_2 = i$, and $z_3 = -2$ into the points $w_1 = 1$, $w_2 = i$, and $w_3 = -1$.   Ans. $w = (3z + 2i)/(iz + 6)$.

2. Find the linear fractional transformation that maps the points $z_1 = -i$, $z_2 = 0$, and $z_3 = i$ into the points $w_1 = -1$, $w_2 = i$, and $w_3 = 1$.   Into what curve must this transformation map the y axis?

3. Find the bilinear transformation that maps the points $z_1 = \infty$, $z_2 = i$, and $z_3 = 0$ into the points $w_1 = 0$, $w_2 = i$, and $w_3 = \infty$.
$$Ans. \; w = -1/z.$$

4. Find the bilinear transformation that maps the points z_1, z_2, and z_3 into the points $w_1 = 0$, $w_2 = 1$, and $w_3 = \infty$.
$$Ans. \; w = [(z - z_1)(z_2 - z_3)]/[(z - z_3)(z_2 - z_1)].$$

5. Find the fixed points of the transformations

(a) $w = \dfrac{z - 1}{z + 1}$;   (b) $w = \dfrac{6z - 9}{z}$.   Ans. (a) $z = \pm i$; (b) $z = 3$.

6. In the bilinear transformation (9), Sec. 34, if $z_1 = 0$, $z_2 = \infty$, $w_1 = 0$, and $w_2 = \infty$, that is, if $z = 0$ and $z = \infty$ are both fixed points, show that the transformation has the form $w = az$.

7. If the origin is a fixed point of a bilinear transformation, prove that the transformation can be written in the form

$$w = \frac{z}{cz + d}.$$

8. When $z_0 = 0$, show that the transformation (8) reduces to a rotation of all points z about the origin through the angle $\theta_1 + \pi$.

9. When $\mathcal{I}(z_1) < 0$ prove that the transformation (6) maps the lower half plane $y \leqq 0$ onto the circular disk $|w| \leqq 1$.

10. Determine the constants $\exp(i\theta_0)$ and z_1 in the transformation (6), which maps the region $y \geqq 0$ onto $|w| \leqq 1$, so that the images of the points $z = \infty$, $z = 0$, and $z = 1$ are the points $w = -1$, $w = 1$, and $w = i$, respectively.   When $z = x$ and $x > 0$, show that $v > 0$ and $-1 < u < 1$, so that the image of the positive x axis is the upper half of the circle $|w| = 1$.   Thus verify the mapping shown in Fig. 13, Appendix 2.

11. The transformation (6) maps the point $z = \infty$ into the point $w = \exp(i\theta_0)$. If it maps the origin $z = 0$ into the point $w = 1$ and the point $z = 1$ into the mid-point $w = \exp(i\theta_0/2)$ of the arc $0 < \phi < \theta_0$ of the circle $|w| = 1$, show that the transformation can be written

$$w = \exp(i\theta_0)\, \frac{z + \exp(-i\theta_0/2)}{z + \exp(i\theta_0/2)} \qquad (0 < \theta_0 < 2\pi).$$

Draw a figure showing corresponding regions and points, including the point z_1 whose image is $w = 0$. (Note the special cases in Exercises 10 and 12.)

12. Verify that the special case $\theta_0 = \pi/2$ of the transformation in Exercise 11 can be written

$$zw - iz + (w - 1)\exp\frac{i\pi}{4} = 0$$

and that it maps the half plane $y > 0$ and segments of the boundary $y = 0$ in the manner indicated in Fig. 21.

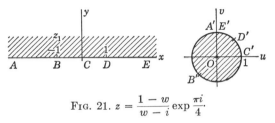

$$\text{Fig. 21. } z = \frac{1 - w}{w - i}\exp\frac{\pi i}{4}.$$

13. If a bilinear transformation maps all points of the x axis upon the u axis, prove that the coefficients in the transformation are all real, except possibly for a common complex factor. Note that the converse statement is evident.

14. Derive the transformation (8) of this section. Successive linear fractional transformations may be used first to map the disk $|z| \leq 1$ onto the upper half of the z' plane and then to map that half plane onto the disk $|w| \leq 1$.

15. When the term in zw is not absent, the bilinear transformation can be written $zw + B'z + C'w + D' = 0$. Write the three simultaneous equations that are satisfied by B', C', and D' if that transformation maps three distinct points z_1, z_2, z_3 into three distinct points w_1, w_2, w_3, respectively, and give the condition on the determinant of the coefficients of B', C', and D' under which the equations can be solved for B', C', and D' in terms of z_n and w_n ($n = 1, 2, 3$). When z_n and w_n fail to satisfy the condition, show that B, C, and D in the linear transformation $Bz + Cw + D = 0$ can be determined, up to a common factor, so that z_n maps into w_n under that transformation. Thus justify the statement made in Sec. 34 that just one bilinear transformation maps z_n into w_n $(n = 1, 2, 3)$.

16. Any set of elements that satisfies all the following conditions is called a *group*.   (a) There is a rule of combining each pair T, T' of elements, distinct or not, such that that combination TT', called the "product," is an element of the set.   (b) The product is associative: $T(T'T'') = (TT')T''$.   (c) The set contains an identity element T_0, such that $TT_0 = T_0T = T$ for each element T.   (d) Each element T has an inverse T^{-1} such that $TT^{-1} = T^{-1}T = T_0$.   Justify the statement in Sec. 34 that the set of all linear fractional transformations is a group.

17. Use special cases $w = az + b$ of the linear fractional transformation to show that TT' and $T'T$ are not always the same.   That is, the "product" does not always satisfy the commutative law.

18. A linear fractional transformation T can be represented by a square array, a square *matrix*, of its coefficients:

$$\begin{pmatrix} a & b \\ c & d \end{pmatrix} \qquad \text{when } T(z) = \frac{az + b}{cz + d}.$$

(a) If a', b', c', d' are the corresponding coefficients in a second transformation T', show that the matrix of the composite transformation $T[T'(z)]$ can be written

$$TT': \begin{pmatrix} aa' + bc' & ab' + bd' \\ ca' + dc' & cb' + dd' \end{pmatrix}$$

This is the *matrix product* of the matrices for T and T'.   (b) With the aid of this rule of multiplication show that $(TT')T'' = T(T'T'')$, as stated in Sec. 34.

36. The Function $z^{\frac{1}{2}}$.   The multiple-valued function

$$(1) \qquad\qquad f(z) = z^{\frac{1}{2}} = \sqrt{r}\, \exp \frac{i\theta}{2},$$

where $z = r \exp (i\theta)$, takes on two values at each point z except the origin, depending on the choice of θ.   One value is the negative of the other because $\exp (i\theta/2)$ changes in sign alone when θ is increased by 2π.

According to Sec. 28, the function f can be written

$$(2) \qquad\qquad z^{\frac{1}{2}} = \exp (\tfrac{1}{2} \log z) \qquad\qquad (r > 0).$$

It is a composite of the entire function exp and the function log. Whenever $\log z$ in equation (2) represents a branch of the multiple-valued logarithmic function (Sec. 26), that equation therefore defines a single-valued analytic function of z, a branch of the double-valued function $z^{\frac{1}{2}}$.

The principal branch f_1 of the function (1) is

(3) $$f_1(z) = \exp\left(\frac{1}{2} \operatorname{Log} z\right) = \sqrt{r}\, \exp\frac{i\theta}{2}$$
$$(r > 0,\ -\pi < \theta < \pi).$$

The ray $\theta = \pi$ is the branch cut for f_1. Note that, even if f_1 were defined on that ray by extending the range of θ in equation (3) to include the value $\theta = \pi$ or $\theta = -\pi$, the function is not continuous there. Although f_1 is analytic at some points in every neighborhood of each point $z = x$ $(x \leqq 0)$, $f_1'(z)$ cannot exist throughout the neighborhood. Therefore each point of the branch cut, including the branch point $z = 0$, is a singular point of f_1. The function $-f_1$,

$$-f_1(z) = \sqrt{r}\, \exp\frac{i(\theta + 2\pi)}{2} \qquad (r > 0,\ -\pi < \theta < \pi),$$

is another branch with the same branch cut. The values $\pm f_1(z)$ represent the totality of values $f(z)$ at all points, excluding those on the branch cut.

Other branches of $z^{\frac{1}{2}}$ are

(4) $$f_2(z) = \sqrt{r}\, \exp\frac{i\theta}{2} \qquad (r > 0,\ 0 < \theta < 2\pi)$$

and $-f_2$, each having the ray $\theta = 0$ as its branch cut. In fact, a branch with $\theta = \alpha$ as branch cut is given by these conditions:

(5) $$f_\alpha(z) = \sqrt{r}\, \exp\frac{i\theta}{2} \qquad (r > 0,\ \alpha < \theta < \alpha + 2\pi).$$

Since a cut serves to make θ or $\arg z$ a single-valued function of the point z, curves running out from the origin could be used, instead of rays, as branch cuts. But in order to make θ single-valued, it is essential that all branch cuts for $z^{\frac{1}{2}}$ run out from the common branch point $z = 0$.

Since $z = w^2$ when $w = z^{\frac{1}{2}}$, mapping by means of the latter function is the same as mapping with its inverse $w = z^2$ (Sec. 31 and Figs. 1, 2, 3 in Appendix 2) and interchanging the w and z planes.

The branch f_2 defined by equation (4) maps the domain consisting of the entire z plane, except for the ray $\theta = 0$, onto the domain $v > 0$, the upper half of the w plane. It maps each domain $|z| < r_0$, $0 < \theta < 2\pi$, consisting of all interior points of a circular disk except for those points that lie on the radius $\theta = 0$, $0 \leqq r < r_0$, onto the open half disk $|w| < \sqrt{r_0}$, $v > 0$ (Fig. 22). Both mappings are one to one. But note that points interior to the disk near the radius $\theta = 0$ have images near the boundary line $v = 0$ of the half disk.

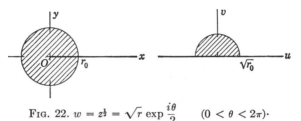

FIG. 22. $w = z^{\frac{1}{2}} = \sqrt{r} \exp \dfrac{i\theta}{2}$ $(0 < \theta < 2\pi)$.

37. Other Irrational Functions.   A branch cut for the function $z^{1/n}$, where n is an integer, can be selected as any ray from the origin.   Let us choose the negative real axis as a branch cut for the function $f(z) = z^{\frac{1}{3}}$, for example.   Each of the three functions

(1) $$f_k(z) = \sqrt[3]{r} \exp \frac{i(\theta + 2\pi k)}{3}$$

$$(k = 0, 1, 2; r > 0, -\pi < \theta < \pi)$$

is a branch of f, since f_k is single-valued and analytic at all points except for points on the cut $\theta = \pi$ and the branch point $z = 0$. The principal branch f_0 maps the cut z plane onto the angular domain $\rho > 0$, $-\pi/3 < \phi < \pi/3$ in the w plane, where

$$w = \rho \exp (i\phi) = f_0(z).$$

The branch f_1 maps the cut z plane onto the domain $\rho > 0$, $\pi/3 < \phi < \pi$, and f_2 maps it onto $\rho > 0$, $\pi < \phi < 5\pi/3$.   Those mappings are one to one.

If $z - z_0 = r' \exp (i\theta')$, a branch of the double-valued function $(z - z_0)^{\frac{1}{2}}$ is defined by the formula

(2) $$(z - z_0)^{\frac{1}{2}} = \sqrt{r'} \exp \frac{i\theta'}{2} \qquad (r' > 0, 0 < \theta' < 2\pi).$$

This single-valued function of z is analytic in its domain of definition because it is an analytic function of the entire function

$z - z_0$. The branch cut is the ray $\theta' = 0$ extending to the right of the branch point $z = z_0$. The branch (2) maps the cut z plane ($r' > 0$, $0 < \theta' < 2\pi$) in a one to one mapping upon the upper half ($\rho > 0$, $0 < \phi < \pi$) of the w plane.

As an instructive, but less elementary, example of irrational functions, consider a branch of the double-valued function

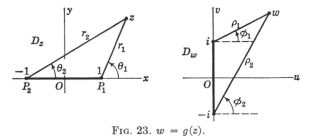

FIG. 23. $w = g(z)$.

$(z^2 - 1)^{\frac{1}{2}}$. It is helpful to represent z by each of two pairs of polar coordinates (Fig. 23):

$$(3) \qquad z - 1 = r_1 \exp (i\theta_1), \qquad z + 1 = r_2 \exp (i\theta_2).$$

We shall show that the function g,

$$(4) \qquad g(z) = (z - 1)^{\frac{1}{2}} (z + 1)^{\frac{1}{2}} = \left(\sqrt{r_1} \exp \frac{i\theta_1}{2} \right) \left(\sqrt{r_2} \exp \frac{i\theta_2}{2} \right),$$

is a branch of $(z^2 - 1)^{\frac{1}{2}}$ that is defined throughout the domain

$$(5) \quad D_z: \qquad 0 \leqq \theta_1 < 2\pi, \qquad 0 \leqq \theta_2 < 2\pi,$$
$$r_1 > 0, \qquad r_2 > 0, \qquad r_1 + r_2 > 2.$$

The polar coordinates in formula (4) are to be confined to the ranges prescribed by conditions (5). Since $r_1 + r_2$ is required to be greater than the length of the segment P_1P_2 of the x axis between the two points $z = \pm 1$, the domain D_z includes all points except those on the closed segment P_1P_2. Note that $g(z)$ can be written as $\sqrt{r_1 r_2} \exp [i(\theta_1 + \theta_2)/2]$.

According to definition (4), g is the product of two branches of type (2) whose branch cuts are the rays $\theta_1 = 0$ and $\theta_2 = 0$. Consequently g is analytic wherever $z \neq -1$ or $\theta_2 \neq 0$. The branch $\sqrt{r_1} \exp (i\theta_1/2)$ is continuous, in fact, analytic, at each interior point of the segment P_1P_2; but the value of the branch $\sqrt{r_2} \exp (i\theta_2/2)$ jumps from $\sqrt{r_2}$ to $-\sqrt{r_2}$ as the point z

crosses that segment. Therefore $g(z)$ has the jump $2\sqrt{r_1 r_2}$ there, so that g is not analytic on P_1P_2.

We can show that g is analytic on the ray $\theta_1 = 0, r_1 > 0$, because that ray lies along $\theta_2 = 0$. For if we write

$$(6) \qquad G(z) = \left(\sqrt{r_1}\exp\frac{i\Theta_1}{2}\right)\left(\sqrt{r_2}\exp\frac{i\Theta_2}{2}\right)$$

$$(r_1 r_2 > 0, \ -\pi < \Theta_k < \pi, \ k = 1, 2),$$

then G is a product of two principal branches which is analytic on the ray $\theta_1 = \Theta_1 = 0$, in fact, wherever $\Theta_1 \neq \pi$ and $r_1 > 0$. Now $G(z) = g(z)$ when point z lies above or on the ray $\theta_1 = 0$, for then $\Theta_k = \theta_k$ $(k = 1, 2)$. When point z lies below that ray, then $\Theta_k = \theta_k - 2\pi$; thus $\exp(i\Theta_k/2) = -\exp(i\theta_k/2)$, and again $G(z) = g(z)$. Therefore g is analytic throughout the domain $x > 1$, and on the ray $\theta_1 = 0$ in particular.

Since g is single-valued and analytic throughout D_z, but not on P_1P_2, and since $[g(z)]^2 = z^2 - 1$, then g is a branch of $(z^2 - 1)^{\frac{1}{2}}$ with branch cut P_1P_2 and branch points $z = \pm 1$.

Under the mapping

$$(7) \qquad w = \rho\exp(i\phi) = g(z),$$

or

$$\rho = \sqrt{r_1 r_2}, \qquad \phi = \frac{\theta_1 + \theta_2}{2},$$

the image of each point of the upper half plane $0 < \theta_k < \pi$ is some point of the upper half plane $0 < \phi < \pi$; similarly, ϕ ranges between π and 2π when θ_k does. The images of the rays $\theta_1 = 0$ and $\theta_2 = \pi$ are the positive and negative real axes $\phi = 0$ and $\phi = \pi$, respectively. Points near the cut P_1P_2 map into points near the segment of the v axis between $w = i$ and $w = -i$. The rest of the v axis is the image of the y axis.

When $0 < \theta_k < \pi$ $(k = 1, 2)$, or when $\theta_1 = 0$, then

$$g(-z) = [-(z+1)]^{\frac{1}{2}}[-(z-1)]^{\frac{1}{2}}$$

$$= \sqrt{r_1 r_2}\exp\frac{i(\theta_2+\pi)}{2}\exp\frac{i(\theta_1+\pi)}{2};$$

thus $g(-z) = -g(z)$. When $\pi < \theta_k < 2\pi$, or when $\theta_2 = \pi$, the arguments of $-(z \pm 1)$ are $\theta_k - \pi$, and again $g(-z) = -g(z)$. The branch g is therefore an *odd function*,

$$(8) \qquad\qquad g(-z) = -g(z) \qquad\qquad (z \text{ in } D_z),$$

although the double-valued function $(z^2 - 1)^{\frac{1}{2}}$ is, in a sense, even.

No two distinct points have the same image w if $w \neq 0$. For if $g(z) = w$ and $g(Z) = w$, then $[g(z)]^2 = [g(Z)]^2$; that is,

$$z^2 - 1 = Z^2 - 1$$

and either $Z = z$ or else $Z = -z$. Since $g(z) = w$, then

$$g(-z) = -w \neq w;$$

therefore $Z = z$. We conclude that every pair of distinct points of D_z maps into some pair of distinct points of a domain D_w which we may describe as follows (Fig. 23).

$$(9) \quad D_w: \quad -\frac{\pi}{2} \leqq \phi_1 < \frac{3\pi}{2}, \quad -\frac{\pi}{2} \leqq \phi_2 < \frac{3\pi}{2},$$
$$\rho_1 > 0, \qquad \rho_2 > 0, \qquad \rho_1 + \rho_2 > 2,$$

where $w - i = \rho_1 \exp(i\phi_1)$, $w + i = \rho_2 \exp(i\phi_2)$.

Now a branch g^{-1} of the double-valued function $(w^2 + 1)^{\frac{1}{2}}$ can be defined on domain D_w, consisting of all points of the w plane except those on the segment $-1 \leqq v \leqq 1$ of the v axis, by writing

$$(10) \quad g^{-1}(w) = (w - i)^{\frac{1}{2}}(w + i)^{\frac{1}{2}} = \sqrt{\rho_1 \rho_2} \ \exp\frac{i\phi_1}{2} \exp\frac{i\phi_2}{2},$$

where the polar coordinates satisfy conditions (9). By the methods used above for the function g, we find that g^{-1} is analytic throughout D_w, with the segment of the v axis between the branch points $w = \pm i$ as its branch cut. Also, the transformation $z = g^{-1}(w)$ maps each point of D_w into a point of D_z such that $y > 0$ when $v > 0$, $y < 0$ when $v < 0$, $y = 0$ and $x > 1$ when $v = 0$ and $u > 0$, and $y = 0$ and $x < -1$ when $v = 0$ and $u < 0$. Since

$$z^2 = [g^{-1}(w)]^2 = w^2 + 1,$$

then $w^2 = z^2 - 1$, and thus either $w = g(z)$ or else $w = -g(z)$. The manner in which g^{-1} and g map the upper and lower half planes and the real axes shows that $w = g(z)$. Hence each point of D_w is the image of a point $z = g^{-1}(w)$ of D_z under the transformation $w = g(z)$.

The branch g therefore maps D_z in a one to one manner upon D_w. Furthermore, when $w = g(z)$, we can show that $z = g^{-1}(w)$. Therefore the analytic functions g and g^{-1} are inverses of each other.

Branches of double-valued functions

(11) $$w = (z^2 + Az + B)^{\frac{1}{2}} = [(z - z_0)^2 - z_1^2]^{\frac{1}{2}},$$

where $A = -2z_0$ and $B = z_0^2 - z_1^2$, and mapping by those branches, can be treated with the aid of the results found for g above and the successive transformations

(12) $$z - z_0 = z_1 Z, \qquad W = (Z^2 - 1)^{\frac{1}{2}}, \qquad w = z_1 W.$$

38. The Transformation $w = \exp z$. The transformation

$$w = e^z, \qquad \text{or} \qquad \rho e^{i\phi} = e^x e^{iy},$$

where $w = \rho \exp (i\phi)$, can be written

$$\rho = e^x, \qquad \phi = y.$$

The transformation therefore maps the lines $x = c$ onto the circles $\rho = \exp c$, and the lines $y = c$ onto the rays $\phi = c$.

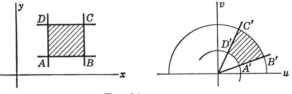

FIG. 24. $w = e^z$.

The rectangular region $c_1 \leqq x \leqq c_2$, $c_3 \leqq y \leqq c_4$ maps onto the region

$$\exp c_1 \leqq \rho \leqq \exp c_2, \qquad c_3 \leqq \phi \leqq c_4$$

bounded by circles and rays. This mapping is one to one if $c_4 - c_3 < 2\pi$. The two regions and corresponding parts of their boundaries are shown in Fig. 24. In particular, if $c_3 = 0$ and $c_4 = \pi$, so that $0 \leqq y \leqq \pi$, the rectangle maps onto half of a circular ring, as shown in Fig. 8, Appendix 2.

When x ranges through all positive and negative values, the radius vector ρ ranges through all positive values; when $x \to -\infty$, $\rho \to 0$. When y varies from zero to π, ϕ varies from zero to π. Thus the infinite strip $0 \leqq y \leqq \pi$ maps onto the upper half of the w plane, $0 \leqq \phi \leqq \pi$. The image of the point $z = 0$ is the point $w = 1$, and that of $z = \pi i$ is $w = -1$. Corresponding parts of the boundaries of the two regions are shown in Fig. 6 of Appendix 2. This mapping of a strip upon a half plane is especially useful in the applications.

The semi-infinite strip $x \leq 0$, $0 \leq y \leq \pi$ maps onto the semi-circle $\rho \leq 1$, $0 \leq \phi \leq \pi$ (Fig. 7, Appendix 2).

The infinite strip $-\pi \leq y \leq \pi$ maps onto the entire w plane, but the mapping is not one to one on the ray $\phi = \pi$. When $-\pi < y < \pi$, then $-\pi < \phi < \pi$, and the transformation $w = \exp z$ can be written

$$z = \text{Log } w = \text{Log } \rho + i\phi \qquad (\rho > 0, -\pi < \phi < \pi).$$

The principal branch Log w has the ray $\phi = \pi$ as its branch cut. Each point of the cut w plane is the image of just one point of the open strip $-\pi < y < \pi$ in the z plane, and conversely. The exponential function also maps the strip $\pi < y < 3\pi$ one to one onto that same cut w plane ($\phi \neq \pi$, $\rho > 0$); in fact, the image of each strip $(2n - 1)\pi < y < (2n + 1)\pi$ $(n = 0, \pm 1, \pm 2, \ldots)$ is that cut plane.

EXERCISES

1. Show that the transformation $w = z^{\frac{1}{2}} = \sqrt{r} \exp (i\theta/2)$, where $0 < \theta < 2\pi$, maps the domain between the two parabolas

$$r = \frac{2b^2}{1 - \cos \theta}, \qquad r = \frac{2c^2}{1 - \cos \theta}$$

in a one to one mapping onto the strip $b < v < c$, where $c > b > 0$.

2. Show that the transformation $z = w^{\frac{1}{2}}$, where $w^{\frac{1}{2}}$ is the principal branch of the double-valued function, maps the triangular region bounded by the lines $y = x$, $y = -x$, and $x = 1$ onto the region bounded by the v axis and the parabola $\rho = 2/(1 + \cos \phi)$. Show corresponding parts of the boundaries of the two regions.

3. The branch g of $(z^2 - 1)^{\frac{1}{2}}$ was defined in Sec. 37 in terms of the coordinates r_1, r_2, θ_1, and θ_2. Show geometrically why the conditions $r_1 > 0$, $0 < \theta_1 + \theta_2 < \pi$ describe the quadrant $x > 0$, $y > 0$ of the z plane. (Note that $\theta_1 + \theta_2 = \pi$ at each point on the positive y axis, and that $\theta_1 + \theta_2$ decreases as the point moves to the right along a ray $\theta_2 = c$, where $0 < c < \pi/2$.) If point z is outside that quadrant, what condition does $\theta_1 + \theta_2$ satisfy? Then show that the image of that quadrant is the quadrant $u > 0$, $v > 0$ of the w plane, under the transformation $w = g(z)$.

4. For the transformation $w = g(z)$ of the first quadrant of the z plane onto the first quadrant of the w plane (Exercise 3), show that

$$(a) \quad u = \frac{1}{\sqrt{2}} \sqrt{r_1 r_2 + x^2 - y^2 - 1}, \quad v = \frac{1}{\sqrt{2}} \sqrt{r_1 r_2 - x^2 + y^2 + 1},$$

where $r_1^2 r_2^2 = (x^2 + y^2 + 1)^2 - 4x^2$, and that (b) the image of the branch B $(x > 0, y > 0)$ of the hyperbola $x^2 - y^2 = 1$ is the ray $v = u$, $u > 0$.

5. In Exercise 4 show that the domain D that lies under the branch B of the hyperbola and in the first quadrant of the z plane is described by the conditions $r_1 > 0$, $0 < \theta_1 + \theta_2 < \pi/2$. Then show that the image of D is the octant $0 < v < u$. Sketch the domains.

6. When g is the branch of $(z^2 - 1)^{\frac{1}{2}}$ defined in Sec. 37 and when $z_0 = r_0 \exp (i\theta_0)$, where $r_0 > 0$ and $0 \leq \theta_0 < 2\pi$, show that a branch g_0 of $(z^2 - z_0^2)^{\frac{1}{2}}$ whose branch cut is the line segment between the points z_0 and $-z_0$ is defined by the formula

$$g_0(z) = z_0\, g(Z) \qquad\qquad \text{where } Z = \frac{z}{z_0}.$$

7. Write $z - 1 = r_1 \exp (i\theta_1)$ and $z + 1 = r_2 \exp (i\Theta_2)$, in which $0 < \theta_1 < 2\pi$ and $-\pi < \Theta_2 < \pi$, to define a branch of the function

(a) $(z^2 - 1)^{\frac{1}{2}}$,   (b) $\left(\dfrac{z-1}{z+1}\right)^{\frac{1}{2}}$,

whose branch cut consists of the two rays $\theta_1 = 0$ and $\Theta_2 = \pi$.

8. In the notation used in Sec. 37 show that the function h, where

$$h(z) = \left(\frac{z-1}{z+1}\right)^{\frac{1}{2}} = \sqrt{\frac{r_1}{r_2}} \exp \frac{i(\theta_1 - \theta_2)}{2},$$

is a branch with the same domain of definition D_z and the same branch cut $P_1 P_2$ (Fig. 23) as g; that the transformation $w = h(z)$ maps D_z onto the right-hand half of the w plane ($\rho > 0$, $-\pi/2 < \phi < \pi/2$) with the point $w = 1$ as the image of the point $z = \infty$. The inverse transformation is

$$z = \frac{1 + w^2}{1 - w^2} \qquad\qquad (u > 0).$$

9. Show that the transformation $w = h(z)$ defined in Exercise 8 maps the region outside the unit circle $|z| = 1$ in the upper half of the z plane onto the angular region in the first quadrant between the line $v = u$ and the u axis. Show the regions graphically.

10. Write $z = r \exp (i\Theta)$, $z - 1 = r_1 \exp (i\Theta_1)$, $z + 1 = r_2 \exp (i\Theta_2)$, where the values of all three angles lie between $-\pi$ and π, and define a branch of the function $[z(z^2 - 1)]^{\frac{1}{2}}$ whose branch cut consists of the two segments $x \leq -1$ and $0 \leq x \leq 1$ of the x axis.

11. Under the transformation $w = \exp z$, show that lines $ky = x$ map onto spirals $\rho = \exp (k\phi)$.

12. Verify the mapping of regions and boundaries shown in Fig. 7 of Appendix 2, under the transformation $w = \exp z$.

13. Under the transformation $w = \exp z$, find the image of the semi-infinite strip $x \geq 0$, $0 \leq y \leq \pi$ and exhibit corresponding portions of the boundaries.

14. Define a branch of $\log (z - 1)$ that maps the cut z plane, including all points except those on the segment $x \geq 1$ of the real axis, onto the strip $0 < v < 2\pi$ in the w plane.

39. The Transformation $w = \sin z$. Since

$$\sin z = \sin x \cosh y + i \cos x \sinh y,$$

the transformation $w = \sin z$ can be written

$$u = \sin x \cosh y, \qquad v = \cos x \sinh y.$$

If $x = \pi/2$, then $u = \cosh y$ and $v = 0$. Thus the line $x = \pi/2$ maps onto the part $u \geq 1$ of the real axis in the w plane. This

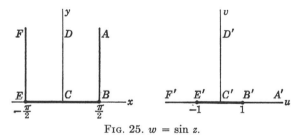

FIG. 25. $w = \sin z$.

mapping is one to one for either the upper or lower half of the line $x = \pi/2$; when y varies from zero to infinity through positive values, or through negative values, u varies from one to infinity.

If $y = 0$, then $u = \sin x$ and $v = 0$. Hence the entire x axis maps onto the segment $-1 \leq u \leq 1$ of the u axis, but this mapping is not one to one. In fact, the segment $-\pi/2 \leq x \leq \pi/2$ of the x axis maps uniquely upon that segment. The upper half of the y axis maps onto the upper half of the v axis, and the lower half onto the lower half, since $u = 0$ and $v = \sinh y$ when $x = 0$. The mapping of those lines is shown in Fig. 25.

The line segment $y = c$, $-\pi/2 \leq x \leq \pi/2$, maps upon the semiellipse whose parametric equations are

$$u = \cosh c \sin x, \qquad v = \sinh c \cos x.$$

If $c > 0$, then $v \geq 0$, and these equations represent the upper half of the ellipse

$$\frac{u^2}{\cosh^2 c} + \frac{v^2}{\sinh^2 c} = 1;$$

if $c < 0$, they represent the lower half (Fig. 26). Each point of the line segment maps into one point of the semiellipse, and conversely, according to the above parametric equations. The foci of the ellipse are the points $w = \pm 1$ independent of the value of c.

The line $x = c$, where $-\pi/2 < c < \pi/2$, maps onto the curve

$$u = \sin c \cosh y, \qquad v = \cos c \sinh y,$$

which is the right-hand half of the hyperbola

$$\frac{u^2}{\sin^2 c} - \frac{v^2}{\cos^2 c} = 1,$$

if $c > 0$, and the left-hand half if $c < 0$. The mapping is one to one. The points $w = \pm 1$ are the foci of this hyperbola.

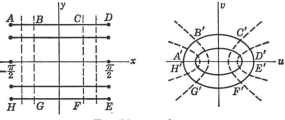

Fig. 26. $w = \sin z$.

Each given point in the upper half of the w plane is a point on a definite one of the semiellipses; it therefore corresponds to just one point of a definite horizontal line segment, that is, to just one point of the semi-infinite strip

$$-\frac{\pi}{2} \leqq x \leqq \frac{\pi}{2}, \qquad y \geqq 0$$

in the z plane. Also, to each point of the strip there corresponds just one point w. Hence the mapping of that strip upon the upper half of the w plane is one to one (Fig. 9, Appendix 2). The right-hand half of this strip maps onto the first quadrant of the w plane (Fig. 10, Appendix 2).

The rectangle $-\pi \leqq x \leqq \pi$, $c_1 \leqq y \leqq c_2$ maps onto the region bounded by two confocal ellipses, as shown in Fig. 27. But note that both the sides $x = \pm\pi$ map onto the line segment $u = 0$, $v = -\sinh y$ ($c_1 \leqq y \leqq c_2$); thus, if $c_1 > 0$, the image of the rectangular domain is the elliptic ring with a cut along the negative v axis. As a point z describes the boundary of the rectangle, its image makes a circuit around one ellipse, then along the cut and around the other ellipse, and back again along the cut to the starting point, as shown in the figure.

The rectangular region $-\pi/2 \leq x \leq \pi/2,\ 0 \leq y \leq c$ maps uniquely onto a semielliptic region in the manner shown in Fig. 11 of Appendix 2.

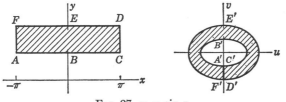

FIG. 27. $w = \sin z$.

40. Successive Transformations. Since $\cos z = \sin (z + \pi/2)$, the transformation

$$w = \cos z$$

can be written successively as

$$w = \sin z', \qquad z' = z + \frac{\pi}{2}.$$

The last transformation is a translation of each point in the z plane to the right through the distance $\pi/2$. Therefore the transformation $w = \cos z$ is the same as the transformation $w = \sin z$ preceded by a translation to the right through $\pi/2$ units.

The transformation

$$w = \sinh z$$

can be written $iw = \sin (iz)$, or

$$w' = \sin z', \qquad z' = iz, \qquad w' = iw.$$

It is therefore the combination of the transformation $w = \sin z$ with a rotation of the axes in each plane through the angle $\pi/2$. Similarly, the transformation

$$w = \cosh z$$

is essentially the same as $w = \cos z$.

As another example of successive transformations, consider

$$w = (\sin z)^{\frac{1}{2}},$$

where the fractional power denotes the principal branch. We write

$$w' = \sin z, \qquad w = (w')^{\frac{1}{2}}.$$

We noted in the preceding section that the first maps the semi-infinite strip $0 \leqq x \leqq \pi/2$, $y \geqq 0$ onto the first quadrant. The second transforms the quadrant into an octant. The successive transformations of regions and boundaries that map the strip in the z plane onto an octant of the w plane are shown in Fig. 28.

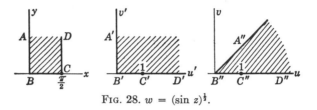

Fig. 28. $w = (\sin z)^{\frac{1}{2}}$.

The linear fractional transformation

$$w = \frac{z - 1}{z + 1}$$

maps the half plane $x \geqq 0$ onto the unit circle $|w| \leqq 1$ (Fig. 12, Appendix 2). It is readily shown that this transformation also maps the half plane $y \geqq 0$ onto the half plane $v \geqq 0$. Since the transformation $w' = \text{Log } w$, or $w = \exp w'$, maps the half plane $v \geqq 0$ onto the strip $0 \leqq v' \leqq \pi$ (Fig. 6, Appendix 2), it follows that the transformation

$$w' = \text{Log } \frac{z - 1}{z + 1}$$

maps the half plane onto the strip. The order of corresponding points on the boundaries is shown in Fig. 19 of Appendix 2.

41. Table of Transformations of Regions. Appendix 2 consists of a set of figures showing the transformation of a number of simple and useful regions by various elementary functions. In each case there is a one to one correspondence between points of the region and of its image. Corresponding parts of boundaries are indicated by the lettering. Some mappings that have not been discussed in the text are shown in that table. Their verification can be left as exercises for the student. Several of the transformations given in Appendix 2 can be derived by means of the Schwarz-Christoffel transformation (Chap. 10).

EXERCISES

1. Show that the transformation $w = \cosh z$ maps the points $z = iy$ ($0 \leqq y \leqq \pi/2$) onto the segment $0 \leqq u \leqq 1$ of the u axis.

2. Under the transformation $w = \cosh z$, show that the image of the semi-infinite strip $x \geqq 0$, $0 \leqq y \leqq \pi/2$ is the first quadrant of the w plane and indicate corresponding parts of the boundaries of the region.

3. Under the transformation $w = \sin z$, show that the images of the sides of the rectangle $0 \leqq x \leqq \pi/2$, $0 \leqq y \leqq 1$ are the line segments

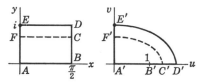

FIG. 29. $w = \sin z$, $A'D' = \cosh 1$, $A'E' = \sinh 1$.

and arc $D'E'$ indicated in Fig. 29, where $D'E'$ is a quarter of the ellipse $(u/\cosh 1)^2 + (v/\sinh 1)^2 = 1$.

4. Complete the mapping indicated in Fig. 29 by using the mapping of line segments $y = c$ ($0 \leqq x \leqq \pi/2$) to prove that the transformation $w = \sin z$ establishes a one to one correspondence between points of the rectangular region and the region $A'B'D'E'$.

5. Verify the mapping by $\sin z$ shown in Fig. 10, Appendix 2.

6. Verify the mapping by $\sin z$ shown in Fig. 11, Appendix 2.

7. Describe the transformation $w = \cosh z$ in terms of the transformation $w = \sin z$ and rotations and translations.

8. Show that the transformation $w = \sin^2 z$ maps the region $0 \leqq x \leqq \pi/2$, $y \geqq 0$ onto the region $v \geqq 0$, and indicate corresponding parts of the boundaries.

9. Under the transformation $w = (\sin z)^{\frac{1}{2}}$, show that the strip $-\pi/2 \leqq x \leqq \pi/2$, $y \geqq 0$ maps onto the part of the first quadrant lying below the line $v = u$, and determine the corresponding parts of the boundaries.

10. Verify the mapping, under the transformation $w = 1/z$, of the regions and parts of the boundaries indicated (a) in Fig. 4, Appendix 2; (b) in Fig. 5, Appendix 2.

11. Verify the mapping shown in Fig. 12, Appendix 2, under the transformation $w = (z - 1)/(z + 1)$.

12. Show that the bilinear transformation $z' = (z - 1)/(z + 1)$ maps the x axis onto the x' axis, the segment $-1 < x < 1$ of that axis onto the negative half of the x' axis, the half plane $y > 0$ onto the half plane

$y' > 0$, and $y < 0$ onto $y' < 0$. When the principal branch of $(z')^{\frac{1}{2}}$ is used, show that the composite transformation

$$w = (z')^{\frac{1}{2}} = \left(\frac{z-1}{z+1}\right)^{\frac{1}{2}}$$

maps the z plane, except for the segment $-1 \leqq x \leqq 1$ of the x axis, onto the half plane $u > 0$ (compare Exercise 8, Sec. 38).

13. Using the polar representation of z, show that the transformation

$$w = z + \frac{1}{z}$$

maps both the upper and lower half of the circle $r = 1$ onto the line segment $-2 \leqq u \leqq 2$, $v = 0$.

14. Show that the transformation $w = z + 1/z$ maps the circle $r = c$ onto the ellipse

$$u = \left(c + \frac{1}{c}\right)\cos\theta, \qquad v = \left(c - \frac{1}{c}\right)\sin\theta.$$

15. Verify the mapping indicated in Fig. 16, Appendix 2, under the transformation $w = z + 1/z$.

16. Describe the mapping by the function $w = \cosh z$ in terms of the transformations $w = e^z$ and $2w = z + 1/z$.

CHAPTER 5

INTEGRALS

The reader may pass directly to the chapters on conformal mapping and applications at this time if he wishes. It would seem natural to present those chapters next, since we have just completed a study of mapping by elementary functions. However, we have not yet established the continuity of the first- and second-order partial derivatives of the real and imaginary components, $u(x,y)$ and $v(x,y)$, of an analytic function. If we take up the subject of conformal mapping at this time, we shall have to assume that continuity; to establish it, we need to use some of the theory of integrals of analytic functions.

The theory of line integrals, together with the theory of power series and residues, constitutes a very important portion of the theory of functions of complex variables. The theory is noted for its mathematical elegance. The theorems are generally concise and powerful, and most of the proofs are simple. But the theory is also noted for its great utility in both pure and applied mathematics. We present a substantial introduction to that theory in this and succeeding chapters.

42. Definite Integrals. In order to introduce the line integral of $f(z)$ in a fairly simple way, we first define the definite integral of a complex-valued function F of a real variable t.

We write

$$(1) \qquad F(t) = U(t) + iV(t) \qquad (a \leqq t \leqq b),$$

where U and V are real-valued *sectionally continuous*, or piecewise continuous, functions of t on a bounded interval (a,b); that is, each of these functions is such that the interval consists of a finite number of subintervals in each of which the function is continuous and has finite limits from the interior at both end points. Such functions are therefore continuous except for at most a finite number of finite jumps in the interval. Then we

95

define the definite integral of F in terms of two real definite integrals, each of which exists, by the equation

$$(2) \qquad \int_a^b F(t)\, dt = \int_a^b U(t)\, dt + i \int_a^b V(t)\, dt.$$

From this definition it follows that

$$(3) \qquad \Re \int_a^b F(t)\, dt = \int_a^b U(t)\, dt = \int_a^b \Re[F(t)]\, dt.$$

Furthermore, if k is a complex constant, $k = k_1 + ik_2$, then

$$\int_a^b kF\, dt = \int_a^b (k_1 U - k_2 V)\, dt + i \int_a^b (k_1 V + k_2 U)\, dt$$
$$= (k_1 + ik_2)\left(\int_a^b U\, dt + i \int_a^b V\, dt\right);$$

that is,

$$(4) \qquad \int_a^b kF(t)\, dt = k \int_a^b F(t)\, dt.$$

Such properties as those on the reversal of limits of integration, and integrals of sums, clearly hold true as they do for real integrals.

To establish another basic property, let r_0 and θ_0 denote the absolute value and argument of the complex number represented by the integral (2), when $r_0 \neq 0$; that is,

$$(5) \qquad \int_a^b F(t)\, dt = r_0 \exp(i\theta_0), \qquad r_0 = \left|\int_a^b F(t)\, dt\right|.$$

When $k = \exp(-i\theta_0)$, it follows from equation (4) that

$$\int_a^b e^{-i\theta_0}F(t)\, dt = e^{-i\theta_0}\int_a^b F(t)\, dt = r_0.$$

Note that r_0 is real and positive. Then, in view of equation (3),

$$r_0 = \Re \int_a^b e^{-i\theta_0}F\, dt = \int_a^b \Re(e^{-i\theta_0}F)\, dt > 0;$$

but $\quad \int_a^b \Re(e^{-i\theta_0}F)\, dt \leqq \int_a^b |\Re(e^{-i\theta_0}F)|\, dt \leqq \int_a^b |e^{-i\theta_0}F|\, dt$

provided $a < b$. Since $|\exp(-i\theta_0)| = 1$, it follows that

$$r_0 \leqq \int_a^b |F|\, dt;$$

that is,

$$(6) \qquad \left|\int_a^b F(t)\, dt\right| \leqq \int_a^b |F(t)|\, dt \qquad (a \leqq b).$$

This inequality is also true if $r_0 = 0$, since its left-hand member then vanishes.

43. Contours. Classes of curves that are adequate for the study of line integrals will now be introduced.

A continuous arc is defined as a set of points (x,y) such that

$$(1) \qquad\qquad x = \phi(t), \qquad y = \psi(t) \qquad\qquad (a \leqq t \leqq b),$$

where ϕ and ψ are continuous functions of the real parameter t. The definition establishes a continuous mapping of points t from the interval (a,b) to the arc and an ordering of the points (x,y) according to increasing values of t. If no two distinct values of t correspond to the same point (x,y), the arc is called a Jordan arc. But if $\phi(a) = \phi(b)$ and $\psi(a) = \psi(b)$, and if no other two values of t correspond to the same point (x,y), the continuous arc is a *simple closed curve*, or a Jordan curve.

The broken line

$$(2) \qquad x = t \quad (0 \leqq t \leqq 2), \qquad y = \begin{cases} t & (0 \leqq t \leqq 1) \\ 1 & (1 \leqq t \leqq 2), \end{cases}$$

that is, $y = x$ $(0 \leqq x \leqq 1)$, $y = 1$ $(1 \leqq x \leqq 2)$, is an example of a Jordan arc. Here the parameter t is the same as the coordinate x. The circle

$$(3) \qquad\qquad x = r_0 \cos t, \qquad y = r_0 \sin t \qquad (0 \leqq t \leqq 2\pi)$$

is an example of a simple closed curve.

If the functions ϕ and ψ in equations (1) have continuous derivatives $\phi'(t)$ and $\psi'(t)$ which do not vanish simultaneously for any value of t, the arc has a continuously turning tangent. The arc or curve is then *smooth*. Its length exists and is given by the formula

$$(4) \qquad\qquad L = \int_a^b \sqrt{[\phi'(t)]^2 + [\psi'(t)]^2}\, dt \qquad\qquad (a \leqq b).$$

A *contour* is a continuous chain of a finite number of smooth arcs. If equations (1) represent a contour, then ϕ and ψ are continuous, whereas ϕ' and ψ' are sectionally continuous. The broken line (2), for example, is a contour. If the contour is closed and does not intersect itself, it is a piecewise smooth Jordan curve, called a *closed contour*. Boundaries of triangles and rectangles are examples. The length of a contour is the sum of the lengths of the smooth arcs; it is represented by the integral (4) when equations (1) represent the contour.

Any Jordan curve C, and hence any closed contour, separates the plane into two domains which each have the points of C as their only boundary points. One of those domains, called the interior of C, is bounded; the other, the exterior of C, is unbounded. It will be convenient to accept this statement, known as the Jordan curve theorem, as geometrically evident; the proof is not simple.[1]

Let a new parameter r be introduced into the parametric equations (1) of a contour by substituting

$$(5) \qquad\qquad t = p(r),$$

where p is continuous with a sectionally continuous derivative $p'(r)$, and where $p'(r) > 0$, so that t increases with r. Then, if $p(c) = a$ and $p(d) = b$, the parametric equations take the form

$$(6) \quad x = \phi[p(r)] = \Phi(r), \qquad y = \psi[p(r)] = \Psi(r) \qquad (c \leqq r \leqq d).$$

These equations represent a continuous mapping of points from the interval $c \leqq r \leqq d$ to the contour C, ordered according to increasing values of r, and therefore of t. Now

$$\phi'(t) = \Phi'(r) \frac{dr}{dt} = \frac{\Phi'(r)}{p'(r)}, \qquad \psi'(t) = \frac{\Psi'(r)}{p'(r)},$$

and the integral in formula (4) for the length of C transforms to

$$\int_c^d \sqrt{[\Phi'(r)]^2 + [\Psi'(r)]^2} \; \frac{1}{p'(r)} \, p'(r) \, dr.$$

Therefore $\qquad L = \int_c^d \sqrt{[\Phi'(r)]^2 + [\Psi'(r)]^2} \, dr \qquad (c \leqq d);$

that is, the number L given by formula (4) is invariant under such changes in the parametric representation of C.

44. Line Integrals. The integral of a function f of the complex variable z from a point $z = \alpha$ to a point $z = \beta$ is defined in terms of the values $f(z)$ at points along an arc C extending from point α to point β. The integral is therefore a line integral. Its value may depend upon the choice of the arc C as well as upon f, α, and β. Although the integral

$$(1) \qquad\qquad \int_C f(z) \, dz \qquad \text{or} \qquad \int_\alpha^\beta f(z) \, dz$$

can be defined directly as a limit of a sum, a definition in terms

[1] See chap. 6 of the book by Dienes cited in Appendix 1.

of definite integrals of the type introduced in Sec. 42 has some advantages.

Let C be a contour extending from α to β and write $z = x + iy$. Then, when z is on C,

$$(2) \qquad\qquad x = \phi(t), \qquad y = \psi(t) \qquad\qquad (a \leq t \leq b),$$

where ϕ and ψ are continuous and ϕ' and ψ' are sectionally continuous; also $z = \alpha$ when $t = a$ and $z = \beta$ when $t = b$. Let f be sectionally continuous on C; that is, the real and imaginary components of f are sectionally continuous functions of t. Then we *define* the integral (1) by the equation

$$(3) \qquad \int_C f(z)\, dz = \int_a^b f[\phi(t) + i\psi(t)][\phi'(t) + i\psi'(t)]\, dt.$$

The integral on the right exists, since its integrand is a sectionally continuous complex-valued function of the real variable t (Sec. 42).

If u and v denote the components of f, then when z is on C,

$$f(z) = u + iv = u[\phi(t),\psi(t)] + iv[\phi(t),\psi(t)]$$

and our definition (3) can be written either in terms of real definite integrals with sectionally continuous integrands,

$$(4) \qquad \int_C f(z)\, dz = \int_a^b (u\phi' - v\psi')\, dt + i \int_a^b (u\psi' + v\phi')\, dt,$$

or in terms of real line integrals,

$$(5) \qquad \int_C f(z)\, dz = \int_C (u\, dx - v\, dy) + i \int_C (u\, dy + v\, dx).$$

Note that these representations can be written formally by replacing f by $u + iv$ and dz by $dx + i\, dy$ and expanding the integrand.

Unless otherwise indicated, let us agree that paths of integration are to be restricted to contours, and integrands to sectionally continuous functions on those contours. Then the line integral (1) will also be called a *contour integral*.

According to equation (3) or (4), the integral from β to α over a given contour C is described in terms of definite integrals from $t = b$ to $t = a$, and hence

$$(6) \qquad\qquad \int_\beta^\alpha f(z)\, dz = - \int_\alpha^\beta f(z)\, dz$$

where these are contour integrals over C in opposite directions. Three further properties of contour integrals follow from equations (3) and (4), namely,

$$(7) \qquad \int_C kf(z) \, dz = k \int_C f(z) \, dz$$

for any complex constant k,

$$(8) \qquad \int_C [f(z) + g(z)] \, dz = \int_C f(z) \, dz + \int_C g(z) \, dz,$$

and, when C consists of a contour C_1 from α to some point γ and a contour C_2 from γ to β, then

$$(9) \qquad \int_C f(z) \, dz = \int_{C_1} f(z) \, dz + \int_{C_2} f(z) \, dz.$$

When z is on C, we interpret the symbol $|dz|$ thus:

$$|dz| = |\phi'(t) + i\psi'(t)| \, dt = \sqrt{(dx)^2 + (dy)^2}.$$

Our definition (4), Sec. 43, of the length of the contour C can then be abbreviated by the formula

$$(10) \qquad L = \int_C |dz|$$

if it is understood that the value of the real integral here is positive.

In view of inequality (6), Sec. 42, we can write the inequality

$$\left| \int_a^b f(\phi + i\psi)(\phi' + i\psi') \, dt \right| \leq \int_a^b |f| \, |\phi' + i\psi'| \, dt \qquad (a \leq b).$$

If we use the abbreviation

$$\int_C |f(z)| \, |dz| = \int_a^b |f[\phi(t) + i\psi(t)]| \, |\phi'(t) + i\psi'(t)| \, dt \qquad (a \leq b),$$

the foregoing inequality for the contour integral of a sectionally continuous function takes the form

$$(11) \qquad \left| \int_C f(z) \, dz \right| \leq \int_C |f(z)| \, |dz|.$$

If $|f(z)| \leq M$ whenever z is on the contour C, where M is some constant, and if L denotes the length of C, the value of the real integral on the right of inequality (11) does not exceed ML; hence

$$(12) \qquad \left| \int_C f(z) \, dz \right| \leq ML.$$

Properties (11) and (12) are especially useful in the theory of contour integrals.

The value of a contour integral is independent of the change in the parametric representation of its arc described under equation (5), Sec. 43. This is seen by writing the real integrals in equation (4) in terms of the new parameter r and following the procedure used in Sec. 43 to show the invariance of arc length.

Although a further examination of geometrical and logical, or topological, foundations of the theory of line integrals would be interesting, we shall proceed with the theory itself.

The real definite integral can be interpreted as an area. It has other interpretations. Except in special cases, no corresponding helpful interpretation, geometrical or physical, is available for the line integral in the complex plane. Nevertheless, as noted earlier, the theory of integration in the complex plane is remarkably useful in physics, engineering, and mathematics.

45. Examples. Let us find the value of the integral

$$I_1 = \int_{C_1} z^2 \, dz$$

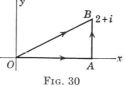

FIG. 30

when C_1 is the straight-line segment OB from $z = 0$ to $z = 2 + i$ (Fig. 30). If the coordinate y is used as the parameter t, the parametric equations of C_1 reduce to $x = 2y$ $(0 \leqq y \leqq 1)$. The integrand z^2 is everywhere continuous; on C_1 it becomes

$$z^2 = x^2 - y^2 + 2xyi = 3y^2 + 4y^2i$$

and $[\phi'(t) + i\psi'(t)] \, dt$, or $dx + i \, dy$, becomes $(2 + i) \, dy$; hence

$$I_1 = \int_0^1 (3y^2 + 4y^2i)(2 + i) \, dy$$

$$= (3 + 4i)(2 + i) \int_0^1 y^2 \, dy = \tfrac{2}{3} + \tfrac{11}{3}i.$$

If the path of integration is C_2, the contour OAB shown in Fig. 30, let us evaluate the integral

$$I_2 = \int_{C_2} z^2 \, dz = \int_{OA} z^2 \, dz + \int_{AB} z^2 \, dz.$$

On arc OA, $z = x$. Parametric equations of that arc are $x = x$, $y = 0$ $(0 \leqq x \leqq 2)$; hence dz is replaced by dx. On AB,

$z = 2 + iy$ $(0 \leq y \leq 1)$, and dz is replaced by $i\,dy$.   Therefore

$$I_2 = \int_0^2 x^2\,dx + \int_0^1 (2 + iy)^2 i\,dy$$
$$= \tfrac{8}{3} + i\left[\int_0^1 (4 - y^2)\,dy + 4i \int_0^1 y\,dy\right] = \tfrac{2}{3} + \tfrac{11}{3}i.$$

Incidentally, the equations of contour OAB here can be written in the form $x = \phi(t)$, $y = \psi(t)$ $(0 \leq t \leq 3)$, where

$$\phi(t) = \begin{cases} t & (0 \leq t \leq 2) \\ 2 & (2 \leq t \leq 3), \end{cases}$$
$$\psi(t) = \begin{cases} 0 & (0 \leq t \leq 2) \\ t - 2 & (2 \leq t \leq 3). \end{cases}$$

We note that $I_2 = I_1$.   Thus the integral of z^2 over the closed contour $OABO$ has the value $I_2 - I_1 = 0$, and we shall soon see that this is a consequence of the fact that the integrand z^2 is analytic interior to and on the contour.

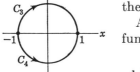

As a third example, let the integrand be the function

$$f(z) = \bar{z},$$

which is everywhere continuous.   If the path C_3 is the upper half of the circle $|z| = 1$ from

FIG. 31

$z = -1$ to $z = 1$ (Fig. 31), its parametric equations can be written

$$x = \cos\theta, \qquad y = \sin\theta, \qquad \text{or} \qquad z = e^{i\theta} \qquad (0 \leq \theta \leq \pi).$$

Then, by replacing dz by $(-\sin\theta + i\cos\theta)\,d\theta$, we find that

$$I_3 = \int_{C_3} \bar{z}\,dz = \int_\pi^0 (\cos\theta - i\sin\theta)(-\sin\theta + i\cos\theta)\,d\theta$$
$$= \int_\pi^0 e^{-i\theta}\,ie^{i\theta}\,d\theta = i\int_\pi^0 d\theta = -\pi i.$$

The integral I_4 between the same two points along the lower semicircle C_4 (Fig. 31), represented by the equations

$$x = \cos\theta, \qquad y = \sin\theta \qquad \text{or} \qquad z = e^{i\theta} \qquad (\pi \leq \theta \leq 2\pi),$$

is found in like manner:

$$I_4 = \int_{C_4} \bar{z}\,dz = i\int_\pi^{2\pi} d\theta = \pi i.$$

Note that $I_4 \neq I_3$ and that the integral I_C of $\bar{z}$ around the entire circle C in the counterclockwise direction does not vanish, since

$$I_C = \int_C \bar{z}\, dz = I_4 - I_3 = 2\pi i.$$

When z is on the unit circle C,

$$\frac{1}{z} = \frac{\bar{z}}{|z|^2} = \bar{z};$$

thus the integrands of the integrals I_3, I_4, and I_C can be replaced by $1/z$. In particular,

$$I_C = \int_C \frac{dz}{z} = 2\pi i.$$

As a final example, let C_5 denote the line segment from the point $z = i$ to $z = 1$. Without evaluating the integral

$$I_5 = \int_{C_5} \frac{dz}{z^4},$$

let us determine an upper bound for its absolute value. The integrand is continuous on C_5, since its only discontinuity is at the origin.

If the parameter t is chosen as the coordinate x, the parametric equations of C_5 reduce to $y = 1 - x \quad (0 \leqq x \leqq 1)$. When z is on C_5,

$$|z^4| = (x^2 + y^2)^2 = [x^2 + (1 - x)^2]^2 = (2x^2 - 2x + 1)^2,$$

and, to find a lower bound for this quantity, we note that

$$|z^4| = [2(x - \tfrac{1}{2})^2 + \tfrac{1}{2}]^2 \geqq \tfrac{1}{4}$$

since $(x - \tfrac{1}{2})^2 \geqq 0$. Consequently, for all z on C_5,

$$\left| \frac{1}{z^4} \right| \leqq 4,$$

a fact that is also evident from a figure. Thus we may write $M = 4$ in the inequality (12), Sec. 44. Since the length of C_5 is $\sqrt{2}$, it follows that

$$|I_5| \leqq 4\sqrt{2}.$$

EXERCISES

For each function f and path C given in Exercises 1 to 6, find the value of

$$\int_C f(z)\, dz$$

after observing that f is at least sectionally continuous on C and that C is a contour.

1. $f(z) = y - x - 3x^2i$; C is the straight-line segment from $z = 0$ to $z = 1 + i$.   *Ans.* $1 - i$.

2. $f(z) = y - x - 3x^2i$; C consists of two straight-line segments, one from $z = 0$ to $z = i$ and the other from $z = i$ to $z = 1 + i$.
Ans. $\frac{1}{2}(1 - i)$.

3. $f(z) = (z + 2)/z$ and C is

(a) the semicircle $z = 2e^{i\theta}$ where θ varies from 0 to π;
(b) the semicircle $z = 2e^{i\theta}$ where θ varies from 0 to $-\pi$;
(c) the circle $z = 2e^{i\theta}$ where θ varies from $-\pi$ to π.
Ans. (a) $-4 + 2\pi i$; (b) $-4 - 2\pi i$; (c) $4\pi i$.

4. $f(z) = z - 1$, and C is this arc from $z = 0$ to $z = 2$:

(a) the semicircle $z - 1 = e^{i\theta}$ $(0 \leq \theta \leq \pi)$;
(b) the segment of the x axis.   *Ans.* (a) 0; (b) 0.

5. C is the arc from $z = -1 - i$ to $z = 1 + i$ of the curve $y = x^3$ and

$$f(z) = \begin{cases} 4y & \text{when } y > 0, \\ 1 & \text{when } y < 0. \end{cases} \quad Ans.\ 2 + 3i.$$

6. $f(z) = e^z$, and C is this path from $z = \pi i$ to $z = 1$:

(a) the straight-line segment;
(b) the broken-line segment along the coordinate axes.
Ans. (a) $1 + e$; (b) $1 + e$.

7. If C is the boundary of the square with vertices at the points $z = 0$, $z = 1$, $z = 1 + i$, and $z = i$, show that

$$\int_C (3z + 1)\, dz = 0.$$

8. If C is the boundary of the square in Exercise 7, evaluate

$$\int_C \pi \exp(\pi \bar{z})\, dz. \qquad Ans.\ 4(e^\pi - 1).$$

9. Evaluate the integral I_3, Sec. 45, using these equations of C_3:

$$x = t, \qquad y = \sqrt{1 - t^2} \qquad (-1 \leq t \leq 1).$$

10. Let C be the arc of the circle $|z| = 2$ that lies in the first quadrant. Without finding the actual value of the integral, show that

$$\left| \int_C \frac{dz}{z^2 + 1} \right| \leq \frac{\pi}{3}.$$

11. When C denotes the boundary of the triangle with vertices at the points $z = 0$, $z = -4$, and $z = 3i$, show that

$$\left| \int_C (e^z - \bar{z}) \, dz \right| \leq 60.$$

12. If C is a circle $|z| = R$, where $R > 1$, show that

$$\left| \int_C \frac{\text{Log } z}{z^2} \, dz \right| < 2\pi \frac{\pi + \text{Log } R}{R}$$

and hence that the value of the integral tends to zero as $R \to \infty$.

13. By writing the integral in terms of real integrals, prove that

$$\int_\alpha^\beta dz = \beta - \alpha$$

whenever the path of integration from point $z = \alpha$ to point $z = \beta$ is (a) a smooth Jordan arc; (b) a contour.

14. Prove that

$$2 \int_\alpha^\beta z \, dz = \beta^2 - \alpha^2$$

whenever the path of integration is (a) a smooth Jordan arc; (b) a contour. (c) As a consequence, show that the integral of z around any closed contour vanishes.

15. When C_0 is a circle

$$z - z_0 = r_0 e^{i\theta} \qquad (0 \leq \theta \leq 2\pi, r_0 > 0).$$

described counterclockwise, show that

$$\int_{C_0} f(z) \, dz = ir_0 \int_0^{2\pi} f(z_0 + r_0 e^{i\theta}) e^{i\theta} \, d\theta$$

if f is continuous on C_0.

16. As particular cases of Exercise 15, show that

$$\int_{C_0} \frac{dz}{z - z_0} = 2\pi i, \qquad \int_{C_0} \frac{dz}{(z - z_0)^n} = 0 \qquad (n = 2, 3, \ldots).$$

46. The Cauchy-Goursat Theorem. According to Green's theorem on real line integrals, if two functions $P(x,y)$ and $Q(x,y)$, together with their partial derivatives of the first order, are continuous throughout a closed region R consisting of the interior of a closed contour C together with the boundary C itself, then

$$\int_C (P \, dx + Q \, dy) = \iint_R \left(\frac{\partial Q}{\partial x} - \frac{\partial P}{\partial y} \right) dx \, dy,$$

where C is described in the *positive* (counterclockwise) *sense,* the direction such that the points interior to R lie on the left of C.

Now consider a function

$$f(z) = u(x,y) + iv(x,y)$$

which is analytic at all points within and on the closed contour C *and is such that $f'(z)$ is continuous there.* Then u and v and their partial derivatives of the first order are continuous there, and consequently

$$\int_C (u\,dx - v\,dy) = -\iint_R \left(\frac{\partial v}{\partial x} + \frac{\partial u}{\partial y}\right) dx\,dy,$$

$$\int_C (v\,dx + u\,dy) = \iint_R \left(\frac{\partial u}{\partial x} - \frac{\partial v}{\partial y}\right) dx\,dy.$$

In view of the Cauchy-Riemann conditions, the integrands of the two double integrals vanish throughout the region R. According to equation (5), Sec. 44, the line integrals on the left are the real and imaginary coefficients of the complex number representing the line integral of $f(z)$. It follows that

$$\int_C f(z)\,dz = 0.$$

This result was originated by Cauchy in the early part of the last century.

As elementary examples, we note that, for every closed contour C,

$$\int_C dz = 0, \qquad \int_C z\,dz = 0, \qquad \int_C z^2\,dz = 0,$$

because the functions 1, z, and z^2 are entire and their derivatives are everywhere continuous.

Goursat[1] was the first to prove that the condition that $f'(z)$ be continuous can be omitted from the hypothesis in the theorem. The removal of that condition is important. One of the consequences, for example, is that derivatives of analytic functions are also analytic, as we shall show. The revised form of the theorem, the *Cauchy-Goursat theorem,* can be stated as follows.

Theorem. *If a function f is analytic at all points interior to and on a closed contour C, then*

$$\int_C f(z)\,dz = 0.$$

---

[1] E. Goursat (1858–1936), pronounced *gour-sah'*.

The proof is presented in the following sections. It will be a simple matter to extend the result to curves that are more general, including, for example, the entire boundary of the region between two polygons, one inside the other.

47. A Preliminary Theorem. The derivative $f'(z_0)$ exists when $f(z)$ is analytic at the point z_0; that is, given any positive number ϵ, a positive number δ_0, depending on z_0 and ϵ, exists such that

(1) $\qquad \left| \dfrac{f(z) - f(z_0)}{z - z_0} - f'(z_0) \right| < \epsilon \qquad$ whenever $0 < |z - z_0| < \delta_0$.

In order to prove the Cauchy-Goursat theorem, we first show that a sufficiently fine subdivision of the region bounded by the closed curve C can be made so that the first inequality here is true for every point z in each subdivision when z_0 is properly chosen in that subdivision. Thus there is some degree of uniformity in the approach of $\Delta f/\Delta z$ to $f'(z)$.

Lemma. *Let $f(z)$ be analytic at all points of a closed region R consisting of the interior of a closed contour C together with the points on C itself. Given any positive number ϵ, it is always possible to divide R into a finite number n of squares and partial squares, whose boundaries will be denoted by C_j, such that a point z_j exists within or on each C_j for which the inequality*

(2) $\qquad \left| \dfrac{f(z) - f(z_j)}{z - z_j} - f'(z_j) \right| < \epsilon \qquad (j = 1, 2, \ldots, n)$

is satisfied by every point z ($z \neq z_j$) within or on C_j.

Let the region R be covered with a set of equal squares formed by drawing lines parallel to the coordinate axes. Those portions of any square which lie outside of R are to be removed, leaving R subdivided into squares and partial squares (Fig. 32).

Now suppose that, for a given positive number ϵ, there

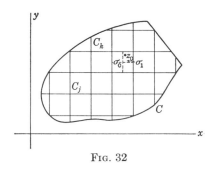

FIG. 32

is at least one of these subregions in which no point z_j exists such that the inequality (2) is true at every point z in that subregion.

If it is a square, let it be divided into four equal squares. If it is a partial square, let the whole square be so divided, and let the portions that lie outside of R be discarded. If in any one of those smaller regions no point z_j exists such that inequality (2) is satisfied there, let that region be subdivided in the same manner, etc.

After a finite number of such steps of subdividing every subregion that requires it, we may arrive at a subdivision such that the inequality (2) is true for every subregion present. In that case the lemma is true.

But suppose that points z_j do not exist such that condition (2) is satisfied after subdividing some one of the original subregions a finite number of times. Let σ_0 denote that subregion if it is a square; if it is a partial square, let σ_0 denote the entire square. Then, after the square σ_0 is subdivided once, at least one of the four smaller squares, denoted by σ_1, contains points of R but no appropriate points z_j after any finite number of subdivisions. After σ_1 is subdivided once, at least one of the smaller squares σ_2 fails to qualify in that respect, etc. If at any step k more than one of the smaller squares could be chosen, let σ_k be taken as the square that is lowest and farthest to the left, in order to make the choice specific.

Each square σ_k of the infinite sequence

$$\sigma_0, \sigma_1, \sigma_2, \ldots, \sigma_{k-1}, \sigma_k, \ldots$$

is contained in the preceding one, σ_{k-1}, and has a side half as long; also, σ_k contains points of R. There is a point z_0 common to every one of the squares of this nested infinite sequence of squares (Exercise 13, Sec. 50). Each neighborhood of z_0, $|z - z_0| < \delta$, contains a square of the sequence, since this is so whenever the length of the diagonal of the square is less than δ. Each neighborhood therefore contains points of R, and hence z_0 is a limit point of the set R. Since the region R is a closed set, the limit point z_0 lies in R.

Thus $f(z)$ is analytic at z_0 and, corresponding to the given number ϵ used in our inequality (2), there is a number δ_0 such that condition (1) is satisfied at z_0. But the neighborhood $|z - z_0| < \delta_0$ involved in that condition contains the square σ_K when the integer K is large enough that the diagonal of that square does not exceed δ_0. Consequently the point z_0 does serve as the point z_j such that inequality (2) is satisfied in the subregion consisting of the square σ_K or a part of σ_K. Contrary to our hypothesis, it is not necessary to subdivide σ_K. Thus we have arrived at a contradiction, and the proof of the lemma is complete.

48. Proof of the Cauchy-Goursat Theorem. We shall show that the inequality

$$(1) \qquad \left| \int_C f(z) \, dz \right| < \epsilon'$$

is true for every positive number ϵ'. For the given closed curve C and the given function f, the integral here has a definite constant value. The integral must therefore have the value zero.

For a given positive number ϵ, let C_j $(j = 1, 2, \ldots, n)$ be the boundaries of a set of squares and partial squares into which the region R can be subdivided, according to the above lemma, so that points z_j exist for which the inequality (2) of the preceding section is true. We can state that inequality in the following form. Each of the functions

$$(2) \qquad \delta_j(z) = \frac{f(z) - f(z_j)}{z - z_j} - f'(z_j) \qquad (j = 1, 2, \ldots, n)$$

satisfies the inequality

$$(3) \qquad |\delta_j(z)| < \epsilon.$$

Note that each function $\delta_j(z)$ is continuous; in particular, its limit as z approaches z_j is zero, and we shall define $\delta_j(z_j)$ to be zero.

We now let z represent any point on the boundary C_j. The value of $f(z)$ at any point on C_j can be written, according to equation (2),

$$(4) \qquad f(z) = f(z_j) - z_j f'(z_j) + f'(z_j)z + (z - z_j)\delta_j(z).$$

Integrating around C_j and recalling that (Sec. 46)

$$\int_{C_j} dz = 0, \qquad \int_{C_j} z \, dz = 0,$$

we see that

$$(5) \qquad \int_{C_j} f(z) \, dz = \int_{C_j} (z - z_j)\delta_j(z) \, dz.$$

Let the integral around each C_j be taken in the counterclockwise sense. The sum of all those integrals is the integral around the closed curve C in the counterclockwise sense; that is,

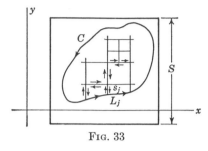

FIG. 33

$$\sum_{j=1}^{n} \int_{C_j} f(z) \, dz = \int_C f(z) \, dz,$$

because the line integrals along the common boundary line of every pair of adjacent sub-regions cancel each other; the integral is taken in one sense along that line in one region and in the opposite sense in the other (Fig. 33). Only the integrals along the arcs that are parts of C remain. Therefore, in view of equation (5),

$$\int_C f(z) \, dz = \sum_{j=1}^{n} \int_{C_j} (z - z_j) \delta_j(z) \, dz,$$

and hence

$$\left| \int_C f(z) \, dz \right| \leq \sum_{j=1}^{n} \left| \int_{C_j} (z - z_j) \delta_j(z) \, dz \right|$$

$$\leq \sum_{j=1}^{n} \int_{C_j} |z - z_j| \, |\delta_j(z)| \, |dz|.$$

It follows from the inequality (3) that

(6)
$$\left| \int_C f(z) \, dz \right| < \epsilon \sum_{j=1}^{n} \int_{C_j} |z - z_j| \, |dz|.$$

Each boundary C_j coincides either entirely or partially with the boundary of a square. In either case let s_j denote the length of a side of that square. Now z is on C_j, and z_j is either interior to or on C_j, so that

$$|z - z_j| \leq s_j \sqrt{2},$$

and

(7)
$$\int_{C_j} |z - z_j| \, |dz| \leq s_j \sqrt{2} \int_{C_j} |dz|.$$

The last integral represents the length of C_j. It is $4s_j$ if C_j is a square, and it does not exceed $(4s_j + L_j)$ if C_j is a partial square, where L_j is the arc of C that forms a part of C_j. When C_j is a square and A_j denotes the area of that square, then, according to the inequality (7),

$$(8) \qquad \int_{C_j} |z - z_j| \, |dz| \leq 4 \sqrt{2} \, s_j^2 = 4 \sqrt{2} \, A_j.$$

When C_j is a partial square,

$$(9) \quad \int_{C_j} |z - z_j| \, |dz| < s_j \sqrt{2} \, (4s_j + L_j) < 4 \sqrt{2} \, A_j + \sqrt{2} \, SL_j,$$

where S is the length of a side of some square that encloses the entire curve C as well as all squares used originally in covering C (Fig. 33). Thus the sum of all A_j's does not exceed S^2.

If L denotes the length of C, it now follows from the inequalities (6), (8), and (9) that

$$\left| \int_C f(z) \, dz \right| < \epsilon (4 \sqrt{2} \, S^2 + \sqrt{2} \, SL).$$

For each positive number ϵ', the right-hand member here can be made equal to ϵ' by assigning the proper value to the positive number ϵ. Hence the inequality (1) is established, and the Cauchy-Goursat theorem is proved.

49. Simply and Multiply Connected Domains. A *simply connected* domain D is an open connected region (a domain) such that every closed contour within it encloses only points of D. The interior of a closed contour is an example; but the exterior is not simply connected, nor is the annular region between two concentric circles. A domain that is not simply connected is said to be *multiply connected*.

The Cauchy-Goursat theorem can be stated in the following alternate form.

If $f(z)$ is analytic throughout a simply connected domain D, then for every closed contour C within D

$$(1) \qquad \int_C f(z) \, dz = 0.$$

The closed contour C here can be replaced by a closed chain of smooth Jordan arcs which intersects itself, since each loop in the chain is a closed contour interior to D. Also, C may contain an arc that is traversed twice in opposite directions, since the integrals along the arc in the two directions cancel each other. Subtleties arise if the number of such arcs, or self-intersections, is not finite.

The theorem can be extended in the following way to permit D to represent certain multiply connected domains.

Theorem. *Let C denote a closed contour and C_j a finite number ($j = 1, 2, \ldots , n$) of closed contours interior to C, such that the interiors of C_j have no points in common. Let R be the closed region consisting of all points on C and its interior except for points interior to each C_j (Fig. 34), and let B denote the entire*

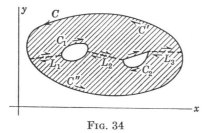

FIG. 34

oriented boundary of R, consisting of C and all C_j, described in a direction such that the points of R lie on the left of B. Then, if $f(z)$ is analytic in R,

$$(2) \qquad \int_B f(z)\, dz = 0.$$

To establish this result, we may introduce one straight-line segment L_1, or a continuous chain of such segments, to connect the outer contour C to the inner contour C_1; another, L_2, to connect C_1 and C_2; and so on—with L_{n+1} connecting C_n and C. In this manner, as indicated by the single-barbed arrows in Fig. 34, two closed contours C' and C'' can be formed, each consisting of the segments L_j and pieces of C and C_j, within and on which f is analytic. The Cauchy-Goursat theorem applies to f on C' and C'', and the sum of the integrals of f over C' and C'', each described in a direction such that their interior points lie on the left of these contours, vanishes. As the integrals in opposite directions along L_j cancel, only the integral over B remains, and formula (2) follows.

As an illustration of this theorem, we note that

$$\int_B \frac{dz}{z^2(z^2 + 9)} = 0$$

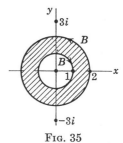

FIG. 35

if boundary B consists of the circle $|z| = 2$ described in the positive direction and the circle $|z| = 1$ described in the negative direction (Fig. 35). The integrand is analytic except at the points $z = 0$ and $z = \pm 3i$, and these three points lie outside the annular region with boundary B.

50. Indefinite Integrals. Let z_0 and z represent two points in a simply connected domain D throughout which f is analytic

(Fig. 36). If C_1 and C_2 are two contours connecting z_0 to z and lying entirely within D, then C_1 and C_2 together form a closed curve, a closed contour, except possibly for self-intersections, along which the Cauchy-Goursat theorem applies. Thus, if points on C_1 and C_2 are denoted by z',

$$\int_{C_2} f(z') \, dz' - \int_{C_1} f(z') \, dz' = 0;$$

that is, the integral from z_0 to z,

$$(1) \qquad\qquad F(z) = \int_{z_0}^{z} f(z') \, dz',$$

has the same value for all such paths.

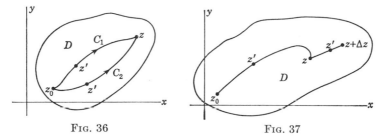

FIG. 36   FIG. 37

We shall now show that the derivative of $F(z)$ exists and is equal to $f(z)$. Let $z + \Delta z$ be a point in D (Fig. 37). Then

$$
\begin{aligned}
F(z + \Delta z) - F(z) &= \int_{z_0}^{z+\Delta z} f(z') \, dz' - \int_{z_0}^{z} f(z') \, dz' \\
&= \int_{z}^{z+\Delta z} f(z') \, dz',
\end{aligned}
$$

where the path of integration from z to $z + \Delta z$ may be selected as a straight line. Since we can write (Exercise 13, Sec. 45)

$$f(z) = \frac{f(z)}{\Delta z} \int_{z}^{z+\Delta z} dz' = \frac{1}{\Delta z} \int_{z}^{z+\Delta z} f(z) \, dz',$$

then

$$\frac{F(z + \Delta z) - F(z)}{\Delta z} - f(z) = \frac{1}{\Delta z} \int_{z}^{z+\Delta z} [f(z') - f(z)] \, dz'.$$

But f is continuous at the point z. Hence for each positive number ϵ, a positive number δ exists for which

$$|f(z') - f(z)| < \epsilon$$

when $|z' - z| < \delta$, or, in particular, when $|\Delta z| < \delta$. Therefore, when $|\Delta z| < \delta$,

$$\left| \frac{F(z + \Delta z) - F(z)}{\Delta z} - f(z) \right| < \frac{\epsilon}{|\Delta z|} \int_{z}^{z+\Delta z} |dz'| = \epsilon;$$

that is,

$$\lim_{\Delta z \to 0} \frac{F(z + \Delta z) - F(z)}{\Delta z} = f(z).$$

Thus the derivative of the integral (1) exists at each point z in D, and

(2) $$F'(z) = f(z).$$

The integral of an analytic function is therefore an analytic function of its upper limit, provided the path of integration is confined to a simply connected domain throughout which the integrand is analytic.

We can see from its definition (1) that $F(z)$ is changed by an additive constant when the lower limit z_0 is replaced by a new constant. The function F is an *indefinite integral* or antiderivative of f, written

$$F(z) = \int f(z) \, dz;$$

that is, it is an analytic function whose derivative is $f(z)$. In view of formula (1), the definite integral can be evaluated as the *change in the value of the indefinite integral*, as in the case of real integrals; for

(3) $$\int_{\alpha}^{\beta} f(z) \, dz = \int_{z_0}^{\beta} f(z) \, dz - \int_{z_0}^{\alpha} f(z) \, dz = F(\beta) - F(\alpha).$$

It is assumed that the paths of integration are confined to a simply connected domain in which f is analytic.

It should be noted that, if G is any analytic function other than F such that $G'(z) = f(z)$, then the derivative of the function $w = G - F$ is zero. Thus, if $w = u + iv$, then

$$\frac{\partial u}{\partial x} + i \frac{\partial v}{\partial x} = 0,$$

and therefore $\partial u/\partial x$ and $\partial v/\partial x$ both vanish throughout the domain in which the functions F and G are analytic. In view of the Cauchy-Riemann conditions, $\partial u/\partial y$ and $\partial v/\partial y$ also vanish, and therefore u and v are constant. Thus w is a constant, and it follows that the two indefinite integrals $F(z)$ and $G(z)$ differ by a constant. As a consequence, any indefinite integral of f can be used in place of F in formula (3).

An indefinite integral of the function $f(z) = z^2$, for example, is the entire function $F(z) = z^3/3$. Since the function z^2 is entire, we can write

$$\int_0^{1+i} z^2 \, dz = \tfrac{1}{3}z^3 \Big]_0^{1+i} = \tfrac{1}{3}(1+i)^3$$

for every contour between the points $z = 0$ and $z = 1 + i$.

As another example, let us evaluate

(4) $$\int_{-1}^1 z^{\frac{1}{2}} \, dz$$

along any contour lying in the upper half of the z plane and joining the two limits, where

(5) $$z^{\frac{1}{2}} = \sqrt{r} \exp \frac{i\theta}{2} \qquad (0 < \theta < 2\pi).$$

This function is not analytic at points on the ray $\theta = 0$, at $z = 1$ in particular. But another branch,

$$f_1(z) = \sqrt{r} \exp \frac{i\theta}{2} \qquad \left(r > 0, \, -\frac{\pi}{2} < \theta < \frac{3\pi}{2} \right),$$

of the multiple-valued function $z^{\frac{1}{2}}$ is analytic everywhere except on the ray $\theta = -\pi/2$. The values of $f_1(z)$ in the upper half plane coincide with those of our function (5), so that our integrand can be replaced by $f_1(z)$. An indefinite integral of f_1 is the function

$$\frac{2}{3} z^{\frac{3}{2}} = \frac{2}{3} r^{\frac{3}{2}} \exp \frac{3i\theta}{2} \qquad \left(r > 0, \, -\frac{\pi}{2} < \theta < \frac{3\pi}{2} \right),$$

analytic in the domain of definition of f_1; thus

$$\int_{-1}^1 z^{\frac{1}{2}} \, dz = \frac{2}{3} r^{\frac{3}{2}} e^{3i\theta/2} \Big]_{z=-1}^{z=1} = \frac{2}{3}(e^0 - e^{3i\pi/2}) = \frac{2}{3}(1+i).$$

The integral (4) over every contour below the x axis has another value. There we can replace the integrand by the branch

$$f_2(z) = \sqrt{r} \exp \frac{i\theta}{2} \qquad \left(r > 0, \frac{\pi}{2} < \theta < \frac{5\pi}{2} \right),$$

whose values coincide with those of the function (5) in the lower half plane.   The analytic function

$$\frac{2}{3} z^{\frac{3}{2}} = \frac{2}{3} r^{\frac{3}{2}} \exp \frac{3i\theta}{2} \qquad \left(r > 0, \frac{\pi}{2} < \theta < \frac{5\pi}{2}\right)$$

is an indefinite integral of $f_2(z)$; thus, along the lower paths,

$$\int_{-1}^{1} z^{\frac{1}{2}} dz = \frac{2}{3} r^{\frac{3}{2}} e^{3i\theta/2} \Big]_{-1}^{1} = \frac{2}{3}(e^{3\pi i} - e^{3\pi i/2}) = \frac{2}{3}(-1 + i).$$

The integral of the function (5) in the positive sense around a closed contour consisting of a path of the second group combined with one of the first therefore has the value

$$\frac{2}{3}(-1 + i) - \frac{2}{3}(1 + i) = -\frac{4}{3}.$$

EXERCISES

1. Determine the domain of analyticity of the function f and apply the Cauchy-Goursat theorem to show that

$$\int_C f(z)\, dz = 0$$

when the closed contour C is the circle $|z| = 1$ and when

(a) $f(z) = \dfrac{z^2}{z - 3}$;   (b) $f(z) = ze^{-z}$;   (c) $f(z) = \dfrac{1}{z^2 + 2z + 2}$;

(d) $f(z) = \operatorname{sech} z$;   (e) $f(z) = \tan z$;   (f) $f(z) = \operatorname{Log}(z + 2)$.

2. If B is the oriented boundary of the region between the circle $|z| = 4$ and the square with sides along the lines $x = \pm 1$, $y = \pm 1$, where B is described so that the region lies on the left of B, state why

$$\int_B f(z)\, dz = 0$$

when

(a) $f(z) = \dfrac{1}{3z^2 + 1}$;   (b) $f(z) = \dfrac{z + 2}{\sin(z/2)}$;   (c) $f(z) = \dfrac{z}{1 - e^z}$.

3. Let C_1 be a closed contour in the domain interior to a closed contour C_2, where both C_1 and C_2 are oriented in the positive (counterclockwise) direction.   If a function f is analytic in the closed region between C_1 and C_2, state why

$$\int_{C_1} f(z)\, dz = \int_{C_2} f(z)\, dz.$$

4. Use the results of Exercise 3 above and Exercise 16, Sec. 45, to show that

$$\int_C \frac{dz}{z - 2 - i} = 2\pi i, \qquad \int_C \frac{dz}{(z - 2 - i)^n} = 0 \qquad (n = 2, 3, \ldots),$$

when C is the boundary of the rectangle $0 \le x \le 3, 0 \le y \le 2$, described in the positive sense.

5. Use the indefinite integral to show that, for every contour C extending from a point α to a point β,

$$\int_C z^n \, dz = \frac{1}{n + 1} (\beta^{n+1} - \alpha^{n+1}) \qquad (n = 0, 1, 2, \ldots).$$

6. Evaluate each of these integrals where the path is an arbitrary contour between the points represented by the limits:

(a) $\displaystyle\int_i^{i/2} e^{\pi z} \, dz;$ (b) $\displaystyle\int_0^{\pi + 2i} \cos \frac{z}{2} \, dz;$ (c) $\displaystyle\int_1^3 (z - 2)^3 \, dz.$

$$Ans. \ (a) \ (1 + i)/\pi; \ (b) \ e + 1/e; \ (c) \ 0.$$

7. If $z_1 \ne 0$ and $z_2 \ne 0$ and $z_1 \ne z_2$, show why

$$\int_{z_1}^{z_2} \frac{dz}{z^2} = \frac{1}{z_1} - \frac{1}{z_2}$$

whenever the contour of integration is interior to a simply connected domain which does not contain the origin. Show how it follows that, for every closed contour C for which the origin is either an interior point or an exterior point,

$$\int_C \frac{dz}{z^2} = 0.$$

8. Let z_0, z_1, and z_2 denote three distinct points of a simply connected domain D. Given that a function f and its derivative f' are both analytic throughout D except at z_0, generalize the result in Exercise 7 to show that, for each contour in D drawn from z_1 to z_2 but not passing through z_0,

$$\int_{z_1}^{z_2} f'(z) \, dz = f(z_2) - f(z_1); \qquad \text{thus} \qquad \int_C f'(z) \, dz = 0$$

when the closed contour C in D does not pass through z_0. Give examples of such functions and domains.

9. Use an indefinite integral to find the value of the integral

$$\int_{-2i}^{2i} \frac{dz}{z}$$

over every contour from $z = -2i$ to $z = 2i$ lying in the right half plane. Note that the principal branch Log z is an indefinite integral of $1/z$ that is analytic in the half plane $x \ge 0$ except at the origin.

10. Solve Exercise 9 for every contour that does not touch the half $x \geqq 0$ of the real axis.   *Ans.* $-\pi i.$

11. Note that the single-valued function

$$f(z) = z^{\frac{1}{2}} = \sqrt{r} \exp \frac{i\theta}{2} \qquad \left(r > 0, \ -\frac{\pi}{2} \leqq \theta < \frac{3\pi}{2} \right),$$

$$f(0) = 0$$

is continuous throughout the half plane $0 \leqq \theta \leqq \pi$, $r \geqq 0$. Let C denote the entire boundary of the half disk $r \leqq 1$, $0 \leqq \theta \leqq \pi$, where C is described in the positive direction. Show that

$$\int_C f(z) \, dz = 0$$

by computing the integrals of f over the semicircle and over the two radii on the x axis. Why does the Cauchy-Goursat theorem not apply here?

12. *Nested Intervals.* An infinite sequence of closed intervals $a_n \leqq x \leqq b_n$ $(n = 0, 1, 2, \ldots)$ is determined according to some rule of selecting half intervals, so that the interval (a_1,b_1) is either the left-hand or right-hand half of a given interval (a_0,b_0); then (a_2,b_2) is one of the two halves of (a_1,b_1), and so on. Prove that there is a point x_0 which belongs to every one of the closed intervals (a_n,b_n).

Suggestion: Note that the left-hand end points a_n represent a bounded nondecreasing sequence of numbers, since $a_0 \leqq a_n \leqq a_{n+1} < b_0$; hence they have a limit A as $n \to \infty$. Show likewise that the end points b_n have a limit B; then that $B = A = x_0$.

13. *Nested Squares.* A square σ_0: $a_0 \leqq x \leqq b_0$, $c_0 \leqq y \leqq d_0$, where $b_0 - a_0 = d_0 - c_0$, is divided into four equal squares by lines parallel to the coordinate axes. One of those four smaller squares σ_1: $a_1 \leqq x \leqq b_1$, $c_1 \leqq y \leqq d_1$, where $b_1 - a_1 = d_1 - c_1$, is selected according to some rule, and it is divided into four equal squares, one of which, σ_2, is selected, etc. (Sec. 47). Prove that there is a point (x_0,y_0) which belongs to every one of the closed regions of the infinite sequence $\sigma_0, \sigma_1, \sigma_2, \ldots$

Suggestion: Apply the results of Exercise 12 to each of the sequences $a_n \leqq x \leqq b_n$ and $c_n \leqq y \leqq d_n$ $(n = 0, 1, 2, \ldots)$.

51. The Cauchy Integral Formula. Another fundamental result will now be established.

Theorem. *Let f be analytic everywhere within and on a closed contour C. If z_0 is any point interior to C, then*

(1) $$f(z_0) = \frac{1}{2\pi i} \int_C \frac{f(z)}{z - z_0} \, dz,$$

where the integral is taken in the positive sense around C.

Formula (1) is *Cauchy's integral formula*. It shows that the value of a function that is analytic in a region is determined throughout the region by its values on the boundary. Thus there is no choice of ways in which the function can be defined at points away from the boundary once the function is defined on the boundary. Every alteration of values of the function at interior points must be accompanied by a change of its values on the boundary, if the function is to remain analytic. We shall see further evidence of this *organic* character of analytic functions as we proceed.

According to the Cauchy integral formula, for example, if C is the circle $|z| = 2$ described in the positive sense, then, taking z_0 to be $-i$, we can write

$$\int_C \frac{z\,dz}{(9 - z^2)(z + i)} = 2\pi i\,\frac{-i}{9 - i^2} = \frac{\pi}{5},$$

since the function $f(z) = z/(9 - z^2)$ is analytic within and on C.

To prove the theorem, let C_0 be a circle about z_0,

$$|z - z_0| = r_0,$$

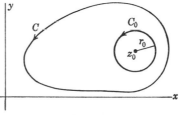

whose radius r_0 is small enough that C_0 is interior to C (Fig. 38). The function $f(z)/(z - z_0)$ is analytic at all points within and on C except the point z_0.

Fig. 38

Hence its integral around the boundary of the ring-shaped region between C and C_0 is zero, according to the Cauchy-Goursat theorem; that is,

$$\int_C \frac{f(z)\,dz}{z - z_0} - \int_{C_0} \frac{f(z)\,dz}{z - z_0} = 0,$$

where both integrals are taken counterclockwise.

Since the integrals around C and C_0 are equal, we can write

(2) $$\int_C \frac{f(z)\,dz}{z - z_0} = f(z_0) \int_{C_0} \frac{dz}{z - z_0} + \int_{C_0} \frac{f(z) - f(z_0)}{z - z_0}\,dz.$$

But $z - z_0 = r_0 e^{i\theta}$ on C_0 and $dz = i r_0 e^{i\theta}\,d\theta$, so that

(3) $$\int_{C_0} \frac{dz}{z - z_0} = i \int_0^{2\pi} d\theta = 2\pi i,$$

for every positive r_0.   Also, f is continuous at the point z_0.   Hence, if we select any positive number ϵ, then a positive number δ exists such that

$$|f(z) - f(z_0)| < \epsilon \qquad \text{whenever } |z - z_0| \leqq \delta.$$

We take r_0 equal to that number δ.   Then $|z - z_0| = \delta$, and

$$\left| \int_{C_0} \frac{f(z) - f(z_0)}{z - z_0} \, dz \right| \leqq \int_{C_0} \frac{|f(z) - f(z_0)|}{|z - z_0|} \, |dz| < \frac{\epsilon}{\delta} \, (2\pi\delta) = 2\pi\epsilon.$$

The absolute value of the last integral in equation (2) can therefore be made arbitrarily small by taking r_0 sufficiently small.   But since the other two integrals in that equation are independent of r_0, in view of equation (3), this one must be independent of r_0 also.   Its value must therefore be zero. Equation (2) then reduces to the formula

$$\int_C \frac{f(z) \, dz}{z - z_0} = 2\pi i f(z_0),$$

and the theorem is proved.

52. Derivatives of Analytic Functions.   A formula for the derivative $f'(z_0)$ can be written formally by differentiating the integral in Cauchy's integral formula

$$(1) \qquad f(z_0) = \frac{1}{2\pi i} \int_C \frac{f(z)}{z - z_0} \, dz$$

with respect to z_0, inside the integral sign.   Thus,

$$(2) \qquad f'(z_0) = \frac{1}{2\pi i} \int_C \frac{f(z)}{(z - z_0)^2} \, dz.$$

As before, we assume that f is analytic within and on the closed contour C and that z_0 is within C.   To establish formula (2), we first note that, according to (1),

$$\frac{f(z_0 + \Delta z_0) - f(z_0)}{\Delta z_0} = \frac{1}{2\pi i \, \Delta z_0} \int_C \left(\frac{1}{z - z_0 - \Delta z_0} - \frac{1}{z - z_0} \right) f(z) \, dz$$

$$= \frac{1}{2\pi i} \int_C \frac{f(z) \, dz}{(z - z_0 - \Delta z_0)(z - z_0)}.$$

The last integral approaches the integral

$$\int_C \frac{f(z) \, dz}{(z - z_0)^2}$$

as Δz_0 approaches zero; for the difference between that integral and this one reduces to

$$\Delta z_0 \int_C \frac{f(z)\, dz}{(z - z_0)^2 (z - z_0 - \Delta z_0)}.$$

Let M be the maximum value of $|f(z)|$ on C and let L be the length of C. Then, if d_0 is the shortest distance from z_0 to C and if $|\Delta z_0| < d_0$, we can write

$$\left| \Delta z_0 \int_C \frac{f(z)\, dz}{(z - z_0)^2 (z - z_0 - \Delta z_0)} \right| < \frac{ML|\Delta z_0|}{d_0^2(d_0 - |\Delta z_0|)},$$

and the last fraction approaches zero when Δz_0 approaches zero. Consequently,

$$\lim_{\Delta z_0 \to 0} \frac{f(z_0 + \Delta z_0) - f(z_0)}{\Delta z_0} = \frac{1}{2\pi i} \int_C \frac{f(z)\, dz}{(z - z_0)^2},$$

and formula (2) is established.

If we differentiate both members of equation (2) and assume that the order of differentiation with respect to z_0 and integration with respect to z can be interchanged, we find that

$$(3) \qquad\qquad f''(z_0) = \frac{2!}{2\pi i} \int_C \frac{f(z)\, dz}{(z - z_0)^3}.$$

This formula can be established by the same method that was used to establish formula (2). For it follows from formula (2) that

$$2\pi i\, \frac{f'(z_0 + \Delta z_0) - f'(z_0)}{\Delta z_0}$$

$$= \int_C \left[\frac{1}{(z - z_0 - \Delta z_0)^2} - \frac{1}{(z - z_0)^2} \right] \frac{f(z)\, dz}{\Delta z_0}$$

$$= \int_C \frac{2(z - z_0) - \Delta z_0}{(z - z_0 - \Delta z_0)^2 (z - z_0)^2}\, f(z)\, dz.$$

Following the same procedure that was used before, we can show that the limit of the last integral, as Δz_0 approaches zero, is

$$2 \int_C \frac{f(z)\, dz}{(z - z_0)^3},$$

and formula (3) follows at once.

We have now established the existence of the derivative of the function f' at each point z_0 interior to the region bounded by the curve C.

We recall our definition that a function f is analytic at a point z_1 if and only if there is a neighborhood about z_1 at each point of which $f'(z)$ exists. Hence f is analytic in some neighborhood of the point. If the curve C used above is a circle $|z - z_1| = r_1$ in that neighborhood, then $f''(z)$ exists at each point inside the circle, and therefore f' is analytic at z_1. We can apply the same argument to the function f' to conclude that its derivative f'' is analytic at z_1, etc. Thus the following fundamental result is a consequence of formula (3).

Theorem. *If a function f is analytic at a point, then its derivatives of all orders, f', f'', . . . , are also analytic functions at that point.*

Since f' is analytic and therefore continuous, and since

$$f'(z) = \frac{\partial u}{\partial x} + i \frac{\partial v}{\partial x} = \frac{\partial v}{\partial y} - i \frac{\partial u}{\partial y},$$

it follows that the partial derivatives of $u(x,y)$ and $v(x,y)$ of the first order are continuous. Since $f''(z)$ is analytic and

$$f''(z) = \frac{\partial^2 u}{\partial x^2} + i \frac{\partial^2 v}{\partial x^2} = \frac{\partial^2 v}{\partial x\, \partial y} - i \frac{\partial^2 u}{\partial x\, \partial y},$$

etc., it follows that the partial derivatives of u and v of all orders are continuous functions of x and y at each point where f is analytic. This result was anticipated in Sec. 20, for the partial derivatives of the second order, in the discussion of harmonic functions.

The argument used in establishing formulas (2) and (3) can be applied successively to obtain a formula for the derivative of any given order. But mathematical induction can now be applied to establish the general formula

$$(4) \qquad f^{(n)}(z_0) = \frac{n!}{2\pi i} \int_C \frac{f(z)\, dz}{(z - z_0)^{n+1}} \qquad (n = 1, 2, \; . \; . \; .).$$

That is, if we assume that this formula is true for any particular integer $n = k$, we can show by proceeding as before that it is true if $n = k + 1$. The details of the proof can be left to the reader, with the suggestion that in the algebraic simplifications he retain the difference $(z - z_0)$ throughout as a single term.

The closed contour C here, as well as in Cauchy's integral formula, can be replaced by *the oriented boundary B of a multiply connected closed region R* of the type described in the theorem in Sec. 49, when f is analytic in R and z_0 is any interior point of R. Our derivations of the Cauchy integral formula and its extensions (4) are still valid when C is replaced by B.

53. Morera's Theorem. In Sec. 50 we proved that the derivative of the function

$$F(z) = \int_{z_0}^{z} f(z') \, dz'$$

exists at each point of a simply connected domain D, in fact, that

$$F'(z) = f(z).$$

We assumed there that f is analytic in D. But in our proof we used only two properties of the analytic function f, namely, that it is continuous in D and that its integral around every closed contour interior to D vanishes. Thus, when f satisfies those two conditions, the function F is analytic in D.

We proved in Sec. 52 that the derivative of every analytic function is analytic. Since $F'(z) = f(z)$, it follows that f is analytic. The following theorem, due to E. Morera (1856–1909), is therefore established.

Theorem. *If a function f is continuous throughout a simply connected domain D and if, for every closed contour C interior to D,*

$$\int_{C} f(z) \, dz = 0,$$

then f is analytic throughout D.

Morera's theorem serves as a converse of the Cauchy-Goursat theorem.

54. Maximum Moduli of Functions. Let f be analytic at a point z_0. If C_0 denotes any one of the circles $|z - z_0| = r_0$ within and on which f is analytic, then, according to Cauchy's integral formula,

$$f(z_0) = \frac{1}{2\pi i} \int_{C_0} \frac{f(z) \, dz}{z - z_0}.$$

It follows that

(1) $$|f(z_0)| \leqq \frac{1}{2\pi r_0} \int_{C_0} |f(z)| \, |dz| = A_0,$$

where A_0 is the mean value of $|f(z)|$ on C_0; that is,

$$(2) \quad A_0 = \frac{1}{2\pi r_0} \int_0^{2\pi} |f(z_0 + r_0 e^{i\theta})| \, r_0 \, d\theta = \frac{1}{2\pi} \int_0^{2\pi} |f(z_0 + r_0 e^{i\theta})| \, d\theta.$$

Thus the value of $|f|$ at the center does not exceed the mean value on C_0.

Let M_0 denote the maximum value of the continuous real-valued function $|f|$ on the closed disk $|z - z_0| \leq r_0$. Thus $|f(z_0)| \leq M_0$. Also $|f(z_0 + r_0 e^{i\theta})| \leq M_0$ and, in view of equation (2),

$$(3) \qquad\qquad A_0 \leq M_0.$$

Suppose that $|f(z_0)| = M_0$. Then it follows from inequality (1) that $M_0 \leq A_0$. But from (3), $M_0 \geq A_0$, and therefore $A_0 = M_0$. Thus the mean value of $|f|$ given by formula (2) coincides with the maximum value M_0 of $|f|$. Now, if $|f(z_0 + r_0 e^{i\theta})| < M_0$ for some θ, that continuous function of θ is less than M_0 over some interval, and its mean value would then be less than M_0. Hence $|f(z)| = M_0$ everywhere on C_0.

Still assuming that $|f(z_0)| = M_0$, let A_1 denote the mean value of $|f|$ on any circle C_1 about z_0 and interior to C_0. Then $|f(z)| \leq M_0$ on C_1, and it follows as before that $M_0 \leq A_1$ and $A_1 \leq M_0$; thus $A_1 = M_0$ and hence $|f(z)| = M_0$ on C_1. Consequently $|f(z)| = M_0$ at every point of the disk $|z - z_0| \leq r_0$. But if the modulus of an analytic function is a constant, the function itself is constant (Exercise 15, Sec. 20). Therefore $f(z)$ is a constant if $|f(z_0)| = M_0$; that is,

$$(4) \qquad\qquad |f(z_0)| < M_0, \qquad \text{unless } f \text{ is a constant.}$$

This *maximum modulus principle* can also be stated as follows.

If a nonconstant function f is analytic at z_0, then every neighborhood of z_0, $|z - z_0| < r_0$, contains points z such that

$$(5) \qquad\qquad |f(z)| > |f(z_0)|.$$

The following theorem is a direct consequence of that principle.

Maximum Modulus Theorem. *If f is analytic throughout a bounded domain D and continuous in the closure $\bar{D}$ and if M denotes the maximum value of $|f(z)|$ in $\bar{D}$, then, unless f is a constant,*

$$(6) \qquad\qquad |f(z)| < M \qquad \text{for every point } z \text{ in } D.$$

Thus $|f(z)|$ assumes its maximum value M somewhere on the boundary of D, never at an interior point. Note that the hypotheses are satisfied when f is analytic in $\bar{D}$.   Also note that $|f|$ is continuous in $\bar{D}$ and therefore has a maximum value M that is assumed somewhere in $\bar{D}$, but not in D, in view of condition (5).

If $f = u + iv$, then, as a consequence of the maximum modulus theorem, *the harmonic function $u(x,y)$ in D, continuous in $\bar{D}$, assumes its maximum value on the boundary B of D, but never interior to D unless u is a constant.*   For the function $\exp f$ is analytic in D and continuous in $\bar{D}$, and therefore its modulus e^u assumes its maximum value only on B; hence $u(x,y)$ itself reaches its maximum only on B.

Properties of *minimum* values of $|f|$ and u are left to the exercises.

When f is analytic within and on the circle C_0, $|z - z_0| = r_0$, then

$$f^{(n)}(z_0) = \frac{n!}{2\pi i} \int_{C_0} \frac{f(z)\, dz}{(z - z_0)^{n+1}} \quad (n = 1, 2, \ldots),$$

according to the integral formula for derivatives.   If M' is the maximum of $|f(z)|$ on C_0, *Cauchy's inequality* follows, namely,

(7) $$|f^{(n)}(z_0)| \leqq \frac{n!M'}{r_0^n}.$$

Let M be such that $|f(z)| < M$ within and on C_0, and write $n = 1$.   Then

(8) $$|f'(z_0)| < \frac{M}{r_0},$$

from which we can show that no entire function except a constant is bounded for all z, a conclusion that can be stated as follows.

Liouville's Theorem.   *If f is entire and $|f(z)|$ is bounded for all values of z in the complex plane, then f is a constant.*

Under the hypothesis a constant M exists such that $|f(z)| < M$ for all z.   Therefore at each point z_0 the inequality (8) is true for every positive number r_0.   We can take r_0 as large as we please.   Since $f'(z_0)$ is a fixed number, it follows that $f'(z_0) = 0$, for every z_0, and hence f is a constant.

55. The Fundamental Theorem of Algebra.   This theorem states that, if $P(z)$ is a polynomial in z of degree one or greater,

$$P(z) = a_0 + a_1 z + a_2 z^2 + \cdots + a_m z^m$$
$$(m = 1, 2, \ldots; a_m \neq 0),$$

then the equation $P(z) = 0$ has at least one root.

The proof of this theorem by purely algebraic methods is difficult, but it follows easily from Liouville's theorem. For let us suppose that $P(z)$ is not zero for any value of z. Then the function

$$f(z) = \frac{1}{P(z)}$$

is everywhere analytic. Also $|f(z)|$ approaches zero as $|z|$ tends to infinity, so that $|f(z)|$ is bounded for all z. Consequently $f(z)$ is a constant. We have therefore arrived at a contradiction, for $P(z)$ is not a constant when $m = 1, 2, \ldots$, and $a_m \neq 0$. Hence $P(z)$ is zero for at least one value of z.

In elementary algebra courses the fundamental theorem is usually stated without proof; then as a consequence it is shown that an algebraic equation of degree m has not more than m roots.

EXERCISES

1. If C is the circle $|z| = 3$ described in the positive sense and if

$$g(z_0) = \int_C \frac{2z^2 - z - 2}{z - z_0} \, dz \qquad (|z_0| \neq 3),$$

show that $g(2) = 8\pi i$. What is the value of $g(z_0)$ when $|z_0| > 3$?

2. If C is a closed contour described in the positive sense and

$$g(z_0) = \int_C \frac{z^3 + 2z}{(z - z_0)^3} \, dz,$$

show why $g(z_0) = 6\pi i z_0$ when z_0 is inside C, and $g(z_0) = 0$ when z_0 is outside C.

3. Let C denote the boundary of the square whose sides lie along the lines $x = \pm 2$ and $y = \pm 2$, where C is described in the positive sense. Give the value of each of these integrals:

(a) $\int_C \frac{e^{-z} \, dz}{z - \pi i/2}$; (b) $\int_C \frac{\cos z}{z(z^2 + 8)} \, dz$; (c) $\int_C \frac{z \, dz}{2z + 1}$;

(d) $\int_C \frac{\tan (z/2)}{(z - x_0)^2} \, dz$ $(|x_0| < 2)$; (e) $\int_C \frac{\cosh z}{z^4} \, dz$.

Ans. (a) 2π; (b) $\pi i/4$; (c) $-\pi i/2$; (d) $i\pi \sec^2 (x_0/2)$; (e) 0.

4. Give the value of the integral of $g(z)$ around the closed contour $|z - i| = 2$ in the positive sense when

(a) $g(z) = \frac{1}{z^2 + 4}$; (b) $g(z) = \frac{1}{(z^2 + 4)^2}$.

Ans. (a) $\pi/2$; (b) $\pi/16$.

5. If f is analytic within and on an oriented closed contour C and if z_0 is not on C, show why it follows that

$$\int_C \frac{f'(z)\,dz}{z - z_0} = \int_C \frac{f(z)\,dz}{(z - z_0)^2}.$$

6. Let f denote a function that is *continuous on a closed contour* C. Follow the procedure used in Sec. 52 to prove that the function

$$g(s) = \frac{1}{2\pi i}\int_C \frac{f(z)\,dz}{z - s}$$

is *analytic* for all s interior to C and in fact that, for each such s,

$$g'(s) = \frac{1}{2\pi i}\int_C \frac{f(z)\,dz}{(z - s)^2}.$$

7. If C is the unit circle $z = \exp(i\theta)$ described from $\theta = -\pi$ to $\theta = \pi$ and k is any real constant, first show that

$$\int_C \frac{e^{kz}}{z}\,dz = 2\pi i;$$

then write the integral in terms of θ to derive the formula

$$\int_0^\pi e^{k \cos \theta} \cos (k \sin \theta)\,d\theta = \pi.$$

8. Let f be analytic in a bounded domain D and continuous in the closure $\bar{D}$ and assume that $f(z) \neq 0$ anywhere in $\bar{D}$. If N is the minimum value of $|f(z)|$ in D, consider the function $1/f$ to prove that

$$|f(z)| > N \qquad \text{for every point } z \text{ in } D,$$

unless f is a constant. This is a *minimum modulus theorem*.

9. Give an example to show that $|f(z)|$ may assume its minimum value at an interior point of a domain in which f is analytic, if that minimum value is zero.

10. Illustrate the maximum modulus theorem and Exercise 8 when $f(z) = (z + 1)^2$ and D is the interior of the triangle with vertices at $z = 0$, $z = 2$, and $z = i$, by finding the points in $\bar{D}$ where $|f(z)|$ has its greatest and least values. *Ans.* $z = 2$, $z = 0$.

11. Let f be analytic in a bounded domain D and continuous in $\bar{D}$ and write $f = u + iv$. Prove that the harmonic function $u(x,y)$ assumes its *minimum* value on the boundary of D, never at an interior point, unless u is a constant.

12. Illustrate Exercise 11 and the maximum principle for harmonic functions (Sec. 54) by writing $u = e^x \cos y$ and taking D as the interior of the rectangle $0 < x < 1$, $0 < y < \pi$, and finding those points in $\bar{D}$ where $u(x,y)$ has its least and greatest values.

Ans. $z = 1 + \pi i$, $z = 1$.

13. Let f be an entire function and u its real component. If the harmonic function u has an upper bound u_0, $u(x,y) < u_0$ for all points in the xy plane, prove that $u(x,y)$ is a constant.

14. Complete the derivation of formula (3), Sec. 52.

15. Carry out the induction to establish formula (4), Sec. 52.

CHAPTER 6

POWER SERIES

56. Taylor's Series. We begin with one of the most important results of this chapter.

Theorem. *Let $f(z)$ be analytic at all points within a circle C_0 with center at z_0 and radius r_0. Then at each point z inside C_0*

$$(1) \quad f(z) = f(z_0) + f'(z_0)(z - z_0) + \frac{f''(z_0)}{2!} (z - z_0)^2 + \cdots$$

$$+ \frac{f^{(n)}(z_0)}{n!} (z - z_0)^n + \cdots ;$$

that is, the infinite series here converges to $f(z)$.

This is the expansion of the function f by Taylor's series about the point z_0. As a special case, when z, z_0, and $f(z)$ are real, it includes the expansion of a real-valued function by Taylor's series, introduced in elementary calculus.

To prove the theorem, let z be any fixed point inside the circle C_0 and write $|z - z_0| = r$; thus $r < r_0$. Let z' denote any point on a circle $|z' - z_0| = r_1$, denoted by C_1, where $r < r_1 < r_0$. As illustrated in Fig. 39, then, z is inside C_1, and f is analytic

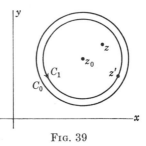

FIG. 39

within and on C_1. According to the Cauchy integral formula, it follows that

$$(2) \qquad f(z) = \frac{1}{2\pi i} \int_{C_1} \frac{f(z') \, dz'}{z' - z}.$$

Now

$$\frac{1}{z' - z} = \frac{1}{(z' - z_0) - (z - z_0)} = \frac{1}{z' - z_0} \frac{1}{1 - \dfrac{z - z_0}{z' - z_0}}.$$

129

But when α is any complex number other than unity, we note that

$$\frac{1}{1-\alpha} = 1 + \alpha + \alpha^2 + \cdots + \alpha^{n-1} + \frac{\alpha^n}{1-\alpha},$$

an identity that becomes evident when both its members are multiplied by $(1 - \alpha)$. Hence the equation above can be written

$$\frac{1}{z'-z} = \frac{1}{z'-z_0}\left[1 + \frac{z-z_0}{z'-z_0} + \cdots + \left(\frac{z-z_0}{z'-z_0}\right)^{n-1}\right.$$
$$\left. + \frac{1}{1 - \dfrac{z-z_0}{z'-z_0}}\left(\frac{z-z_0}{z'-z_0}\right)^n\right],$$

and therefore

$$\frac{f(z')}{z'-z} = \frac{f(z')}{z'-z_0} + (z-z_0)\frac{f(z')}{(z'-z_0)^2} + \cdots$$
$$+ (z-z_0)^{n-1}\frac{f(z')}{(z'-z_0)^n} + (z-z_0)^n\frac{f(z')}{(z'-z)(z'-z_0)^n}.$$

We now divide through by $2\pi i$ and integrate each term counterclockwise around C_1. In view of formula (2) and the integral formulas (Sec. 52),

$$\frac{1}{2\pi i}\int_{C_1}\frac{f(z')\,dz'}{(z'-z_0)^{j+1}} = \frac{1}{j!}f^{(j)}(z_0) \qquad (j = 1, 2, \ldots),$$

we can write the result as follows:

(3) $f(z) = f(z_0) + f'(z_0)(z - z_0) + \cdots$
$$+ \frac{f^{(n-1)}(z_0)}{(n-1)!}(z-z_0)^{n-1} + R_n,$$

where

(4) $$R_n = \frac{(z-z_0)^n}{2\pi i}\int_{C_1}\frac{f(z')\,dz'}{(z'-z)(z'-z_0)^n}.$$

Since $|z - z_0| = r$ and $|z' - z_0| = r_1$ and $|z' - z| \geq r_1 - r$, it follows from equation (4) that, when M denotes the maximum value of $|f(z')|$ on C_1,

$$|R_n| \leq \frac{r^n}{2\pi}\frac{2\pi r_1 M}{(r_1-r)r_1^n} = \frac{r_1 M}{r_1 - r}\left(\frac{r}{r_1}\right)^n.$$

But $r/r_1 < 1$, and therefore

$$\lim_{n\to\infty} R_n = 0.$$

Thus, as n tends to infinity, the limit of the sum of the first n terms in the right-hand member of equation (3) is $f(z)$. That is, $f(z)$ is represented by Taylor's series,

$$(5) \qquad f(z) = f(z_0) + \sum_{n=1}^{\infty} \frac{f^{(n)}(z_0)}{n!} (z - z_0)^n.$$

When $z_0 = 0$, this reduces to *Maclaurin's series*,

$$(6) \qquad f(z) = f(0) + \sum_{n=1}^{\infty} \frac{f^{(n)}(0)}{n!} z^n.$$

57. Observations and Examples. When it is known that f is analytic at all points within the circle C_0, the convergence of Taylor's series to $f(z)$ is assured; no test for the convergence of the series is required. The maximum radius of C_0 is the distance from the point z_0 to the singular point of f that is nearest z_0, since the function is to be analytic at all points inside C_0.

As our first example of a Maclaurin series expansion, let $f(z)$ be e^z. Then $f^{(n)}(z) = e^z$ and $f^{(n)}(0) = 1$. Since e^z is analytic for every value of z, then

$$(1) \qquad e^z = 1 + \sum_{n=1}^{\infty} \frac{z^n}{n!} \qquad\qquad \text{when } |z| < \infty.$$

Similarly, we find that

$$(2) \qquad \sin z = \sum_{n=1}^{\infty} (-1)^{n+1} \frac{z^{2n-1}}{(2n-1)!} \qquad \text{when } |z| < \infty,$$

$$(3) \qquad \cos z = 1 + \sum_{n=1}^{\infty} (-1)^n \frac{z^{2n}}{(2n)!} \qquad \text{when } |z| < \infty,$$

$$(4) \qquad \sinh z = \sum_{n=1}^{\infty} \frac{z^{2n-1}}{(2n-1)!} \qquad\qquad \text{when } |z| < \infty,$$

$$(5) \qquad \cosh z = 1 + \sum_{n=1}^{\infty} \frac{z^{2n}}{(2n)!} \qquad\qquad \text{when } |z| < \infty,$$

and

$$(6) \qquad \frac{1}{1+z} = \sum_{n=0}^{\infty} (-1)^n z^n \qquad\qquad \text{when } |z| < 1.$$

As a special case of the expansion (1), for example, when z is real, the representation

$$e^z = 1 + \sum_{n=1}^{\infty} \frac{x^n}{n!}$$

is valid for every real x.

By substituting Z^2 for z in the expansion (6), we note that

$$\frac{1}{1 + Z^2} = \sum_{n=0}^{\infty} (-1)^n Z^{2n} \qquad \text{when } |Z| < 1,$$

since $|Z^2| < 1$ when $|Z| < 1$. When we make the substitution $z = -\alpha$, expansion (6) gives the sum of the infinite geometric series with α as the common ratio of adjacent terms; that is,

$$(7) \quad 1 + \alpha + \alpha^2 + \cdots + \alpha^n + \cdots = \frac{1}{1 - \alpha} \quad \text{when } |\alpha| < 1.$$

The derivatives of the function $f(z) = z^{-1}$ are

$$f^{(n)}(z) = (-1)^n n! \, z^{-n-1} \qquad (n = 1, 2, \ldots ; z \neq 0),$$

and therefore $f^{(n)}(1) = (-1)^n n!$. Hence the expansion of this function by Taylor's series about the point $z = 1$ is

$$(8) \qquad \frac{1}{z} = \sum_{n=0}^{\infty} (-1)^n (z - 1)^n.$$

This expansion is valid when $|z - 1| < 1$, since the function is analytic at all points except $z = 0$.

As another example, let us expand the function

$$f(z) = \frac{1 + 2z}{z^2 + z^3} = \frac{1}{z^2}\left(2 - \frac{1}{1 + z}\right)$$

in a series of positive and negative powers of z. We cannot apply Maclaurin's series to f itself, since this function is not analytic at $z = 0$; but we can apply it to the function $1/(1 + z)$. Thus, when $0 < |z| < 1$, it is true that

$$\frac{1 + 2z}{z^2 + z^3} = \frac{1}{z^2}(2 - 1 + z - z^2 + z^3 - \cdots)$$

$$= \frac{1}{z^2} + \frac{1}{z} - 1 + z - z^2 + z^3 - \cdots .$$

EXERCISES

1. Show that, for every finite value of z,

$$e^z = e + e \sum_{n=1}^{\infty} \frac{(z-1)^n}{n!}.$$

2. Show that

(a) $\dfrac{1}{z^2} = 1 + \displaystyle\sum_{n=1}^{\infty} (n+1)(z+1)^n$ when $|z+1| < 1$;

(b) $\dfrac{1}{z^2} = \dfrac{1}{4} + \dfrac{1}{4} \displaystyle\sum_{n=1}^{\infty} (-1)^n(n+1) \left(\dfrac{z-2}{2}\right)^n$ when $|z-2| < 2.$

3. Expand $\cos z$ by Taylor's series about the point $z = \pi/2$.

4. Expand $\sinh z$ by Taylor's series about the point $z = \pi i$.

5. Within what circle does the Maclaurin series for the function $\tanh z$ converge to the function? Write the first few terms of that series.

6. Prove that, when $0 < |z| < 4$,

$$\frac{1}{4z - z^2} = \sum_{n=0}^{\infty} \frac{z^{n-1}}{4^{n+1}}.$$

7. Make the substitution $z + 1 = Z$ in the Maclaurin series expansion (6) to obtain a representation of the function Z^{-1} in powers of $Z - 1$ that is valid when $|Z - 1| < 1$. Show that your result agrees with the Taylor series expansion (8).

8. Substitute Z^{-1} for z in expansion (6) and in its condition of validity to obtain an expansion of the function $(1 + Z)^{-1}$ in negative powers of Z that is valid everywhere outside the circle $|Z| = 1$.

$$Ans. \ (1 + Z)^{-1} = \sum_{n=0}^{\infty} (-1)^n Z^{-n-1} \quad (|Z| > 1).$$

9. Prove that when $x \neq 0$,

$$\frac{\sin (x^2)}{x^4} = \frac{1}{x^2} - \frac{x^2}{3!} + \frac{x^6}{5!} - \frac{x^{10}}{7!} + \cdots .$$

10. Represent the function

$$f(z) = \frac{z}{(z-1)(z-3)}$$

by a series of positive and negative powers of $(z - 1)$ which converges to $f(z)$ when $0 < |z - 1| < 2$.

$$Ans. \ f(z) = \frac{-1}{2(z - 1)} - 3 \sum_{n=1}^{\infty} \frac{(z - 1)^{n-1}}{2^{n+1}}.$$

58. Laurent's Series. Let z' denote any point on either of two concentric circles C_1 and C_2,

$$|z' - z_0| = r_1, \qquad |z' - z_0| = r_2,$$

about a point z_0, where $r_2 < r_1$ (Fig. 40). We shall prove the following theorem.

Theorem. *If f is analytic on C_1 and C_2 and throughout the region between those two circles, then at each point z between them $f(z)$ is represented by a convergent series of positive and negative powers of $(z - z_0)$,*

$$(1) \qquad f(z) = \sum_{n=0}^{\infty} a_n(z - z_0)^n + \sum_{n=1}^{\infty} \frac{b_n}{(z - z_0)^n},$$

where

$$(2) \qquad a_n = \frac{1}{2\pi i} \int_{C_1} \frac{f(z') \ dz'}{(z' - z_0)^{n+1}} \qquad (n = 0, 1, 2, \ . \ . \ .),$$

$$(3) \qquad b_n = \frac{1}{2\pi i} \int_{C_2} \frac{f(z') \ dz'}{(z' - z_0)^{-n+1}} \qquad (n = 1, 2, \ . \ . \ .),$$

each integral being taken counterclockwise.

The series here is called *Laurent's series.*

In case f is analytic at every point on and inside C_1 except the point z_0 itself, the radius r_2 may be taken arbitrarily small. The expansion (1) is then valid when

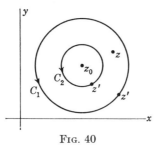

$$0 < |z - z_0| < r_1.$$

If f is analytic at all points on and inside C_1, the integrand of the integral (3) is an analytic function of z' inside and on C_2, because $-n + 1 \leqq 0$; the integral therefore has the value zero and the series becomes Taylor's series.

Fig. 40

Since the integrands of the integrals in formulas (2) and (3) are analytic functions of z' throughout the annular region, any closed contour C around the annulus can be used as the path of integration in place of the circular paths C_1 and C_2. Thus Laurent's series can be written

$$(4) \qquad f(z) = \sum_{n=-\infty}^{\infty} A_n(z - z_0)^n \qquad (r_2 < |z - z_0| < r_1),$$

where

$$(5) \qquad A_n = \frac{1}{2\pi i} \int_C \frac{f(z')\,dz'}{(z' - z_0)^{n+1}} \qquad (n = 0, \pm 1, \pm 2, \ldots).$$

In particular cases, of course, some of the coefficients may be zero. In fact, the function

$$f(z) = \frac{1}{(z - 1)^2},$$

for example, already has the form (4), where $z_0 = 1$. Here $A_{-2} = 1$ and all other A_n's are zero, which is in agreement with formula (5). Since this function is analytic everywhere except at the point $z = 1$, the curve C can be any closed contour enclosing that point.

The coefficients are usually found by other means than the use of the above formulas. For example, when $|z| > 0$, the expansions

$$\frac{e^z}{z^2} = \frac{1}{z^2} + \frac{1}{z} + \frac{1}{2!} + \frac{z}{3!} + \frac{z^2}{4!} + \cdots$$

and

$$e^{1/z} = 1 + \sum_{n=1}^{\infty} \frac{1}{n!z^n}$$

follow from Maclaurin's series. We shall see (Sec. 62) that such representations are unique, so that these must be the Laurent series when $z_0 = 0$.

To prove the theorem we first note that, according to Cauchy's integral formula,

$$(6) \qquad f(z) = \frac{1}{2\pi i} \int_{C_1} \frac{f(z')\,dz'}{z' - z} - \frac{1}{2\pi i} \int_{C_2} \frac{f(z')\,dz'}{z' - z},$$

since C_1 and C_2 form the boundary of a closed region throughout which f is analytic. In the first integral, as in the above proof of Taylor's theorem, we write

$$\frac{1}{z' - z} = \frac{1}{(z' - z_0) - (z - z_0)} = \frac{1}{z' - z_0} + \frac{z - z_0}{(z' - z_0)^2} + \cdots$$
$$+ \frac{(z - z_0)^{n-1}}{(z' - z_0)^n} + \frac{(z - z_0)^n}{(z' - z_0)^n(z' - z)}.$$

In the second integral we write

$$-\frac{1}{z'-z} = \frac{1}{(z-z_0) - (z'-z_0)}$$

and factor $(z - z_0)$ from the denominator to obtain the form

$$-\frac{1}{z'-z} = \frac{1}{z-z_0} + \frac{z'-z_0}{(z-z_0)^2} + \cdots$$

$$+ \frac{(z'-z_0)^{n-1}}{(z-z_0)^n} + \frac{(z'-z_0)^n}{(z-z_0)^n(z-z')}.$$

Then it follows from equation (6) that

$$f(z) = a_0 + a_1(z - z_0) + a_2(z - z_0)^2 + \cdots$$

$$+ a_{n-1}(z - z_0)^{n-1} + R_n + \frac{b_1}{z-z_0} + \frac{b_2}{(z-z_0)^2} + \cdots$$

$$+ \frac{b_n}{(z-z_0)^n} + Q_n,$$

where a_n and b_n are the numbers represented by formulas (2) and (3) and

$$R_n = \frac{(z-z_0)^n}{2\pi i} \int_{C_1} \frac{f(z')\,dz'}{(z'-z_0)^n(z'-z)},$$

$$Q_n = \frac{1}{2\pi i(z-z_0)^n} \int_{C_2} \frac{(z'-z_0)^n f(z')}{z-z'}\,dz'.$$

Let $r = |z - z_0|$; then $r_2 < r < r_1$. The proof that R_n approaches zero as n tends to infinity is the same as that used in establishing Taylor's series. If M is the maximum value of $|f(z')|$ on C_2, then

$$|Q_n| \leqq \left(\frac{r_2}{r}\right)^n \frac{Mr_2}{r-r_2},$$

and therefore Q_n approaches zero as n tends to infinity. This completes the proof of the theorem.

59. Properties of Series. Let S_N represent the sum of the first N terms of any infinite series of complex numbers,

(1) $$\sum_{n=1}^{\infty} z_n.$$

Then, if $z_n = x_n + iy_n$, we can write

(2) $$S_N = \sum_{n=1}^{N} z_n = \sum_{n=1}^{N} x_n + i \sum_{n=1}^{N} y_n,$$

and in order that the limit of S_N may exist as N tends to infinity, it is necessary and sufficient that the limits of each of the above sums of the real numbers x_n and y_n exist. For if those limits exist and are denoted by X and Y, that is, if

$$(3) \qquad X = \sum_{n=1}^{\infty} x_n, \qquad Y = \sum_{n=1}^{\infty} y_n,$$

and if X_N and Y_N represent the two sums on the right in equation (2), then corresponding to each positive number ϵ there is an integer N_ϵ such that

$$|X_N - X| < \frac{\epsilon}{2} \qquad \text{and} \qquad |Y_N - Y| < \frac{\epsilon}{2} \qquad \text{whenever } N > N_\epsilon.$$

But then $|S_N - (X + iY)| < \epsilon$ whenever $N > N_\epsilon$, because

$$|X_N + iY_N - X - iY| \leq |X_N - X| + |Y_N - Y| < \epsilon,$$

and therefore

$$(4) \qquad \lim_{N \to \infty} S_N = X + iY.$$

On the other hand, if condition (4) is satisfied for some pair of real numbers X and Y, then to each positive number ϵ there corresponds an integer M_ϵ such that $|S_N - X - iY| < \epsilon$ when $N > M_\epsilon$. Since $S_N = X_N + iY_N$, it follows that $|X_N - X| < \epsilon$ and $|Y_N - Y| < \epsilon$ when $N > M_\epsilon$; that is, $X_N \to X$ and $Y_N \to Y$ as $N \to \infty$. Thus condition (4) implies conditions (3), and conversely.

A necessary condition for the convergence of a series of real numbers is that the nth term approach zero as n tends to infinity. If the series (1) is to converge, then the series (3) must both converge, and so x_n and y_n must approach zero as n tends to infinity. Therefore z_n must approach zero; that is, a *necessary condition for the convergence of the series* (1) *is that*

$$(5) \qquad \lim_{n \to \infty} |z_n| = 0.$$

In particular, the terms of a convergent series are bounded: $|z_n| < M$ for every positive integer n, where M is some positive constant.

If the series (1) is *absolutely convergent*, that is, if the series

$$\sum_{n=1}^{\infty} |z_n| = \sum_{n=1}^{\infty} \sqrt{x_n{}^2 + y_n{}^2}$$

converges, then it follows from the comparison test for series of positive real numbers that the two series

$$\sum_{n=1}^{\infty} |x_n|, \qquad \sum_{n=1}^{\infty} |y_n|$$

both converge. The series (3) are thus absolutely convergent, and they are therefore convergent, because the absolute convergence of a series of real numbers implies the convergence of the series itself. Since the series (3) converge, the series (1) converges; that is, *absolute convergence of a series of complex numbers implies the convergence of the series itself.*

Theorem. *If a power series*

(6)
$$\sum_{n=0}^{\infty} a_n z^n$$

converges when $z = z_1$, it is absolutely convergent for every value of z such that $|z| < |z_1|$.

Since the series whose terms are $a_n z_1^n$ converges, those terms are all bounded; that is,

$$|a_n z_1^n| < M \qquad (n = 0, 1, 2, \ldots),$$

for some positive constant M. Write

$$\frac{|z|}{|z_1|} = k, \qquad \text{where } |z| < |z_1|;$$

then
$$|a_n z^n| = |a_n z_1^n| \left|\frac{z}{z_1}\right|^n < M k^n.$$

The series whose terms are the positive real numbers $M k^n$ is a geometric series; it is convergent, since $k < 1$. We conclude from the comparison test that the series

$$\sum_{n=0}^{\infty} |a_n z^n|$$

converges, and so the theorem is proved.

The region of convergence of the power series (6) is therefore a circle about the origin. The greatest circle about the origin such that the series converges at each point inside is called the *circle of convergence* of the power series. The series cannot converge at any point z_1 outside that circle, according to the above theorem, for in that case it must converge everywhere inside the circle about the origin passing through z_1. Thus the first circle could not be the circle of convergence.

If z is replaced by $(z - z_0)$, it follows that the region of convergence of the series

$$(7) \qquad \sum_{n=0}^{\infty} a_n(z - z_0)^n$$

is a circle about the point z_0. Similarly, we can see at once that if the series

$$(8) \qquad \sum_{n=1}^{\infty} \frac{b_n}{(z - z_0)^n}$$

converges when $z = z_1$, then it is absolutely convergent for every value of z such that

$$|z - z_0| > |z_1 - z_0|.$$

The region of convergence of the series (8) is therefore the exterior of some circle about the point z_0.

60. Uniform Convergence. Let C_0 denote a circle $|z| = r_0$ interior to which a power series converges, and let the function S represent the sum of that series,

$$(1) \qquad S(z) = \lim_{N \to \infty} \sum_{n=0}^{N} a_n z^n = \sum_{n=0}^{\infty} a_n z^n.$$

The remainder after N terms can be written

$$(2) \qquad R_N(z) = S(z) - \sum_{n=0}^{N-1} a_n z^n = \lim_{m \to \infty} \sum_{n=N}^{m} a_n z^n.$$

When $|z| \leq |z_1|$, where $|z_1| < r_0$, we can write

$$(3) \qquad \left| \sum_{n=N}^{m} a_n z^n \right| \leq \sum_{n=N}^{m} |a_n z^n| \leq \sum_{n=N}^{m} |a_n||z_1|^n.$$

The limit of this last sum, as m tends to infinity, is the remainder in the series of the absolute values of the terms of the series (1). But according to the theorem in the preceding section, the series (1) is absolutely convergent when $z = z_1$, and hence the remainder

$$\rho_N = \lim_{m \to \infty} \sum_{n=N}^{m} |a_n||z_1|^n$$

approaches zero as N tends to infinity; that is, given any positive number ϵ, an integer N_ϵ exists such that $\rho_N < \epsilon$ whenever $N \geqq N_\epsilon$. Since the terms of the last series are all nonnegative real numbers, it follows that, for every integer m greater than N,

$$\sum_{n=N}^{m} |a_n||z_1|^n \leqq \rho_N.$$

In view of the relation (3), then,

$$\left| \sum_{n=N}^{m} a_n z^n \right| \leqq \rho_N$$

for every integer m greater than N, and hence the remainder (2) satisfies the relation

$$|R_N(z)| \leqq \rho_N < \epsilon \qquad \text{when } N \geqq N_\epsilon.$$

Now N_ϵ is independent of z when $|z| \leqq |z_1|$, so that the following theorem is established.

Theorem. *The power series* (1) *is uniformly convergent for all points z within and on any circle $|z| = |z_1|$ that is interior to the circle of convergence.*

The partial sum

$$S_N(z) = \sum_{n=0}^{N-1} a_n z^n$$

of the series (1) is a polynomial, and hence it is a continuous function of z. To show that its limit $S(z)$ is continuous when $|z| \leqq |z_1|$, we first note that since

$$S(z) = S_N(z) + R_N(z),$$

then

(4) $\quad |S(z + \Delta z) - S(z)| = |S_N(z + \Delta z) - S_N(z) + R_N(z + \Delta z)$
$$- R_N(z)|$$
$$\leqq |\Delta S_N| + |R_N(z + \Delta z)| + |R_N(z)|,$$

where $\Delta S_N = S_N(z + \Delta z) - S_N(z)$. We want to show that given any positive number ϵ, a positive number δ exists such that

(5) $\qquad\qquad |S(z + \Delta z) - S(z)| < \epsilon \qquad \text{when } |\Delta z| < \delta.$

In view of the uniform convergence established above, an integer N_ϵ exists such that $|R_N| < \epsilon/3$ for every point in the region $|z| \leq |z_1|$, when $N \geq N_\epsilon$. When $N = N_\epsilon$, a number δ exists such that $|\Delta S_N| < \epsilon/3$ when $|\Delta z| < \delta$, because $S_N(z)$ is continuous. The value of the right-hand member of the inequality (4) is therefore less than ϵ, and the inequality (5) is established.

We have now shown that a power series represents a continuous function of z at each point interior to its circle of convergence.

By substituting $(z - z_0)$ or its reciprocal for z, the above results can be extended at once to series of the types

$$\sum_{n=0}^{\infty} a_n(z - z_0)^n, \qquad \sum_{n=0}^{\infty} \frac{b_n}{(z - z_0)^n},$$

with obvious modifications. Thus, if the second series here is convergent in the annulus $r_1 \leq |z - z_0| \leq r_2$, it is uniformly convergent for all values of z in that annulus and its sum represents a continuous function of z there.

61. Integration and Differentiation of Power Series. It was shown above that a power series represents a continuous function $S(z)$ interior to the circle of convergence. We shall prove in this section that S is analytic within that circle.

Theorem 1. *Let C denote any contour interior to the circle of convergence of a power series, and let g be any function that is continuous on C. The series formed by multiplying each term of the power series by $g(z)$ can be integrated term by term over C; that is,*

$$(1) \qquad \sum_{n=0}^{\infty} a_n \int_C z^n g(z) \, dz = \int_C S(z)g(z) \, dz.$$

Since the sum $S(z)$ of the power series is a continuous function, the integral of the product

$$S(z)g(z) = \sum_{n=0}^{N-1} a_n z^n g(z) + R_N(z)g(z)$$

exists. The terms of the finite sum here are also continuous on the contour C, so that their integrals over C exist, and consequently the integral of the remainder $R_N(z)g(z)$ must exist. Thus

$$(2) \quad \int_C S(z)g(z) \, dz = \sum_{n=0}^{N-1} a_n \int_C z^n g(z) \, dz + \int_C R_N(z)g(z) \, dz.$$

Let M represent the maximum value of $|g(z)|$ at all points z on C, and let L denote the length of C. In view of the uniform convergence of the power series established in Sec. 60, for every positive number ϵ, an integer N_ϵ exists such that at all points z on C,

$$|R_N(z)| < \epsilon \qquad \text{when } N \geq N_\epsilon.$$

Since ϵ and N_ϵ are independent of z, we can write

$$\left| \int_C R_N(z)g(z) \, dz \right| < \epsilon M L \qquad \text{when } N \geq N_\epsilon.$$

It follows, therefore, from equation (2) that

$$\int_C S(z)g(z) \, dz = \lim_{N \to \infty} \sum_{n=0}^{N-1} a_n \int_C z^n g(z) \, dz,$$

which is the same as equation (1), and so Theorem 1 is proved.

When $g(z) = 1$ for all values of z and C is any closed contour interior to the circle of convergence of the power series, then, for every integer n,

$$\int_C z^n g(z) \, dz = \int_C z^n \, dz = 0.$$

It follows from equation (1) that

$$\int_C S(z) \, dz = 0$$

for every closed contour interior to the circle of convergence; thus, according to Morera's theorem, the function S is analytic. The result can be stated as follows.

Theorem 2. *A power series represents an analytic function at every point interior to its circle of convergence.*

If a function f is analytic inside a circle C about the origin and has a singular point z_0 on C such that either f or its derivative of some order has no limit as z tends to z_0 from the interior of C, then the Maclaurin series for $f(z)$ must diverge outside C. If it converged, it would represent an analytic function F in a circle enclosing C. Since $F(z) = f(z)$ interior to C, then f and its derivatives would have limits at z_0.

The function $e^z(z - 1)/(z - 1)$ is an example of one whose Maclaurin series has a circle of convergence that extends beyond its singular point $(z = 1)$. Since that function is the same as the entire function e^z when $z \neq 1$, its Maclaurin series converges everywhere.

Theorem 3. *A power series can be differentiated term by term at every point z interior to the circle of convergence; that is,*

$$(3) \qquad S'(z) = \sum_{n=1}^{\infty} n a_n z^{n-1} \qquad\qquad (|z| < r_0).$$

To establish this theorem, let z_1 denote any point interior to the circle and let C be some closed contour about z_1 and interior to the circle. Then, since S is analytic,

$$S'(z_1) = \frac{1}{2\pi i} \int_C \frac{S(z)\,dz}{(z - z_1)^2}.$$

In equation (1) we write

$$g(z) = \frac{1}{2\pi i (z - z_1)^2};$$

then

$$\int_C z^n g(z)\,dz = \frac{1}{2\pi i} \int_C \frac{z^n\,dz}{(z - z_1)^2} = \frac{d}{dz_1}(z_1{}^n)$$

and

$$\int_C S(z)g(z)\,dz = S'(z_1).$$

Therefore

$$S'(z_1) = \sum_{n=0}^{\infty} a_n \frac{d}{dz_1}(z_1{}^n),$$

and the theorem is proved.

The results here can be extended at once to series of positive or negative powers of $(z - z_0)$.

Theorem 2 is often helpful in establishing the analyticity of functions or in evaluating limits. As a simple example, let us show that the function f defined by the conditions

$$f(z) = \frac{\sin z}{z} \qquad\qquad \text{when } z \neq 0,$$
$$f(0) = 1$$

is entire. Since the Maclaurin series for the sine function converges to $\sin z$ for every z, the series obtained by multiplying all terms of that series by the common factor z^{-1}, that is,

$$(4) \qquad 1 - \frac{z^2}{3!} + \frac{z^4}{5!} - \cdots = \sum_{n=0}^{\infty} (-1)^n \frac{z^{2n}}{(2n + 1)!},$$

converges to $f(z)$ if $z \neq 0$. But series (4) clearly converges to $f(0)$ when $z = 0$. Thus $f(z)$ is represented by the convergent power series (4) for all z, and so f is an entire function. In particular, f is continuous at $z = 0$ and, since $z^{-1} \sin z = f(z)$ when $z \neq 0$, then

$$(5) \qquad \lim_{z \to 0} \frac{\sin z}{z} = \lim_{z \to 0} f(z) = f(0) = 1,$$

a result known beforehand because the limit here is the definition of the derivative of $\sin z$ at $z = 0$.

EXERCISES

1. By differentiating Maclaurin's series for $(1 - z)^{-1}$, obtain the representations

$$\frac{1}{(1 - z)^2} = \sum_{n=1}^{\infty} n z^{n-1}, \qquad \frac{2}{(1 - z)^3} = \sum_{n=2}^{\infty} n(n - 1)z^{n-2} \qquad (|z| < 1).$$

2. Expand the function z^{-1} in powers of $z - 1$; then obtain by differentiation the expansion of z^{-2} in powers of $z - 1$. Give the region of validity.

3. Integrate Maclaurin's series for $(1 + z')^{-1}$ along a contour interior to the circle of convergence from $z' = 0$ to $z' = z$ to obtain the representation

$$\mathrm{Log}\,(z + 1) = \sum_{n=1}^{\infty} (-1)^{n+1} \frac{z^n}{n} \qquad (|z| < 1).$$

4. If $f(z) = (e^{cz} - 1)/z$ when $z \neq 0$ and $f(0) = c$, prove that f is entire.

5. Expand $\sinh z$ in powers of $z - \pi i$ to prove that

$$\lim_{z \to \pi i} \frac{\sinh z}{z - \pi i} = -1.$$

6. If $f(z) = z^{-1}\,\mathrm{Log}\,(z + 1)$ when $z \neq 0$ and $f(0) = 1$, prove that f is analytic throughout the domain $|z| < 1$.

7. If $f(z) = (z^2 - \pi^2/4)^{-1} \cos z$ when $z^2 \neq \pi^2/4$ and $f(\pm \pi/2) = -1/\pi$, prove that f is an entire function.

8. If a function f is analytic at z_0 and $f(z_0) = 0$, use series to show that

$$\lim_{z \to z_0} \frac{f(z)}{z - z_0} = f'(z_0).$$

Also note that this follows directly from the definition of $f'(z_0)$.

9. If f and g are analytic at z_0 and $f(z_0) = g(z_0) = 0$ while $g'(z_0) \neq 0$, prove that

$$\lim_{z \to z_0} \frac{f(z)}{g(z)} = \frac{f'(z_0)}{g'(z_0)}.$$

10. If f is analytic at z_0 and $f(z_0) = f'(z_0) = \cdots = f^{(m)}(z_0) = 0$, prove that the function g is analytic at z_0, where

$$g(z) = \frac{f(z)}{(z - z_0)^{m+1}} \qquad \text{if } z \neq z_0,$$

and

$$g(z_0) = \frac{f^{(m+1)}(z_0)}{(m + 1)!}.$$

62. Uniqueness of Representations by Power Series. The series in equation (3) of the preceding section is a power series that converges to $S'(z)$ everywhere within the circle of convergence C_0 of the series

$$(1) \qquad \sum_{n=0}^{\infty} a_n z^n = S(z).$$

Consequently, that series can be differentiated term by term; that is,

$$S''(z) = \sum_{n=2}^{\infty} n(n - 1)a_n z^{n-2} \qquad (|z| < r_0).$$

Similarly, the derivative of $S(z)$ of any order can be found by successively differentiating the series term by term. Moreover,

$$S(0) = a_0, \qquad S'(0) = a_1, \qquad S''(0) = 2!a_2, \qquad \ldots,$$

so that the coefficients are those of the Maclaurin series expansion of $S(z)$,

$$a_n = \frac{S^{(n)}(0)}{n!}.$$

The generalization to series of positive powers of $(z - z_0)$ is immediate. Thus we have the following theorem on the uniqueness of the representation of functions in power series.

Theorem 1. *If the series*

$$(2) \qquad \sum_{n=0}^{\infty} a_n(z - z_0)^n$$

converges to $f(z)$ at all points interior to some circle $|z - z_0| = r_0$, that series is the Taylor series expansion of the function f in powers of $(z - z_0)$.

As an example, we find by substituting z^2 for z in the Maclaurin series for sin z that

$$(3) \qquad \sin (z^2) = \sum_{n=1}^{\infty} (-1)^{n-1} \frac{z^{4n-2}}{(2n-1)!} \qquad (|z| < \infty).$$

This series must be identical to the series that would be found by expanding the function sin (z^2) directly in Maclaurin's series.

It follows from Theorem 1 that, if the series (2) converges to zero at every point in some neighborhood of z_0, then each of the coefficients a_n must vanish.

Theorem 2. *If the series*

$$(4) \qquad \sum_{n=-\infty}^{\infty} A_n(z - z_0)^n = \sum_{n=0}^{\infty} a_n(z - z_0)^n + \sum_{n=1}^{\infty} \frac{b_n}{(z - z_0)^n}$$

converges to $f(z)$ at all points in some annular region about z_0, then it is the Laurent series expansion of the function f in powers of $(z - z_0)$ for that region.

The proof of this theorem follows from Theorem 1 of the preceding section, extended to series of positive and negative powers of $(z - z_0)$. If we take the curve C as a closed contour around the annulus and interior to it and write

$$g(z) = \frac{1}{2\pi i(z - z_0)^{m+1}},$$

the term by term integration shows that

$$A_m = \frac{1}{2\pi i} \int_C \frac{f(z) \, dz}{(z - z_0)^{m+1}}.$$

These are the coefficients in the Laurent series.

63. Multiplication and Division. Suppose that the two power series

$$(1) \qquad \sum_{n=0}^{\infty} a_n z^n = f(z), \qquad \sum_{n=0}^{\infty} b_n z^n = g(z)$$

both converge in the interior of some circle $|z| = r_0$. The sums $f(z)$ and $g(z)$ are then analytic functions in that region, and hence their product has a Maclaurin series expansion in the region,

$$(2) \qquad f(z)g(z) = \sum_{n=0}^{\infty} c_n z^n \qquad (|z| < r_0).$$

The coefficients c_n are given by the formulas

$$c_0 = f(0)g(0) = a_0 b_0,$$
$$c_1 = f(0)g'(0) + f'(0)g(0) = a_0 b_1 + a_1 b_0,$$
$$c_2 = \frac{1}{2!}[f(0)g''(0) + 2f'(0)g'(0) + f''(0)g(0)]$$
$$= a_0 b_2 + a_1 b_1 + a_2 b_0,$$

etc., where we have made use of the fact that the two series (1) are the same as the Maclaurin series for f and g. With the aid of the formula for the nth derivative of the product of two functions, we can see that

$$(3) \quad f(z)g(z) = a_0 b_0 + (a_0 b_1 + a_1 b_0)z$$
$$+ (a_0 b_2 + a_1 b_1 + a_2 b_0)z^2 + \cdots$$
$$+ \left(\sum_{k=0}^{n} a_k b_{n-k}\right) z^n + \cdots \qquad (|z| < r_0).$$

The series (3) is the same as the series obtained by multiplying the two series (1) together term by term and collecting the terms in like powers of z; it is the *Cauchy product* of the two given series. Thus we can state the following theorem.

Theorem. *The product of two power series converges to the product of their sums at all points interior to both their circles of convergence.*

If $g(z) \neq 0$ in some neighborhood of the origin, the quotient $f(z)/g(z)$ is an analytic function there. It therefore has a Maclaurin series expansion

$$(4) \qquad q(z) = \frac{f(z)}{g(z)} = \sum_{n=0}^{\infty} \gamma_n z^n,$$

where $\gamma_0 = q(0)$, $\gamma_1 = q'(0)$, $\gamma_2 = q''(0)/2!$, etc. The first few of these coefficients can be found in terms of the coefficients a_n and b_n by differentiating the quotient $f(z)/g(z)$ successively. The results are the same as those obtained by carrying out the division of the first of series (1) by the second. This method identifies the first few terms of the quotient of two power series with the power series that represents the quotient. This is generally the result that is needed, although it can be shown that the series are entirely identical.

The addition of two power series term by term is always valid within their common region of convergence. This follows from the definition of the sum of the series. Multiplication by a constant is a special case of the above theorem on the multiplication of two series; consequently, two power series can be subtracted term by term.

64. Examples. Consider first this function f:

$$(1) \qquad f(z) = \frac{-1}{(z-1)(z-2)} = \frac{1}{z-1} - \frac{1}{z-2},$$

which is analytic everywhere except at the two points $z = 1$ and $z = 2$.

Example 1.   Obtain Maclaurin's series for f.

That series represents $f(z)$ when $|z| < 1$. In that domain $|z/2| < 1$. Knowing the sum of geometric series (Sec. 57), we can write

$$f(z) = \frac{1}{2} \frac{1}{1 - z/2} - \frac{1}{1 - z} = \sum_{n=0}^{\infty} \left[\frac{1}{2} \left(\frac{z}{2} \right)^n - z^n \right] \qquad (|z| < 1).$$

Since this series in powers of z converges to $f(z)$ when $|z| < 1$, it is Maclaurin's series for f; that is, the coefficient of z^n in the expansion

$$(2) \qquad f(z) = \sum_{n=0}^{\infty} (2^{-n-1} - 1) z^n \qquad (|z| < 1)$$

must have the value $f^{(n)}(0)/n!$; thus $f^{(n)}(0) = n!(2^{-n-1} - 1)$.

Example 2.   Write the Laurent series that represents f throughout the annulus $1 < |z| < 2$.

In that annular domain $|1/z| < 1$ and $|z/2| < 1$, and thus

$$(3) \quad f(z) = \frac{1}{z} \frac{1}{1 - 1/z} + \frac{1}{2} \frac{1}{1 - z/2} = \sum_{n=0}^{\infty} \frac{1}{z^{n+1}} + \sum_{n=0}^{\infty} \frac{z^n}{2^{n+1}}$$

$$(1 < |z| < 2).$$

There is but one such representation of f in that annulus, so this is Laurent's series for f there. Since the coefficient of z^{-1} has the value $A_{-1} = 1$, our formula (5), Sec. 58, for the coefficients A_n shows that, if C is any closed contour within the annulus that encloses the point $z = 1$, then $\int_C f(z)\, dz = 2\pi i$.

Example 3. Obtain Laurent's series for f in the domain $|z| > 2$.

In that domain $|1/z| < 1$ and $|2/z| < 1$; therefore

$$(4) \quad f(z) = \frac{1}{z}\left(\frac{1}{1 - 1/z} - \frac{1}{1 - 2/z}\right) = \sum_{n=0}^{\infty} \frac{1 - 2^n}{z^{n+1}} \qquad (|z| > 2).$$

This is the required Laurent series. Here the coefficient of z^{-1} is zero; consequently the integral of f around each closed contour that contains both points $z = 1$ and $z = 2$ in its interior has the value zero.

Example 4. Find the first few terms of Laurent's series for the function g in the domain $0 < |z| < \pi$, when

$$g(z) = \frac{1}{z^2 \sinh z} = \frac{1}{z^3}\,\frac{1}{1 + z^2/3! + z^4/5! + \cdots}.$$

The denominator of the last fraction consists of a power series that converges to $z^{-1} \sinh z$ when $z \neq 0$ and to unity when $z = 0$. Thus the sum of that series does not vanish anywhere in the domain $|z| < \pi$, and the power series representation of that fraction can be found by division to be

$$\frac{1}{1 + z^2/3! + z^4/5! + \cdots} = 1 - \frac{1}{3!}z^2 + \left[\frac{1}{(3!)^2} - \frac{1}{5!}\right]z^4 + \cdots$$
$$(|z| < \pi).$$

Hence the Laurent series for g in the domain specified runs

$$(5) \qquad \frac{1}{z^2 \sinh z} = \frac{1}{z^3} - \frac{1}{6}\frac{1}{z} + \frac{7}{360}z + \cdots \qquad (0 < |z| < \pi).$$

65. Zeros of Analytic Functions. If a function f is analytic at z_0, there is a neighborhood of z_0 throughout which f is represented by Taylor's series,

$$(1) \qquad\qquad f(z) = a_0 + \sum_{n=1}^{\infty} a_n(z - z_0)^n \qquad (|z - z_0| < r_0),$$

where $a_0 = f(z_0)$ and $n!a_n = f^{(n)}(z_0)$. If z_0 is a zero of f, then

$a_0 = 0.$ When

$$(2) \qquad f(z_0) = f'(z_0) = f''(z_0) = \cdots = f^{(m-1)}(z_0) = 0$$

but $f^{(m)}(z_0) \neq 0$, then z_0 is called a *zero of order* m and

$$(3) \qquad f(z) = (z - z_0)^m \sum_{n=0}^{\infty} a_{m+n}(z - z_0)^n$$

$$(a_m \neq 0, |z - z_0| < r_0).$$

Let $g(z)$ denote the sum of the series in equation (3),

$$(4) \qquad g(z) = \sum_{n=0}^{\infty} a_{m+n}(z - z_0)^n \qquad (|z - z_0| < r_0).$$

Note that $g(z_0) = a_m \neq 0$. Since series (4) converges, g is a continuous function at z_0. For each positive number ϵ, therefore, a number δ exists such that

$$|g(z) - a_m| < \epsilon \qquad \text{whenever } |z - z_0| < \delta.$$

If $\epsilon = |a_m/2|$ and δ_1 is the corresponding value of δ,

$$|g(z) - a_m| < \tfrac{1}{2}|a_m| \qquad \text{when } |z - z_0| < \delta_1.$$

It follows that $g(z) \neq 0$ at any point in the neighborhood $|z - z_0| < \delta_1$, because if $g(z) = 0$ the inequality here is contradicted.

The argument remains valid if $m = 0$, in which case $g = f$ and $f(z_0) \neq 0$. Thus we have established the following theorem.

Theorem. *Unless a function is identically zero, about each point where the function is analytic there is a neighborhood throughout which the function has no zero, except possibly at the point itself. Thus the zeros of an analytic function are isolated.*

EXERCISES

1. Let g denote the function $\sin(z^2)$. Use Maclaurin's series (3), Sec. 62, for $g(z)$ to show that $g^{(2n-1)}(0) = 0$ and $g^{(4n)}(0) = 0$, where $n = 1, 2, \ldots$.

2. Use the expansion found in Example 4, Sec. 64, to show that, if C is the circle $|z| = 1$,

$$\int_C \frac{dz}{z^2 \sinh z} = -\frac{1}{3}\pi i.$$

3. Obtain the Maclaurin series representation

$$z \cosh (z^2) = z + \sum_{n=1}^{\infty} \frac{1}{(2n)!} z^{4n+1} \qquad (|z| < \infty).$$

4. Represent the function $(z + 1)/(z - 1)$ by (a) Maclaurin's series, and give the region of validity for the representation; (b) Laurent's series for the domain $|z| > 1$.

$$Ans. \ (a) -1 - 2 \sum_{n=1}^{\infty} z^n \quad (|z| < 1); \quad (b) \ 1 + 2 \sum_{n=1}^{\infty} z^{-n} \quad (|z| > 1).$$

5. Obtain the expansion of the function $(z - 1)/z^2$ in (a) Taylor's series in powers of $z - 1$ and give the region of validity; (b) Laurent's series for the domain $|z - 1| > 1$.

$$Ans. \ (a) \sum_{n=1}^{\infty} (-1)^{n+1} n(z - 1)^n \quad (|z - 1| < 1);$$

$$(b) \sum_{n=1}^{\infty} (-1)^{n+1} n(z - 1)^{-n} \quad (|z - 1| > 1).$$

6. Obtain the Laurent series expansion

$$\frac{\sinh z}{z^2} = \frac{1}{z} + \sum_{n=1}^{\infty} \frac{1}{(2n + 1)!} z^{2n-1} \qquad (|z| > 0).$$

7. Give two Laurent series expansions, in powers of z, for the function

$$f(z) = \frac{1}{z^2(1 - z)}$$

and specify the regions in which those expansions are valid.

$$Ans. \sum_{n=0}^{\infty} z^{n-2} \quad (0 < |z| < 1); \ - \sum_{n=0}^{\infty} z^{-n-3} \qquad (|z| > 1).$$

8. Write the two Laurent series in powers of z that represent the function $z^{-1}(1 + z^2)^{-1}$ in certain domains and specify those domains.

9. Obtain the first four terms of the Laurent series expansion

$$\frac{e^z}{z(z^2 + 1)} = \frac{1}{z} + 1 - \frac{1}{2} z - \frac{5}{6} z^2 + \cdots \qquad (0 < |z| < 1).$$

10. Obtain the first few terms of the Laurent series expansions

(a) $\csc z = \dfrac{1}{z} + \dfrac{1}{3!}z - \left[\dfrac{1}{5!} - \dfrac{1}{(3!)^2}\right]z^3 + \cdots$ $(0 < |z| < \pi)$;

(b) $\dfrac{1}{e^z - 1} = \dfrac{1}{z} - \dfrac{1}{2} + \dfrac{1}{12}z - \dfrac{1}{720}z^3 + \cdots$ $(0 < |z| < 2\pi)$.

11. Write the Laurent series expansion of the function $(z - k)^{-1}$ for the domain $|z| > |k|$, where k is real and $k^2 < 1$. Then write $z = \exp(i\theta)$ to obtain these formulas for sums of series of sines and cosines:

$$\sum_{n=1}^{\infty} k^n \sin(n\theta) = \frac{k \sin \theta}{p(k,\theta)}, \qquad \sum_{n=1}^{\infty} k^n \cos(n\theta) = \frac{k \cos \theta - k^2}{p(k,\theta)},$$

where $p(k,\theta) = 1 + k^2 - 2k \cos \theta$ and $k^2 < 1$.

12. Let $F(r,\theta)$ denote a function of z, where $z = r \exp(i\theta)$, that is analytic in some annulus about the origin that includes the circle $r = 1$. Take that circle as the curve C in the formula for the coefficients A_n in the Laurent expansion of $F(r,\theta)$ in powers of z, and show that

$$F(1,\theta) = \frac{1}{2\pi} \int_0^{2\pi} F(1,\theta')\, d\theta' + \frac{1}{\pi} \sum_{n=1}^{\infty} \int_0^{2\pi} F(1,\theta') \cos[n(\theta - \theta')]\, d\theta'.$$

This is the Fourier series expansion of the complex-valued function $F(1,\theta)$ of the real variable θ on the unit circle. If $u(\theta)$ and $v(\theta)$ denote the real and imaginary components of $F(1,\theta)$, show that the above expansion is true when F is replaced everywhere by u or everywhere by v. The restrictions on the real-valued functions u and v here, however, are much more severe than they need be in order that those functions be represented by their Fourier series.[1]

[1] For other sufficient conditions, see, for instance, the author's book "Fourier Series and Boundary Value Problems," pp. 70, 86, 1941.

CHAPTER 7

RESIDUES AND POLES

66. Residues. If there is some neighborhood of a singular point z_0 of a function f throughout which f is analytic, except at the point itself, then z_0 is called an *isolated singular point* of f.

The function $1/z$ furnishes a simple example. It is analytic except at $z = 0$; hence the origin is an isolated singular point of that function. The function

$$\frac{z + 1}{z^3(z^2 + 1)}$$

has three isolated singular points, namely, $z = 0$ and $z = \pm i$.

As another example, the function

$$\frac{1}{\sin (\pi/z)}$$

has an infinite number of isolated singular points all lying on the segment of the real axis from $z = -1$ to $z = 1$, namely, $z = \pm 1$, $z = \pm\frac{1}{2}$, $z = \pm\frac{1}{3}$, etc. But the origin $z = 0$ is also a singular point; it is not isolated, since every neighborhood of the origin contains other singular points of the function.

Again, the function Log z has a singular point at the origin that is not isolated, because each neighborhood of the origin includes points on the negative real axis where Log z is not analytic.

When z_0 is an isolated singular point of f, a positive number r_1 exists such that the function is analytic at each point z for which $0 < |z - z_0| < r_1$. In that domain the function is represented by the Laurent series

$$(1) \quad f(z) = \sum_{n=0}^{\infty} a_n(z - z_0)^n + \frac{b_1}{z - z_0} + \frac{b_2}{(z - z_0)^2} + \cdots,$$

where the coefficients are given by formulas in Sec. 58. In particular,

$$(2) \qquad b_1 = \frac{1}{2\pi i} \int_C f(z)\, dz$$

where C is any closed contour around z_0, described in the positive sense, such that f is analytic on C and interior to C except at the point z_0 itself.

Note that our representation (1) of the function f is that particular Laurent expansion about z_0 which is valid whenever $0 < |z - z_0| < r_1$. The point z can be arbitrarily near z_0. In that expansion, b_1, the coefficient of $(z - z_0)^{-1}$, is called the *residue* of f at the isolated singular point z_0.

Every function has a residue at each of its isolated singular points because Laurent's series about the point represents the function throughout a neighborhood of the point except at the point itself. The value of the residue may be zero, however. According to formula (2), *the residue of f at z_0 is the value of the integral of $(2\pi i)^{-1}f(z)$ in the positive sense around any closed contour C enclosing z_0, if C is such that f is analytic everywhere on and within that closed contour except at z_0.*

We now have a powerful method of evaluating certain integrals around closed contours. For example, let us evaluate the contour integral of the function $e^{-z}(z - 1)^{-2}$ in the positive sense around the circle $C_0:|z| = 2$. The only singular point, $z = 1$, of the function is interior to that circle. We may use Taylor's series for e^{-z} about the point $z = 1$ to write

$$(3) \qquad \frac{e^{-z}}{(z - 1)^2} = \frac{e^{-1}}{(z - 1)^2} - \frac{e^{-1}}{z - 1} + e^{-1} \sum_{n=2}^{\infty} (-1)^n \frac{(z - 1)^{n-2}}{n!}$$

$$(|z - 1| > 0).$$

From this Laurent expansion we see that the residue of our function at $z = 1$ is $-e^{-1}$, and it follows at once that

$$(4) \qquad \int_{C_0} \frac{e^{-z}}{(z - 1)^2}\, dz = -\frac{2\pi i}{e}.$$

As another example, we shall prove that, for the above circle C_0,

$$(5) \qquad \int_{C_0} \exp\left(\frac{1}{z^2}\right) dz = 0.$$

Since $1/z^2$ is analytic everywhere except at the origin, the integrand here also has that character. The singular point is interior to C_0. With the aid of Maclaurin's series for the exponential function, we can write the Laurent expansion

$$\exp\left(\frac{1}{z^2}\right) = 1 + \frac{1}{z^2} + \frac{1}{2!}\frac{1}{z^4} + \frac{1}{3!}\frac{1}{z^6} + \cdots \qquad (|z| > 0).$$

The residue of the integrand at its singular point $z = 0$ is therefore zero ($b_1 = 0$), and the vanishing of the integral (5) is established.

67. The Residue Theorem. If a function has only a finite number of singular points in some domain, then those singular points are necessarily isolated.

Theorem. *Let C be a closed contour within and on which a function f is analytic except for a finite number of singular points $z_1, z_2, \ldots, z_n$ interior to C. If $K_1, K_2, \ldots, K_n$ denote the residues of f at those points, then*

$$(1) \qquad \int_C f(z)\, dz = 2\pi i(K_1 + K_2 + \cdots + K_n),$$

where the integral is taken counterclockwise around C.

Let each of the points z_j be enclosed in a circle C_j with radius small enough that these n circles and the curve C are all separated (Fig. 41). Those circles, together with the curve C, form the boundary of a closed multiply connected region throughout which f is analytic. According to the Cauchy-Goursat theorem, extended to such regions (Sec. 49),

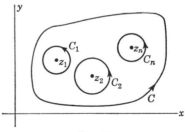

FIG. 41

$$\int_C f(z)\, dz - \int_{C_1} f(z)\, dz - \int_{C_2} f(z)\, dz - \cdots - \int_{C_n} f(z)\, dz = 0.$$

This equation reduces to formula (1), because

$$K_j = \frac{1}{2\pi i} \int_{C_j} f(z)\, dz \qquad (j = 1, 2, \ldots, n),$$

and so the theorem is proved.

As an example, let us evaluate the integral

$$(2) \qquad \int_C \frac{5z - 2}{z(z - 1)} \, dz,$$

where C is the circle $|z| = 2$, described counterclockwise. The two singularities, $z = 0$ and $z = 1$, of the integrand lie inside C. To find the residue K_1 at $z = 0$, we may write

$$\frac{5z - 2}{z(z - 1)} = \left(5 - \frac{2}{z}\right)\left(\frac{-1}{1 - z}\right) = \left(-5 + \frac{2}{z}\right)(1 + z + z^2 + \cdots)$$

$$= \frac{2}{z} - 3 - 3z - 3z^2 - \cdots \qquad (0 < |z| < 1).$$

Hence $K_1 = 2$.

To find the residue K_2 at $z = 1$, we may use the Taylor series

$$\frac{1}{z} = 1 - (z - 1) + (z - 1)^2 - \cdots \qquad (|z - 1| < 1)$$

in order to find the coefficients in the appropriate Laurent expansion of the integrand about the point $z = 1$.   Thus

$$\frac{5z - 2}{z(z - 1)} = \left(5 + \frac{3}{z - 1}\right)\frac{1}{z}$$

$$= \left(5 + \frac{3}{z - 1}\right)[1 - (z - 1) + (z - 1)^2 - \cdots]$$

when $0 < |z - 1| < 1$.   The coefficient of $(z - 1)^{-1}$ in this product is 3; that is, $K_2 = 3$.   Therefore,

$$\int_C \frac{5z - 2}{z(z - 1)} \, dz = 2\pi i(K_1 + K_2) = 10\pi i.$$

In this example it is simpler to write the integrand as the sum of its partial fractions.   Then

$$\int_C \frac{5z - 2}{z(z - 1)} \, dz = \int_C \frac{2}{z} \, dz + \int_C \frac{3}{z - 1} \, dz = 2\pi i(2 + 3) = 10\pi i.$$

As still another method of evaluating the integral (2), we can note that the integral divided by $2\pi i$ is the coefficient b_1 of the Laurent expansion of the integrand about the origin in the domain *outside* the circle $|z| = 1$, according to formula (3) of Sec. 58. That expansion is easily written as follows.   If $|z| > 1$,

$$\frac{5z - 2}{z(z - 1)} = \frac{5z - 2}{z^2} \frac{1}{1 - (1/z)} = (5z - 2) \sum_{n=0}^{\infty} \frac{1}{z^{n+2}}.$$

The coefficient b_1 of $1/z$ in this product is 5.   Hence the value of the integral is $10\pi i$.

68. Poles.   In Laurent's series (1), Sec. 66, which represents a function f in a domain $0 < |z - z_0| < r_1$ about an isolated singular point z_0, the series of negative powers of $z - z_0$ is called the *principal part* of $f(z)$ about z_0.   The structure of the principal part has a major influence upon the behavior of the function near the singular point.

Suppose the principal part contains only a finite number of terms; then an integer m exists such that the coefficients b_{m+1}, b_{m+2}, . . . all vanish, and

$$(1) \quad f(z) = \frac{b_1}{z - z_0} + \frac{b_2}{(z - z_0)^2} + \cdots + \frac{b_m}{(z - z_0)^m}$$
$$+ \sum_{n=0}^{\infty} a_n(z - z_0)^n$$

when $0 < |z - z_0| < r_1$, for some positive number r_1, where $b_m \neq 0$.   The isolated singular point z_0 is then called a *pole of order* m of the function f.

A pole of order $m = 1$ is called a *simple pole*.

When the principal part of f about the point z_0 has an infinite number of terms, the point is called an *essential singular point* of the function.

The function

$$\frac{z^2 - 2z + 3}{z - 2} = \frac{3}{z - 2} + 2 + (z - 2),$$

for example, has a simple pole at $z = 2$.   Its residue there is 3.

As another example, the function

$$\frac{\sinh z}{z^4} = \frac{1}{z^3} + \frac{1}{3!} \frac{1}{z} + \frac{1}{5!} z + \frac{1}{7!} z^3 + \cdots \qquad (|z| > 0)$$

has a pole of order 3 at $z = 0$, with a residue there of $\frac{1}{6}$.   But the function

$$\cosh \frac{1}{z} = 1 + \sum_{n=1}^{\infty} \frac{1}{(2n)!} \frac{1}{z^{2n}} \qquad (|z| > 0)$$

has an essential singular point at $z = 0$.   Its residue there is zero.

When f has a pole of order m at z_0, let us write

$$\phi(z) = (z - z_0)^m f(z) \qquad (0 < |z - z_0| < r_1),$$

an equation that defines the function ϕ in a neighborhood of z_0 except at the point z_0 itself. Then, in view of equation (1), when $0 < |z - z_0| < r_1$ we can write

$$(2) \quad \phi(z) = b_1(z - z_0)^{m-1} + b_2(z - z_0)^{m-2} + \cdots$$

$$+ b_m + \sum_{n=0}^{\infty} a_n(z - z_0)^{n+m},$$

where $b_m \neq 0$. We now define $\phi(z)$ at $z = z_0$ to be the number b_m,

$$\phi(z_0) = b_m.$$

Then the representation (2) is valid throughout a neighborhood of z_0, including that point itself. Since the series in equation (2) is a convergent power series, the function ϕ is analytic at z_0.

Our definition of $\phi(z_0)$ can now be written

$$(3) \quad \phi(z_0) = \lim_{z \to z_0} (z - z_0)^m f(z) = b_m.$$

Since this limit exists and $b_m \neq 0$, it follows that $|f(z)|$ *always becomes infinite as z approaches a pole* z_0.

A function that is not analytic at a point z_0, but that can be made analytic there merely by assigning a suitable v lue to the function at that point, is said to have a *removable singular point* at z_0.

We have now shown that, when a function f has a pole of order m at $z = z_0$, then the function

$$(4) \quad \phi(z) = (z - z_0)^m f(z)$$

has a removable singular point at z_0, and that $\phi(z_0) \neq 0$. Moreover, equation (2) is the expansion of $\phi(z)$ in Taylor's series about the point z_0, so that

$$(5) \quad b_1 = \frac{\phi^{(m-1)}(z_0)}{(m - 1)!}.$$

When $m = 1$, this formula for the residue of f at z_0 can be written, according to equation (3), as

$$(6) \quad b_1 = \phi(z_0) = \lim_{z \to z_0} (z - z_0)f(z).$$

Conversely, suppose f is a function such that the product

$$(z - z_0)^m f(z)$$

can be so defined at z_0 that it is analytic there.   As before, m is a positive integer.   Let $\phi(z)$ denote that product.   Then in some neighborhood of z_0,

$$\phi(z) = (z - z_0)^m f(z) = \phi(z_0) + \phi'(z_0)(z - z_0) + \cdots$$
$$+ \frac{\phi^{(m)}(z_0)}{m!}(z - z_0)^m + \cdots .$$

Therefore at each point except z_0 in the neighborhood it is true that

$$f(z) = \frac{\phi(z_0)}{(z - z_0)^m} + \frac{\phi'(z_0)}{(z - z_0)^{m-1}} + \cdots + \frac{\phi^{(m-1)}(z_0)}{(m-1)!}\frac{1}{z - z_0}$$
$$+ \sum_{n=m}^{\infty} \frac{\phi^{(n)}(z_0)}{n!}(z - z_0)^{n-m},$$

and if $\phi(z_0) \neq 0$, it follows that f has a pole of order m at z_0 with the residue given by equation (5) there.   We state this test for poles as follows.

Theorem.   *Let a function f satisfy these conditions: for some positive integer m a value $\phi(z_0)$ exists, where $\phi(z_0) \neq 0$, such that the function*

$$\phi(z) = (z - z_0)^m f(z)$$

is analytic at z_0.   Then f has a pole of order m at z_0.   Its residue there is given by formula (5) if $m > 1$ and by formula (6) if $m = 1$.

Note that the conditions in the theorem are satisfied whenever f has the form

$$f(z) = \frac{\phi(z)}{(z - z_0)^m} \qquad (m = 1, 2, \ldots),$$

where the function ϕ is analytic at z_0 and $\phi(z_0) \neq 0$.   The residue of the function $\exp(-2z)/z^3$, for instance, at its pole $z = 0$ of order 3 is $(-2)^2/2!$, or 2.

69. Quotients of Analytic Functions.   The basic method for computing the residue of a function at an isolated singular point z_0 is that of finding the coefficient of $(z - z_0)^{-1}$ in the Laurent series that represents the function at all points arbitrarily near z_0.   In case z_0 is an essential singular point we offer no other method.   But for residues at poles, formulas (5) and (6) of the preceding section may be used to advantage when the function ϕ is simple enough.

An alternate method of finding the residue of a function f at a pole z_0 is available when f has the fractional form

$$(1) \qquad f(z) = \frac{p(z)}{q(z)},$$

where *p and q are both analytic at z_0 and $p(z_0) \neq 0$.* We first note that z_0 is a singular point of f when and only when $q(z_0) = 0$. For if $q(z_0) \neq 0$, then there is a neighborhood of z_0 throughout which $q(z) \neq 0$ (Sec. 65). Thus there is some neighborhood of z_0 throughout which p and q are analytic and $q(z) \neq 0$; therefore f is analytic at z_0. On the other hand, if $q(z_0) = 0$, then $q(z) \neq 0$ at any other point in a sufficiently small neighborhood of z_0, and it follows that z_0 is an isolated singular point of f.

When p and q satisfy the conditions $q(z_0) = 0$, $q'(z_0) \neq 0$, and $p(z_0) \neq 0$, the function f has a simple pole at z_0 and the residue of f has the value

$$(2) \qquad b_1 = \frac{p(z_0)}{q'(z_0)}.$$

To prove this statement, we represent the analytic functions p and q of equation (1) by Taylor's series in a neighborhood $|z - z_0| < r_1$ to write

$$(3) \quad (z - z_0)f(z) = \frac{p(z_0) + p'(z_0)(z - z_0) + \cdots}{q'(z_0) + q''(z_0)(z - z_0)/2! + \cdots}$$
$$(0 < |z - z_0| < r_1).$$

The quotient of series here represents a function ϕ that is analytic at z_0, and since $\phi(z_0) = p(z_0)/q'(z_0) \neq 0$, the theorem in the preceding section applies to complete the proof.

In like manner we can see that, *if $p(z_0) \neq 0$ and*

$$q(z_0) = q'(z_0) = \cdots = q^{(m-1)}(z_0) = 0,$$

but $q^{(m)}(z_0) \neq 0$, then the function f has a pole of order m at z_0. When $m = 2$, the residue of f at the pole z_0 of second order is given by the formula

$$(4) \qquad b_1 = 2\frac{p'(z_0)}{q''(z_0)} - \frac{2}{3}\frac{p(z_0)q'''(z_0)}{[q''(z_0)]^2},$$

as we can see by computing $\phi'(z_0)$, where

$$\phi(z) = \frac{p(z_0) + p'(z_0)(z - z_0) + \cdots}{q''(z_0)/2! + q'''(z_0)(z - z_0)/3! + \cdots} \qquad (|z - z_0| < r_1).$$

But when $m > 2$, the corresponding formulas for the residue are lengthy.

To illustrate an application of formula (2), consider the function

$$\cot z = \frac{\cos z}{\sin z}$$

which has the singular points $z = \pm n\pi$ $(n = 1, 2, \ldots)$ and $z = 0$. The derivative of the denominator, $q'(z) = \cos z$, does not vanish at any of those points. Since the numerator p and the denominator q here are entire functions and p does not vanish at those points, the singular points are all simple poles, and the residue of $\cot z$ at each of the poles $z_0 = 0$, $\pm n\pi$ is unity, since

$$b_1 = \frac{p(z_0)}{q'(z_0)} = \frac{\cos z_0}{\cos z_0} = 1.$$

As another example, we compute the residue of the function

$$f(z) = \frac{1}{z(e^z - 1)}$$

at the origin. Here $p(z) = 1$, $q(z) = z(e^z - 1)$, $q(0) = q'(0) = 0$, $q''(0) = 2$, and $q'''(0) = 3$. Thus the origin is a pole of the second order and, according to formula (4), the residue of f there is $-\frac{1}{2}$.

EXERCISES

1. If a function h is analytic at a point z_0 and $h(z_0) \neq 0$, show that z_0 is a simple pole of the function

$$f(z) = \frac{h(z)}{z - z_0}$$

and that $h(z_0)$ is the residue of f at that pole. Give examples.

2. If $h(z_0) = 0$ in Exercise 1, prove that z_0 is a removable singular point of f.

3. Show that all singular points of each of the following functions are poles. Determine the order m of each pole and the residue K of the function at the pole.

(a) $\dfrac{z + 1}{z^2 - 2z}$; (b) $\tanh z$; (c) $\dfrac{1 - \exp(2z)}{z^4}$;

(d) $\dfrac{\exp(2z)}{(z - 1)^2}$; (e) $\dfrac{z}{\cos z}$; (f) $\dfrac{\exp z}{z^2 + \pi^2}$.

Ans. (a) $m = 1$, $K = -\frac{1}{2}, \frac{3}{2}$; (b) $m = 1$, $K = 1$; (c) $m = 3$, $K = -\frac{4}{3}$.

4. Find the residue at $z = 0$ of the function

(a) $\csc^2 z$;   (b) $z^{-3} \csc (z^2)$;   (c) $z \cos \dfrac{1}{z}$.   *Ans.* (a) 0; (b) $\frac{1}{6}$; (c) $-\frac{1}{2}$.

5. Find the value of the contour integral

$$\int_C \frac{3z^3 + 2}{(z - 1)(z^2 + 9)} \, dz$$

taken counterclockwise around the circle (a) $|z - 2| = 2$; (b) $|z| = 4$.
Ans. (a) πi; (b) $6\pi i$.

6. Find the value of the integral

$$\int_C \frac{dz}{z^3(z + 4)}$$

taken counterclockwise around the circle (a) $|z| = 2$; (b) $|z + 2| = 3$.
Ans. (a) $\pi i/32$; (b) 0.

7. If C is the circle $|z| = 2$ described in the positive sense, evaluate the integral

(a) $\displaystyle\int_C \tan z \, dz$;   (b) $\displaystyle\int_C \frac{dz}{\sinh 2z}$;   (c) $\displaystyle\int_C \frac{\cosh \pi z \, dz}{z(z^2 + 1)}$.
Ans. (a) $-4\pi i$; (b) $-\pi i$.

8. Evaluate the integral of f in the positive sense around the unit circle about the origin, when $f(z)$ is

(a) $z^{-2}e^{-z}$;   (b) $z^{-1} \csc z$;   (c) $z^{-2} \csc z$;   (d) $z \exp \dfrac{1}{z}$.
Ans. (a) $-2\pi i$; (b) 0; (d) πi.

9. If a function f is analytic at z_0 and if z_0 is a zero of order m of f, prove that the function $1/f$ has a pole of order m at z_0.

10. Let a function f be analytic throughout a domain D and let z_0 be the only zero of f in D. If C is a closed contour in D that encloses z_0, where C is described in the positive sense, prove that

$$\frac{1}{2\pi i} \int_C \frac{f'(z)}{f(z)} \, dz = m,$$

where the positive integer m is the order of that zero. The quotient f'/f is known as the *logarithmic derivative* of f; it is the derivative of $\log f$.

70. Evaluation of Improper Real Integrals.   One of the important applications of the theory of residues consists in the evaluation of certain types of real definite integrals. These integrals often arise in physical problems, especially in the solution of boundary value problems in partial differential equations.

Sometimes they appear as integrals in the complex plane, even though they are reducible to real definite integrals.[1] The examples treated here and in the following sections illustrate some useful methods.

Real integrals of the type

(1)
$$\int_{-\infty}^{\infty} \frac{p(x)}{q(x)}\, dx,$$

where p and q are polynomials with no factors in common, can be evaluated quite easily by using the theory of residues if the zeros of q can be found. We assume that q has no real zeros; for if $q(x)$ contains a factor $(x - x_0)^k$, where $k = 1, 2, \ldots$, then at the point $x = x_0$ the integrand is infinite and of such an order that the improper integral

$$\int_{a}^{x_0} \frac{p(x)}{q(x)}\, dx,$$

where a is any real constant, does not converge.

The value of the integral (1) exists when and only when the degree of q is at least two greater than the degree of p, and q has no real zeros. The method of partial fractions, which can also be used to evaluate integrals of this type, is closely related to the method of residues.

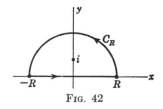

Fig. 42

As our first example, let us use residues to find the value of the elementary integral

(2)
$$I = \int_{0}^{\infty} \frac{dx}{x^2 + 1} = \frac{1}{2} \int_{-\infty}^{\infty} \frac{dx}{x^2 + 1}.$$

The second integral represents an integration, along the entire length of the real axis, of the function

(3)
$$f(z) = \frac{1}{z^2 + 1} = \frac{1}{z + i}\frac{1}{z - i},$$

a function with simple poles at the points $z = i$ and $z = -i$.

Let C_R denote the upper half of a circle $|z| = R$, where $R > 1$ (Fig. 42). Integrating f counterclockwise around the boundary

---

[1] See, for instance, chaps. 6–8 of the author's book "Operational Mathematics," 2d ed., 1958.

of the semicircular region, we have

$$\int_{-R}^{R} f(x)\,dx + \int_{C_R} f(z)\,dz = 2\pi i K_1,$$

where K_1 is the residue of f at the pole $z = i$. From the expression (3) for $f(z)$ we see that

$$K_1 = \frac{1}{z+i}\bigg]_{z=i} = \frac{1}{2i}.$$

Therefore, when $R > 1$,

(4) $$\int_{-R}^{R} \frac{dx}{x^2+1} = \pi - \int_{C_R} \frac{dz}{z^2+1}.$$

Now $|z| = R$ when z is on C_R, and

$$|z^2 + 1| \geqq |z^2| - 1 = R^2 - 1.$$

Consequently,

$$\left| \int_{C_R} \frac{dz}{z^2+1} \right| \leqq \int_{C_R} \frac{|dz|}{R^2-1} = \frac{\pi R}{R^2-1},$$

and this quantity approaches zero as R tends to infinity. It follows from equation (4) that

(5) $$\lim_{R\to\infty} \int_{-R}^{R} \frac{dx}{x^2+1} = \pi;$$

therefore,

(6) $$I = \frac{1}{2} \int_{-\infty}^{\infty} \frac{dx}{x^2+1} = \frac{\pi}{2}.$$

The limit (5) is called the *Cauchy principal value* of the integral in equation (6). In general,

(7) $$\lim_{R\to\infty} \int_{-R}^{R} f(x)\,dx = \text{P.V.} \int_{-\infty}^{\infty} f(x)\,dx.$$

Whenever each of the integrals

$$\int_{-\infty}^{0} f(x)\,dx, \qquad \int_{0}^{\infty} f(x)\,dx$$

has a value, as is the case here, the principal value (7) is the same as the integral. But if $f(x) = x$, for instance, the principal value of the integral is zero, whereas the value of the integral itself does not exist.

71. Another Example. Let us find the value of the integral

(1) $$I = \int_0^\infty \frac{x^2\,dx}{(x^2+9)(x^2+4)^2} = \frac{1}{2}\int_{-\infty}^\infty \frac{x^2\,dx}{(x^2+9)(x^2+4)^2},$$

which again is of the type discussed in the foregoing section.

Following the same method as before, we note that the singular points of the function

(2) $$f(z) = \frac{z^2}{(z^2+9)(z^2+4)^2}$$

consist of simple poles at the points $z = \pm 3i$ and poles of the second order at $z = \pm 2i$. The residue K_1 at the pole $z = 3i$ has the value

$$K_1 = \frac{z^2}{(z+3i)(z^2+4)^2}\bigg]_{z=3i} = -\frac{3}{50i}.$$

To find the residue K_2 at $z = 2i$, we write

$$\phi(z) = (z-2i)^2 f(z) = \frac{z^2}{(z^2+9)(z+2i)^2}.$$

Then $K_2 = \phi'(2i)$, according to formula (5) of Sec. 68; that is,

$$K_2 = \frac{(-4+9)(2i+2i)^2(4i) - (2i)^2[5(2)(4i) + (4i)^2(4i)]}{5^2(4i)^4}$$

which reduces to

$$K_2 = -\frac{13i}{200}.$$

Let C_R again denote the upper half of the circle $|z| = R$, where $R > 3$ now. Integrating counterclockwise around the boundary of the semicircle, we have

(3) $$\int_{-R}^R f(x)\,dx + \int_{C_R} f(z)\,dz = 2\pi i(K_1 + K_2) = \frac{\pi}{100}.$$

But when z is on C_R, we see from formula (2) that

$$|f(z)| \le \frac{R^2}{(R^2-9)(R^2-4)^2}.$$

The length of C_R is πR. It follows as before that the limit, as R tends to infinity, of the second integral in equation (3) is zero.

Therefore,

$$\int_{-\infty}^{\infty} f(x)\ dx = \frac{\pi}{100},$$

or in view of equation (1), $I = \pi/200$.

72. Improper Integrals Involving Trigonometric Functions.

As an example of another type of integral that can be evaluated by means of contour integrals and residue theory, consider the integral

(1)
$$\int_0^{\infty} \frac{\cos x\ dx}{x^2 + 1} = \frac{1}{2} \int_{-\infty}^{\infty} \frac{\cos x\ dx}{x^2 + 1}.$$

Since $|\cos z|$ increases like e^y as y tends to infinity, the method used above does not apply here without some modifications.

Now $\cos x$ is the real part of $\exp (ix)$; therefore,

(2)
$$\int_0^{\infty} \frac{\cos x\ dx}{x^2 + 1} = \frac{1}{2} \mathfrak{R} \int_{-\infty}^{\infty} \frac{e^{ix}\ dx}{x^2 + 1}.$$

We write
$$f(z) = \frac{e^{iz}}{z^2 + 1}$$

and note that

(3)
$$|e^{iz}| = e^{-y} \leqq 1 \qquad\qquad \text{when } y \geqq 0.$$

The singularities of our function f are the simple poles $z = \pm i$. At $z = i$ the residue of f is

$$K_1 = \frac{e^{iz}}{z + i}\bigg]_{z=i} = \frac{1}{2ei},$$

and, therefore,

(4)
$$\int_{-R}^{R} \frac{e^{ix}\ dx}{x^2 + 1} + \int_{C_R} \frac{e^{iz}\ dz}{z^2 + 1} = 2\pi i K_1 = \frac{\pi}{e},$$

where C_R is the upper half of the circle $|z| = R$ $(R > 1)$. In view of the inequality (3), it follows as before that the second integral in equation (4) approaches zero as R tends to infinity, so that

$$\int_{-\infty}^{\infty} \frac{e^{ix}\ dx}{x^2 + 1} = \frac{\pi}{e}.$$

The real part of this integral is therefore the same as the value of the integral itself. According to equation (2), then

$$\int_0^{\infty} \frac{\cos x\ dx}{x^2 + 1} = \frac{\pi}{2e}.$$

EXERCISES

Establish the following integration formulas with the aid of residues:

1. $\displaystyle\int_0^\infty \frac{x^2\,dx}{(x^2+1)(x^2+4)} = \frac{\pi}{6}.$
  2. $\displaystyle\int_0^\infty \frac{dx}{x^4+1} = \frac{\pi\sqrt{2}}{4}.$

3. $\displaystyle\int_0^\infty \frac{x^2\,dx}{x^6+1} = \frac{\pi}{6}.$
  4. $\displaystyle\int_0^\infty \frac{dx}{(x^2+1)^2} = \frac{\pi}{4}.$

5. $\displaystyle\int_0^\infty \frac{\cos ax}{x^2+1}\,dx = \frac{\pi}{2}e^{-a} \quad (a \geqq 0).$
  6. $\displaystyle\int_0^\infty \frac{\cos x\,dx}{(x^2+1)^2} = \frac{\pi}{2e}.$

7. $\displaystyle\int_{-\infty}^\infty \frac{\cos x\,dx}{(x^2+a^2)(x^2+b^2)} = \frac{\pi}{a^2-b^2}\left(\frac{e^{-b}}{b} - \frac{e^{-a}}{a}\right) \qquad (a > b > 0).$

8. $\displaystyle\int_0^\infty \frac{\cos ax}{(x^2+b^2)^2}\,dx = \frac{\pi}{4b^3}(1+ab)e^{-ab} \qquad (a > 0,\, b > 0).$

9. $\displaystyle\int_{-\infty}^\infty \frac{x\sin ax}{x^4+4}\,dx = \frac{\pi}{2}e^{-a}\sin a \qquad (a > 0).$

Use residues to find the values of the following integrals:

10. $\displaystyle\int_{-\infty}^\infty \frac{dx}{x^2+2x+2}.$

11. $\displaystyle\int_{-\infty}^\infty \frac{x\,dx}{(x^2+1)(x^2+2x+2)}.$ *Ans.* $-\pi/5.$

12. $\displaystyle\int_0^\infty \frac{x^2\,dx}{(x^2+1)^2}.$

13. $\displaystyle\int_0^\infty \frac{x\sin x\,dx}{(x^2+1)(x^2+4)}.$

14. $\displaystyle\int_{-\infty}^\infty \frac{\sin x\,dx}{x^2+4x+5}.$ *Ans.* $-(\pi/e)\sin 2.$

15. $\displaystyle\int_{-\infty}^\infty \frac{\cos x\,dx}{(x+a)^2+b^2}.$

73. Definite Integrals of Trigonometric Functions. The method of residues is useful in the evaluation of definite integrals of the type

(1) $$\int_0^{2\pi} F(\sin\theta, \cos\theta)\,d\theta,$$

where F is a quotient of polynomials in $\sin\theta$ and $\cos\theta$. If we consider θ as the argument of z on the unit circle $z = e^{i\theta}$, then we can write

(2) $\sin\theta = \dfrac{z - z^{-1}}{2i}, \quad \cos\theta = \dfrac{z + z^{-1}}{2}, \quad dz = ie^{i\theta}\,d\theta = iz\,d\theta,$

and the integral (1) then represents the contour integral of a rational function of z around the unit circle. The contour integral can be evaluated by the residue theorem if we can find the zeros of the polynomial in the denominator.

As an example, we compute the value of the integral

$$I = \int_0^{2\pi} \frac{d\theta}{\frac{5}{4} + \sin \theta}.$$

Note that the denominator of the integrand is never zero. In terms of points z on the unit circle, we can write, according to equations (2),

$$\frac{5}{4} + \sin \theta = \frac{5}{4} + \frac{z - 1/z}{2i} = \frac{1}{4iz}(2z^2 + 5iz - 2)$$

and $$I = \int_C \frac{4\,dz}{2z^2 + 5iz - 2} = \int_C \frac{2\,dz}{(z + 2i)(z + \frac{1}{2}i)},$$

where C is the circle $|z| = 1$ (Fig. 43). The only singular point of the integrand that is interior to C is the simple pole $z = -\frac{1}{2}i$, and the residue of the integrand there is $2/(-\frac{1}{2}i + 2i)$, or $4/3i$. Therefore

$$I = 2\pi i \frac{4}{3i} = \frac{8}{3}\pi.$$

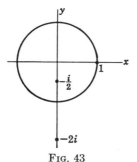

FIG. 43

74. Integration around a Branch Point.
We now illustrate a method of evaluating a real integral when the singularities of the integrand of the contour integral include a branch point and a branch cut.

Let x^{-k}, where $0 < k < 1$ and $x > 0$, denote the principal value of that power of x, namely, the positive real number $\exp(-k \operatorname{Log} x)$. We shall evaluate the improper real integral

(1) $$\int_0^\infty \frac{x^{-k}}{x + 1}\,dx \qquad (0 < k < 1),$$

which represents the beta function with arguments k and $1 - k$ (Exercise 9). The integral exists when $0 < k < 1$, because the integrand behaves like x^{-k} near $x = 0$ and like x^{-k-1} as x tends to infinity.

Let z^{-k} denote this branch of the power function:

(2) $$z^{-k} = \exp(-k \log z) = \exp[-k(\operatorname{Log} r + i\theta)]$$
$$(0 < \theta < 2\pi, r > 0),$$

where $z = r \exp (i\theta)$.   Then, in terms of the principal value r^{-k},

(3) $z^{-k} = r^{-k} \exp (-ik\theta)$ $(0 < \theta < 2\pi, r > 0)$,

and when $\theta = 0$ here, $z^{-k} = r^{-k} = x^{-k}$.   The function

$$f(z) = \frac{z^{-k}}{z + 1}$$

is analytic everywhere except at the simple pole $z = -1$ and the branch point $z = 0$ and branch cut $\theta = 0$.   When $\theta = 0$, $f(z)$ becomes the integrand of the integral (1).   The residue of f at

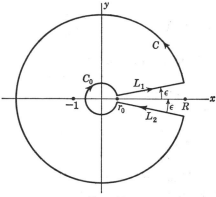

FIG. 44

$z = -1$ is the value of z^{-k} at that point, namely, $\exp (-ik\pi)$. Thus the integral of f around the closed contour shown in Fig. 44, consisting of circular arcs C and C_0 of radius R and r_0, respectively, and segments L_1 and L_2 of the rays $\theta = \epsilon$ and $\theta = 2\pi - \epsilon$, can be written

(4) $\int_{L_1} f(z) \, dz + \int_C f(z) \, dz + \int_{L_2} f(z) \, dz + \int_{C_0} f(z) \, dz$
$$= 2\pi i \exp (-ik\pi)$$

when $R > 1$, $r_0 < 1$, and ϵ is a small positive constant.

On the segment L_1, $z = r \exp (i\epsilon)$ and $z^{-k} = r^{-k} \exp (-ik\epsilon)$. On L_2, $z = r \exp [i(2\pi - \epsilon)] = r \exp (-i\epsilon)$ and

$$z^{-k} = r^{-k} \exp [-ik(2\pi - \epsilon)].$$

The sum of the integrals of f over L_1 and L_2 is therefore this combination of definite integrals with respect to the variable r:

$$\exp (i\epsilon - ik\epsilon) \int_{r_0}^{R} \frac{r^{-k} \, dr}{re^{i\epsilon} + 1} + \exp [-i\epsilon - ik(2\pi - \epsilon)] \int_{R}^{r_0} \frac{r^{-k} \, dr}{re^{-i\epsilon} + 1}.$$

The integrands here are continuous functions of r and ϵ in the closed region $r_0 \leq r \leq R$, $0 \leq \epsilon \leq \pi/2$; hence the integrals, as well as their coefficients, are continuous functions of ϵ at $\epsilon = 0$, and

$$(5) \quad \lim_{\epsilon \to 0} \left(\int_{L_1} f\, dz + \int_{L_2} f\, dz \right) = [1 - \exp\,(-2ik\pi)] \int_{r_0}^{R} \frac{r^{-k}\, dr}{r + 1}$$

$$= 2i \exp\,(-ik\pi) \sin k\pi \int_{r_0}^{R} \frac{x^{-k}\, dx}{x + 1}.$$

The integral of f over C, where $z = R \exp\,(i\theta)$, can be written

$$(6) \quad \int_{C} f(z)\, dz = iR \int_{\epsilon}^{2\pi - \epsilon} \frac{R^{-k} \exp\,(-ik\theta)}{Re^{i\theta} + 1} e^{i\theta}\, d\theta \qquad (R > 1).$$

The integrand of the definite integral here is a continuous function of θ on the interval $0 \leq \theta \leq 2\pi$. Therefore the integral has a limit, as $\epsilon \to 0$, which is simply the integral from zero to 2π. Similarly, the limit of the integral

$$(7) \quad \int_{C_0} f(z)\, dz = ir_0 \int_{2\pi - \epsilon}^{\epsilon} \frac{r_0^{-k} \exp\,(-ik\theta)}{r_0 e^{i\theta} + 1} e^{i\theta}\, d\theta \qquad (0 < r_0 < 1),$$

as $\epsilon \to 0$, exists. Thus the limit, as ϵ tends to zero, of the left-hand member of equation (4) exists, and since the right-hand member is independent of ϵ, it follows from equations (5), (6), and (7) that

$$(8) \quad 2i \exp\,(-ik\pi) \sin k\pi \int_{r_0}^{R} \frac{x^{-k}\, dx}{x + 1} + I + I_0 = 2\pi i \exp\,(-ik\pi),$$

where

$$(9) \quad \begin{aligned} I &= iR^{1-k} \int_{0}^{2\pi} \frac{\exp\,(i\theta - ik\theta)}{Re^{i\theta} + 1}\, d\theta, \\ I_0 &= -ir_0^{1-k} \int_{0}^{2\pi} \frac{\exp\,(i\theta - ik\theta)}{r_0 e^{i\theta} + 1}\, d\theta. \end{aligned}$$

Now $I \to 0$ as $R \to \infty$, and $I_0 \to 0$ as $r_0 \to 0$, because

$$|I| \leq \frac{2\pi R}{R - 1} R^{-k} \qquad \text{and} \qquad |I_0| \leq \frac{2\pi}{1 - r_0} r_0^{1-k}$$

and $1 - k > 0$. Also, the limit of the first integral in equation (8) as $R \to \infty$ and $r_0 \to 0$ is the integral (1), while the member on the right of equation (8) is independent of R and r_0. We take successive limits in that equation as $R \to \infty$ and $r_0 \to 0$ to get the integration formula

(10)
$$\int_0^\infty \frac{x^{-k}}{x+1}\, dx = \frac{\pi}{\sin k\pi} \qquad (0 < k < 1).$$

EXERCISES

Use residues to establish the following integration formulas.

1. (a) $\displaystyle\int_{-\pi}^{\pi} \frac{\cos\theta\, d\theta}{5 + 4\cos\theta} = -\frac{\pi}{3}$;   (b) $\displaystyle\int_{-\pi}^{\pi} \frac{d\theta}{1 + \sin^2\theta} = \pi\sqrt{2}.$

2. (a) $\displaystyle\int_0^{2\pi} \frac{d\theta}{1 + k\cos\theta} = \frac{2\pi}{\sqrt{1 - k^2}}$ $\qquad (k^2 < 1);$

 (b) $\displaystyle\int_0^{2\pi} \frac{d\theta}{1 + k\sin\theta} = \frac{2\pi}{\sqrt{1 - k^2}}$ $\qquad (k^2 < 1).$

3. $\displaystyle\int_0^{\pi} \frac{\cos 2\theta\, d\theta}{1 + k^2 - 2k\cos\theta} = \frac{\pi k^2}{1 - k^2}$ $\qquad (k^2 < 1).$

4. $\displaystyle\int_0^{\pi} \frac{d\theta}{(a + \cos\theta)^2} = \pi a(a^2 - 1)^{-\frac{3}{2}}$ $\qquad (a > 1).$

5. $\displaystyle\int_0^{2\pi} \frac{\cos^2 3\theta\, d\theta}{5 - 4\cos 2\theta} = \frac{3}{8}\pi.$

6. $\displaystyle\int_0^{\pi} \sin^{2n}\theta\, d\theta = \pi \frac{(2n)!}{(2^n n!)^2}$ $\qquad (n = 1, 2, \ldots).$

7. Given that $\displaystyle\int_0^\infty \exp(-x^2)\, dx = \frac{1}{2}\sqrt{\pi}$, integrate $\exp(-z^2)$ around the boundary of the rectangle $-a \leq x \leq a$, $0 \leq y \leq b$, and let a tend to infinity to prove that

$$\int_0^\infty \exp(-x^2)\cos(2bx)\, dx = \frac{1}{2}\sqrt{\pi}\exp(-b^2).$$

8. Derive the formula

$$\int_{-\infty}^\infty \frac{e^{kx}\, dx}{1 + e^x} = \frac{\pi}{\sin k\pi} \qquad (0 < k < 1)$$

by using a contour integral around the rectangular path along the lines $y = 0$, $x = \pm a$, and $y = 2\pi$ (Fig. 45) and letting a tend to infinity.

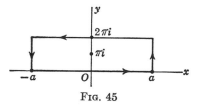

FIG. 45

9. The *beta function* is this function of two real variables:

$$B(r,s) = \int_0^1 t^{r-1}(1 - t)^{s-1}\, dt \qquad (r > 0, s > 0).$$

Make the substitution $t = (x + 1)^{-1}$ to show that the integral evaluated in Sec. 74 is $B(k, 1 - k)$; thus

$$B(k, 1 - k) = \frac{\pi}{\sin k\pi} \qquad (0 < k < 1).$$

10. With the aid of the closed contour shown in Fig. 44, prove that

$$\int_0^\infty \frac{x^k}{(x^2 + 1)^2}\, dx = \frac{\pi}{4} \frac{1 - k}{\cos (\frac{1}{2}k\pi)} \quad [-1 < k < 3, x^k = \exp (k \operatorname{Log} x)].$$

11. Given that $\int_0^\infty \exp (-x^2)\, dx = \frac{1}{2}\sqrt{\pi}$, integrate $\exp (-z^2)$ around the boundary of the circular sector $0 \leqq \theta \leqq \pi/4, 0 \leqq r \leqq R$, and let R tend to infinity to prove that

$$\int_0^\infty \cos (x^2)\, dx = \int_0^\infty \sin (x^2)\, dx = \frac{1}{4}\sqrt{2\pi}.$$

Note: To show that the integral over the circular arc tends to zero, show that its absolute value is less than I, where

$$I = R \int_0^{\pi/4} \exp (-R^2 \cos 2\theta)\, d\theta,$$

and then that

$$I = \frac{R}{2} \int_0^{\pi/2} \exp (-R^2 \sin \phi)\, d\phi < \frac{R}{2} \int_0^{\pi/2} \exp \left(-\frac{2R^2}{\pi} \phi\right) d\phi;$$

for it is clear from the graph of the sine function that $\sin \phi \geqq 2\phi/\pi$ when $0 \leqq \phi \leqq \pi/2$. Carry out the integration in the last member of the inequality for I to show that this member approaches zero as R tends to infinity.

12. Show that

$$\int_0^\infty \frac{\sin x}{x}\, dx = \frac{\pi}{2}$$

by integrating the function $z^{-1}e^{iz}$ around the indented contour shown in Fig. 46, consisting of the semicircles C_0 and C, with radii r_0 and R, and the segments L_1 and L_2 of the x axis, and then letting r_0 tend to zero and R tend to infinity. (See the note in Exercise 11 for a method of showing that the integral over C tends to zero as R tends to infinity.) Use the integration formula derived here to show that the function

$$S(k) = \frac{2}{\pi} \int_0^\infty \frac{\sin kt}{t}\, dt$$

is this step function: $S(k) = 1$ when $k > 0$, $S(k) = -1$ when $k < 0$, $S(0) = 0$.

13. Derive the formulas

$$(a) \int_0^\infty \frac{\text{Log } x}{x^2 + 1}\, dx = 0; \quad (b) \int_0^\infty \frac{\text{Log } x}{(x^2 + 1)^2}\, dx = -\frac{\pi}{4}.$$

Note: The closed contour shown in Fig. 46 can be used here, together with the results found in Sec. 70 and Exercise 4, Sec. 72.

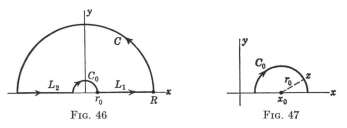

FIG. 46   FIG. 47

14. Let a point $z = x_0$ on the x axis be a simple pole of a function f, and let K_0 be the residue of f at that pole. Show that, for some positive number r_1, f has the form

$$f(z) = \frac{K_0}{z - x_0} + g(z) \qquad (0 < |z - x_0| < r_1),$$

where g is analytic throughout the neighborhood $|z - x_0| < r_1$. If C_0 is the upper half of the circle $|z - x_0| = r_0$ (Fig. 47) described in the clockwise sense, where $r_0 < r_1$, prove that

$$\lim_{r_0 \to 0} \int_{C_0} f(z)\, dz = -iK_0\pi.$$

15. Derive the integration formula

$$\int_0^\infty \frac{\sin^2 x}{x^2}\, dx = \frac{\pi}{2}.$$

Note: If we write $2 \sin^2 x = 1 - \cos 2x = \Re(1 - e^{2xi})$, the closed contour shown in Fig. 46 can be used. See Exercise 14 for the evaluation of the limit of the contour integral over C_0.

16. The integral of the function

$$h(x) = \frac{1}{x(x^2 - 4x + 5)}$$

over an interval that includes the origin does not exist. Show that the principal value of the integral of that function along the entire x axis,

$$\text{P.V.} \int_{-\infty}^\infty h(x)\, dx = \lim_{r_0 \to 0} \left[\int_{-\infty}^{-r_0} h(x)\, dx + \int_{r_0}^\infty h(x)\, dx \right] \qquad (r_0 > 0),$$

does exist by finding that value with the aid of the closed contour in Fig. 46 and the result found in Exercise 14.   *Ans.* $2\pi/5$.

CHAPTER 8

CONFORMAL MAPPING

75. Rotation of Tangents. Let us examine the change in direction of curves at a point z_0 under a transformation $w = f(z)$ when the function f is analytic at that point and $f'(z_0) \neq 0$. The image of a smooth arc in a neighborhood of z_0 is a smooth arc in the w plane because the mapping function f is analytic at z_0. The derivative

$$(1) \qquad f'(z_0) = \lim_{\Delta z \to 0} \frac{\Delta w}{\Delta z},$$

where $\Delta w = f(z_0 + \Delta z) - f(z_0)$, exists and is independent of the manner in which Δz approaches zero.

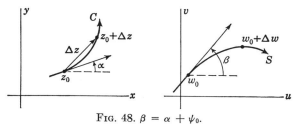

FIG. 48. $\beta = \alpha + \psi_0$.

When $f'(z_0) \neq 0$, let ψ_0 denote one of the values of the argument of the number $f'(z_0)$ and let R_0 denote $|f'(z_0)|$; thus

$$(2) \qquad f'(z_0) = R_0 \exp{(i\psi_0)} \qquad (R_0 > 0).$$

Then the two equations

$$(3) \qquad \lim_{\Delta z \to 0} \left| \frac{\Delta w}{\Delta z} \right| = R_0,$$

$$(4) \qquad \lim_{\Delta z \to 0} \left(\arg \frac{\Delta w}{\Delta z} \right) = \psi_0$$

are consequences of equation (1) (see Exercise 7, Sec. 77).

Now let C be a smooth curve through the point z_0, and let S be its image under the transformation $w = f(z)$ (Fig. 48). If a

174

positive sense of direction along C is prescribed, a corresponding positive sense along S is determined by the mapping function f. When $z_0 + \Delta z$ is a point on C in the positive sense from z_0, the limit of the argument of Δz as Δz approaches zero is the angle of inclination α of the directed tangent line to C at z_0. If $w_0 = f(z_0)$ and $w_0 + \Delta w$ is the image of $z_0 + \Delta z$, then the argument of Δw approaches the angle of inclination β of the directed tangent to S at w_0.

Since $\Delta w = \Delta z(\Delta w/\Delta z)$, a value of the argument of Δw is given by the formula

$$\arg \Delta w \ = \ \arg \Delta z \ + \ \arg \frac{\Delta w}{\Delta z}.$$

As Δz tends to zero, it follows that

(5) $\beta = \alpha + \psi_0.$

Thus the directed tangent to a curve C at z_0 is rotated through the angle

(6) $\psi_0 = \arg f'(z_0)$

by the transformation $w - f(z)$, provided f is analytic at z_0 and $f'(z_0) \neq 0$.

76. Conformal Mapping.   Since the angle ψ_0 is determined by the mapping function f and the point z_0, it is the same for all

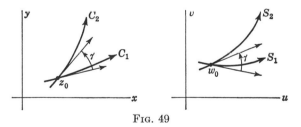

FIG. 49

curves through z_0. If α_1 and α_2 are the angles of inclination at z_0 of two directed arcs C_1 and C_2 and if β_1 and β_2 are the corresponding angles for the images S_1 and S_2 of those arcs, then

$$\beta_1 = \alpha_1 + \psi_0 \qquad \text{and} \qquad \beta_2 = \alpha_2 + \psi_0$$

and therefore $\beta_2 - \beta_1 = \alpha_2 - \alpha_1$. That is, the angle $\gamma = \beta_2 - \beta_1$ from S_1 to S_2 is the same in magnitude and sense as the angle $\alpha_2 - \alpha_1$ from C_1 to C_2 (Fig. 49).

A mapping that preserves angles in that manner between every pair of curves at each point of some domain is said to be *conformal* in the domain.   We can state our result as follows.

Theorem.   *At each point z of a domain where f is analytic and $f'(z) \neq 0$ the mapping $w = f(z)$ is conformal.*

Henceforth the terms *conformal mapping* and *conformal transformation* will be used to signify transformations by means of analytic functions with nonvanishing derivatives.

According to equation (3) of the preceding section,

$$\lim_{\Delta z \to 0} \frac{|\Delta w|}{|\Delta z|} = |f'(z_0)| = R_0.$$

Therefore the transformation magnifies the lengths of short lines by approximately the factor R_0.   The image of each small figure near the point *conforms* to the original figure in the sense that it has approximately the same shape.   The coefficient of magnification R_0, as well as the angle of rotation ψ_0, varies from point to point.   Large figures may transform into figures that bear no resemblance to the original.

A point at which $f'(z) = 0$ is called a *critical point* of the transformation.

The point $z = 0$ is a critical point of the transformation

$$w = z^2 + 1.$$

If we write $z = r \exp (i\theta)$ and $w - 1 = \rho \exp (i\phi)$, then

$$\rho \exp (i\phi) = r^2 \exp (2i\theta)$$

and it follows that each ray $\theta = c$ from the point $z = 0$ maps onto a ray $\phi = 2c$ from the point $w = 1$.   Thus the angle between any two rays drawn from that critical point is doubled by this transformation.

Taylor's series for the function f, about a critical point z_0, can be used to show that, if the first $m - 1$ derivatives of the function vanish at z_0 and $f^{(m)}(z_0) \neq 0$, then the angle at z_0 between any pair of curves is multiplied by m under the transformation $w = f(z)$.   The proof is left to the exercises.

An *isogonal* mapping preserves magnitudes of angles but not necessarily the sense.   The transformation $w = \bar{z}$, a reflection in the real axis, is isogonal but not conformal.   If this is followed by a conformal transformation, the resulting transformation $w = f(\bar{z})$ is also isogonal but not conformal.

77. Examples.   Since the elementary functions used in Chap. 4 are analytic, the mapping discussed there is conformal except at singular points and critical points.

Every conformal transformation must map orthogonal curves into orthogonal curves. In particular, if f is analytic and $f'(z) \neq 0$ at a point, the transformation

$$u + iv = f(x + iy)$$

maps the curves $u(x,y) = c_1$, $v(x,y) = c_2$ that intersect at that point into the lines $u = c_1$, $v = c_2$ in the w plane.   Since the lines

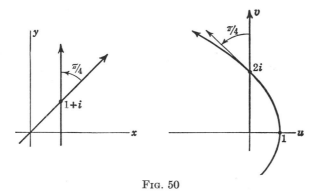

FIG. 50

are orthogonal, *the curve $u(x,y) = c_1$ is orthogonal to the curve $v(x,y) = c_2$.*

As another illustration, the transformation

$$w = z^2 = x^2 - y^2 + 2ixy$$

maps the line $y = x$ into the line $u = 0$, and the line $x = 1$ onto the parabola whose parametric equations are

$$u = 1 - y^2, \qquad v = 2y;$$

this is the parabola $v^2 = -4(u - 1)$ (Fig. 50).   If the direction of increasing y is taken as the positive sense on the two lines in the z plane, the angle from the first to the second is $\pi/4$.   When $y > 0$ and y increases along the line $y = x$, v increases along the line $u = 0$, since $v = 2y^2$, and so the positive sense of the first image is upward.   This is also true for the parabola, as we see from the second parametric equation $v = 2y$. It is readily verified that the angle from the first image to the second at the point $w = 2i$, which is the image of the point $z = 1 + i$, is $\pi/4$ as required by the conformality of the mapping.

The argument of the derivative of the function $w = z^2$ at the point $z = 1 + i$ is

$$\psi_0 = \arg 2z = \arg (2 + 2i) = \frac{\pi}{4}.$$

This is the angle through which the tangent to each curve at that point is turned by the transformation. The coefficient of magnification $|f'(z_0)|$ of distances at that point is $2\sqrt{2}$.

EXERCISES

1. Show that the transformation $w = z^2$ changes directions of curves at the point $z = 2 + i$ by the angle $\arctan \frac{1}{2}$. Illustrate this by using some particular curve. Show that the coefficient of magnification of distances at that point is $2\sqrt{5}$.

2. Show that the transformation $w = z^n$ changes directions at the point $z = r_0 \exp (i\theta_0)$ by the angle $(n - 1)\theta_0$, when $r_0 > 0$ and $n > 0$. What is the coefficient of magnification of distances at the point?

Ans. nr_0^{n-1}.

3. What change of directions is produced by the transformation $w = 1/z$ (a) at the point $z = 1$; (b) at the point $z = i$?

Ans. (a) A change in sense only; (b) none.

4. Under the transformation $w = 1/z$, show that the images of the lines $y = x - 1$ and $y = 0$ are the circle $u^2 + v^2 - u - v = 0$ and the line $v = 0$. Show those curves graphically, determine corresponding directions along them, and verify the conformality of the mapping at the point $z = 1$.

5. Show why the transformation $w = \exp z$ is everywhere conformal. Note that the mapping of directed line segments shown in Figs. 7 and 8 of Appendix 2 agrees with that conclusion.

6. Show that the transformation $w = \sin z$ is conformal at all points except $z = \pm\pi/2$, $z = \pm 3\pi/2$, ... Note that the mapping of directed line segments shown in Figs. 9, 10, and 11 of Appendix 2 agrees with that conclusion.

7. For a function g of Δz and a number $g_0 = R_0 \exp (i\psi_0)$, assume that

$$\lim_{\Delta z \to 0} g(\Delta z) = R_0 \exp (i\psi_0) \qquad (R_0 > 0).$$

Then to each positive number ϵ, where $\epsilon < R_0$, there corresponds a number δ such that the point $g(\Delta z)$ lies in a neighborhood of g_0 of radius ϵ whenever $|\Delta z| < \delta$. Draw a figure that shows such a neighborhood and the angle $\Delta\psi = \arg [g(\Delta z)] - \psi_0$, where $\psi_0 - \pi < \arg [g(\Delta z)] < \psi_0 + \pi$. Show that $|\sin \Delta\psi| < \epsilon/R_0$ when $|\Delta z| < \delta$ and hence that

$$\lim_{\Delta z \to 0} \arg [g(\Delta z)] = \psi_0;$$

thus justify formula (4), Sec. 75. Also justify formula (3), Sec. 75.

8. If a function f is analytic at a point z_0 and

$$f(z_0) = w_0, \qquad f'(z_0) = f''(z_0) = \cdots = f^{(m-1)}(z_0) = 0,$$

while $f^{(m)}(z_0) \neq 0$, use Taylor's series to show that for some number r_1 the increment $\Delta w = f(z_0 + \Delta z) - f(z_0)$ has the form

$$\Delta w = \frac{1}{m!} f^{(m)}(z_0)(\Delta z)^m [1 + \Delta z\, h(\Delta z)] \qquad (|\Delta z| < r_1),$$

where h is continuous at $\Delta z = 0$. Under the transformation $w = f(z)$ of arc C into arc S shown in Fig. 48, show that the angles of inclination now satisfy the relation

$$\beta = m\alpha + \arg [f^{(m)}(z_0)]$$

and, if δ now denotes the angle from S_1 to S_2 in Fig. 49, that $\delta = m\gamma$. Thus the transformation is not conformal at z_0.

78. Conjugate Harmonic Functions. We noted in Sec. 20 that the real and imaginary coefficients of every analytic function of a complex variable z are harmonic functions of x and y. That is, they satisfy Laplace's partial differential equation

$$(1) \qquad \frac{\partial^2 u}{\partial x^2} + \frac{\partial^2 u}{\partial y^2} = 0,$$

and their partial derivatives up to the second order are continuous functions of x and y.

The functions u and v are conjugate harmonic functions when $u + iv$ is an analytic function of z. Then, in view of the Cauchy-Riemann conditions, the differential of v can be written

$$(2) \qquad dv = \frac{\partial v}{\partial x}\, dx + \frac{\partial v}{\partial y}\, dy = -\frac{\partial u}{\partial y}\, dx + \frac{\partial u}{\partial x}\, dy.$$

Now suppose that u is a given harmonic function in some simply connected domain D. We can show that its harmonic conjugate v exists, and we can write an explicit formula for $v(x,y)$.

The last member of equation (2) is an exact differential if

$$\frac{\partial}{\partial y}\left(-\frac{\partial u}{\partial y}\right) = \frac{\partial}{\partial x}\left(\frac{\partial u}{\partial x}\right);$$

this condition is true because the function u satisfies Laplace's equation (1). It follows that the value of the line integral

$$\int_{(x_0,y_0)}^{(x,y)} \left[-\frac{\partial u(x',y')}{\partial y'}\,dx' + \frac{\partial u(x',y')}{\partial x'}\,dy'\right]$$

is independent of the path between the limits as long as the path is a contour interior to D. When the point (x_0,y_0) is kept fixed, the integral represents a single-valued function of x and y; its value is changed by an additive constant when the fixed point (x_0,y_0) is changed.

We now show that the formula

$$(3) \quad v(x,y) = \int_{(x_0,y_0)}^{(x,y)} \left[-\frac{\partial u(x',y')}{\partial y'}\,dx' + \frac{\partial u(x',y')}{\partial x'}\,dy'\right] + c,$$

where c is any real constant, represents a harmonic conjugate of u. According to formulas in advanced calculus for the derivatives of line integrals,

$$(4) \qquad \frac{\partial v}{\partial x} = -\frac{\partial u}{\partial y} \quad \text{and} \quad \frac{\partial v}{\partial y} = \frac{\partial u}{\partial x}.$$

These are the Cauchy-Riemann conditions. Since the partial derivatives of u through the second order are continuous, it is evident from equations (4) that those derivatives of v are also continuous. It follows (Sec. 18) that

$$u(x,y) + iv(x,y)$$

is an analytic function f of z in D. Since $if(z) = -v + iu$, both v and $-v$, where v is given by formula (3), are harmonic conjugates of the given function u.

The function $u = xy$, for example, is harmonic everywhere. According to formula (3),

$$v = \int_{(0,0)}^{(x,y)} (-x'\,dx' + y'\,dy') + c.$$

The integration here may be carried out by inspection; also it is easily done by first integrating along the line $y' = 0$ from the origin to the point $(x,0)$ and then along the line $x' = x$ to the point (x,y).   The result is

$$v = -\tfrac{1}{2}x^2 + \tfrac{1}{2}y^2 + c;$$

this function, as well as $-v$, is a harmonic conjugate of xy.   Here the analytic function is f or if, where

$$f(z) = xy + \tfrac{1}{2}(y^2 - x^2)i + ic = -\tfrac{1}{2}iz^2 + ic.$$

79. Inverse Functions.   In earlier chapters we showed that the inverses of several of the elementary functions are analytic.   The inverse of the function $w = \exp z$, for example, is the function

$$z = \log w = \text{Log } \rho + i\phi,$$

and the range of ϕ can be prescribed so as to make this function single-valued and analytic in any simply connected domain that does not include the point $w = 0$.   Moreover,

$$\frac{dz}{dw} = \frac{1}{w} = \frac{1}{e^z} = \frac{1}{dw/dz}.$$

At this time it is convenient to note the corresponding general properties of inverses of analytic functions.

Theorem.   *Let a function f be analytic at a point $z = z_0$ where $f'(z_0) \neq 0$; also let w_0 denote the number $f(z_0)$.   Then there exists a neighborhood of the point w_0 in the w plane in which the function*

$$(1) \hspace{3cm} w = f(z)$$

has a unique inverse

$$(2) \hspace{3cm} z = F(w),$$

in the sense that the function F is single-valued and analytic there and $F(w_0) = z_0$ and that $w = f[F(w)]$; moreover,

$$(3) \hspace{3cm} F'(w) = \frac{1}{f'(z)}.$$

Equation (1) can be written in the form

$$(4) \hspace{2.5cm} u = u(x,y), \hspace{1cm} v = v(x,y).$$

Since w is analytic at the point $z_0 = x_0 + iy_0$, it is analytic in some neighborhood of that point.   The functions u and v and their partial derivatives are continuous in the neighborhood.

In addition to the continuity of the functions u and v and their derivatives, the further condition under which the simultaneous equations (4) have unique solutions for x and y as continuous functions of u and v is that the Jacobian of the functions u and v,

$$\begin{vmatrix} \dfrac{\partial u}{\partial x} & \dfrac{\partial u}{\partial y} \\[2mm] \dfrac{\partial v}{\partial x} & \dfrac{\partial v}{\partial y} \end{vmatrix},$$

be different from zero at the point (x_0, y_0).[1] In view of the Cauchy-Riemann conditions, the value of this determinant can be written

$$\left(\frac{\partial u}{\partial x}\right)^2 + \left(\frac{\partial v}{\partial x}\right)^2 = |f'(z)|^2,$$

and by hypothesis this is not equal to zero at the point z_0. In fact, since f' is analytic at z_0 and $f'(z_0) \neq 0$, there is a neighborhood of the point z_0 that contains no zeros of f' (Sec. 65). Thus it is established that one and only one pair of continuous functions $x(u,v)$, $y(u,v)$ exists in a neighborhood of the point $w_0 = u_0 + iv_0$ such that the functions

(5) $$x = x(u,v), \qquad y = y(u,v)$$

satisfy equations (4) and such that

$$x_0 = x(u_0,v_0), \qquad y_0 = y(u_0,v_0).$$

Equations (5) can be written in the complex form

$$z = F(w),$$

where F is a continuous function. To show that its derivative exists, we write

(6) $$\frac{\Delta z}{\Delta w} = \frac{1}{\Delta w/\Delta z}.$$

Since w is an analytic function of z, it is continuous, and since z is a continuous function of w, it follows that whenever Δw approaches zero, Δz approaches zero, and conversely. Now dw/dz exists and is different from zero; hence it follows from

[1] See, for instance, Goursat-Hedrick, "Mathematical Analysis," vol. 1, p. 45.

equation (6) that

$$\frac{dz}{dw} = \lim_{\Delta w \to 0} \frac{\Delta z}{\Delta w} = \lim_{\Delta z \to 0} \frac{1}{\Delta w/\Delta z} = \frac{1}{dw/dz}.$$

This is the same as equation (3).

Since $F'(w)$ exists in a neighborhood of w_0, the function F is analytic there.

Formula (3) could have been used to obtain the differentiation formulas for the inverses of our elementary functions.

Let us return to the example used at the beginning of this section, using the function $w = \exp z$. If $z_0 = 0$ here, then $w_0 = \exp(0) = 1$ and $f'(0) = 1 \neq 0$. According to the theorem, there is a unique inverse corresponding to these points. Now we know that the multiple-valued function

$$z = \log w = \operatorname{Log} \rho + i(\phi + 2n\pi) \qquad (\rho > 0, -\pi < \phi < \pi)$$

is an inverse of the function $\exp z$. But if

$$F(w_0) = z_0,$$

as stated in the theorem, then $\log 1 = 0$. Since $\phi = 0$ and $\rho = 1$ when $w = 1$, it follows that $n = 0$ in the above formula for $\log w$. Thus the unique inverse prescribed here is the function

$$F(w) = \operatorname{Log} \rho + i\phi \qquad (\rho > 0, -\pi < \phi < \pi).$$

80. Transformation of Harmonic Functions. The problem of finding a function that is harmonic in a specified domain and that satisfies prescribed conditions on the boundary of the domain is one of the oldest and most prominent types of boundary value problems in partial differential equations. If the values of the function itself are prescribed along the boundary, the problem is called a *Dirichlet problem,* or a *boundary value problem of the first kind.* If values of the normal derivative of the harmonic function are prescribed on the boundary, the problem is one of the *second kind,* called a *Neumann problem.* Modifications and combinations of those types of boundary conditions also arise.

Each analytic function furnishes a pair of harmonic functions. Since the function $\exp(iz)$, for example, is entire, its components

(1) $\qquad G(x,y) = e^{-y} \cos x, \qquad H(x,y) = e^{-y} \sin x$

are everywhere harmonic. The function H satisfies the conditions

$$(2) \qquad \frac{\partial^2 H}{\partial x^2} + \frac{\partial^2 H}{\partial y^2} = 0,$$

(3) $H(0,y) = 0,$ $H(\pi,y) = 0,$

(4) $H(x,0) = \sin x,$ $\lim_{y \to \infty} H(x,y) = 0,$

which make up a Dirichlet problem for the strip $0 < x < \pi$, $y > 0$. Of course the same function H satisfies other boundary conditions for this and other domains; for instance, its normal derivative $\partial H / \partial x$ on the line $x = \pi/2$ is zero.

Sometimes the solution of a given problem can be discovered by this method of conjugate functions. But the success of this procedure will depend on the simplicity of the problem and on our familiarity with the real and imaginary parts of several analytic functions. An important additional aid in solving such problems will now be noted.

Let H denote any harmonic function of the independent variables x and y, and let new independent variables u and v be introduced such that the complex variable $z = x + iy$ is an analytic function of $w = u + iv$,

$$z = f(w).$$

We have seen in Sec. 78 that, corresponding to the given harmonic function $H(x,y)$, a conjugate harmonic function $G(x,y)$ exists; $H + iG$ is an analytic function of z. Since z is an analytic function of w, the function $H + iG$ is also an analytic function of w, and therefore H is a harmonic function of u and v. Our result can be stated as follows.

Theorem. *Every harmonic function of x and y transforms into a harmonic function of u and v under the change of variables*

$$x + iy = f(u + iv),$$

where f is an analytic function.

As a consequence, a function that is harmonic in some neighborhood remains harmonic under a change of variables arising from a conformal transformation

$$w = F(z),$$

where $F(z)$ is analytic and $F'(z) \neq 0$ in the neighborhood, since the inverse function $z = f(w)$ is analytic (Sec. 79).

As an illustration of the theorem, the function $H = e^{-y} \sin x$ is harmonic in any region of the xy plane. Under the transformation

$$z = w^2,$$

we have $x = u^2 - v^2$, $y = 2uv$, and hence the function

$$H = e^{-2uv} \sin (u^2 - v^2)$$

is harmonic in the corresponding region of the uv plane; that is,

$$\frac{\partial^2 H}{\partial u^2} + \frac{\partial^2 H}{\partial v^2} = 0.$$

81. Transformation of Boundary Conditions. The conditions that a harmonic function H or its normal derivative be a prescribed constant along portions of the boundary of a region are the most common although not the only important types of boundary conditions. Some of those conditions remain unaltered under the change of variables involved in conformal transformations.

A curve along which a function H is constant is called a *level curve* of the function. Under the change in variables a level curve $H(x,y) = c$ in the xy plane transforms into the level curve

$$H[x(u,v),\ y(u,v)] = c$$

in the uv plane. In particular then, any portion of the boundary of a region in the xy plane upon which H has a constant value transforms into a corresponding curve in the uv plane along which H has the same constant value. That is, a boundary condition $H = c$ in the original problem carries over to the transformed problem.

If the normal derivative of H vanishes along some curve in the xy plane, then the normal derivative of H expressed as a function of u and v also vanishes along the corresponding curve in the uv plane.

To see that this is so, let us first recall that the gradient of a function H is a vector whose direction is that along which the directional derivative of H has its maximum value at the point considered. The magnitude of the gradient is the value of that maximum rate of change. It is shown in advanced calculus that the projection of that vector upon any direction is the directional derivative of the function H in that direction. In particular, the projection of the gradient on the x axis is $\partial H/\partial x$, and on the y axis is $\partial H/\partial y$. Thus the gradient vector is represented by the formula

$$\text{grad } H = \frac{\partial H}{\partial x} + i\frac{\partial H}{\partial y}.$$

The gradient is perpendicular to the level curve $H(x,y) = c$ at each point.

Suppose that the normal derivative of $H(x,y)$ vanishes, $dH/dn = 0$, along some curve C (Fig. 51). Since dH/dn is the

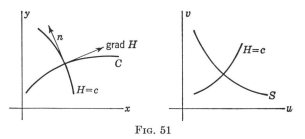

Fig. 51

projection of the gradient on the normal, the normal to C must be perpendicular to the gradient of H at each point. The tangent to C therefore coincides with the gradient, and C is orthogonal to the level curves $H(x,y) = c$. The image S of C, under a conformal transformation, is therefore orthogonal to the level curves

$$H[x(u,v),\ y(u,v)] = c,$$

which are the images of $H(x,y) = c$. Therefore the normal derivative of H as a function of u and v, along the curve S, must also vanish.

The invariance of the two special types of boundary conditions can be stated as follows.

Theorem. *Under a transformation $z = f(w)$, where f is analytic and $f'(w) \neq 0$, boundary conditions of either of the two types*

$$H = c \qquad \text{or} \qquad \frac{dH}{dn} = 0$$

on a harmonic function H, where c is a constant, remain unchanged.

A boundary condition that is not of one of those two types may transform into a condition that is substantially different

from the original one.   Boundary conditions for the transformed
problem may, of course, be obtained from the particular transformation in any case.   It is of some interest to note that under
a conformal transformation the ratio of a directional derivative of
H in the z plane to the directional derivative of H in the cor-
responding direction in the w plane can be shown to be $|dw/dz|$.
This ratio is not generally constant along a curve (see Exercises
3 and 8 below).

EXERCISES

1. The harmonic function

$$H = 2 - x + \frac{x}{x^2 + y^2}$$

assumes the value 2 on the circle $x^2 + y^2 = 1$.   Under the change of
variables $z = e^w$, find H as a function of u and v, and show directly that
$H = 2$ on the image $u = 0$ of the circle, thus verifying one of the results
of the preceding section for this special case.

2. The normal derivative of the harmonic function

$$H = e^{-x} \cos y$$

is zero along the line $y = 0$; that is, $\partial H/\partial y = 0$ on that line.   Find H in
terms of u and v under the change of variables $z = w^2$, and show directly
that the normal derivatives of H along the images $u = 0$ and $v = 0$ of
the line $y = 0$ also vanish.

3. The normal derivative of the harmonic function

$$H = 2y + e^{-x} \cos y$$

is constant, $\partial H/\partial y = 2$, along the line $y = 0$.   Under the change of
variables $z = w^2$, show that the normal derivative is not constant along
the image of that line but that $\partial H/\partial u = 4v$ along $u = 0$ and $\partial H/\partial v = 4u$
along $v = 0$.

4. Let H be a harmonic function throughout a simply connected
domain D of the xy plane.   Then a function G exists such that $H + iG$ is
an analytic function of z in D (Sec. 78).   Deduce that the partial
derivatives of H, of all orders, are continuous functions of x and y in D

5. If a function H is a solution of a Neumann problem (Sec. 80), show
why $H + c$ is also a solution of that problem, where c is any constant.

6. Use partial differentiation under a change of variables to show that

$$\frac{\partial^2 H}{\partial x^2} + \frac{\partial^2 H}{\partial y^2} = \left(\frac{\partial^2 H}{\partial u^2} + \frac{\partial^2 H}{\partial v^2} \right) \left| \frac{dw}{dz} \right|^2,$$

where $w = u + iv$ is an analytic function of $z = x + iy$ and $dw/dz \neq 0$. Note that it follows from this formula for the transformation of the Laplacian that a harmonic function H remains harmonic under the change of variables.

7. Let a function p of x and y satisfy *Poisson's equation*

$$\frac{\partial^2 p}{\partial x^2} + \frac{\partial^2 p}{\partial y^2} = S(x,y)$$

in a domain D_z of the xy plane, where S is a prescribed function. If D_w is the image of the domain D_z under a transformation $z = f(w)$ that is conformal in D_w, show that $p[x(u,v), y(u,v)]$ satisfies another Poisson equation

$$\frac{\partial^2 p}{\partial u^2} + \frac{\partial^2 p}{\partial v^2} = S[x(u,v), y(u,v)]|f'(w)|^2$$

when (u,v) is in D_w (see Exercise 6).

8. (*a*) Under the change of variables described in Exercise 6, show that

$$|\text{grad } H(x,y)| = |\text{grad } H[x(u,v), y(u,v)]| \left| \frac{dw}{dz} \right|.$$

(*b*) Why is the angle at a point in the xy plane between a curve C and the vector grad H equal to the angle at the image point in the uv plane between the image S of C and grad H? (*c*) If σ is distance along C and s is distance along S, use the results of parts (*a*) and (*b*) to show that the directional derivative transforms as follows:

$$\frac{dH}{d\sigma} = \frac{dH}{ds} \left| \frac{dw}{dz} \right|.$$

CHAPTER 9

APPLICATIONS OF CONFORMAL MAPPING

We shall now use conformal mapping to solve a number of physical problems involving Laplace's equation in two independent variables. Problems in the conduction of heat, electrostatic potential, and the flow of fluids will be treated. Since they are intended to illustrate methods, the problems will be kept on a fairly elementary level.

82. Steady Temperatures. Let K denote the thermal conductivity of the material in a solid body. Then the flux of heat by conduction across any surface within the solid is

$$(1) \qquad\qquad \Phi = -K\frac{dT}{dn},$$

where T denotes the temperature and n the distance normal to the surface. The flux Φ is the rate of flow of heat per unit time per unit area. It is therefore measured in such units as calories per second per square centimeter.

We consider only cases in which the temperature is a function of x and y, because the use of analytic functions and conformal mapping is limited to those cases. Since the temperature T does not vary with time, the flow of heat is in a steady state, and since T does not vary with the coordinate perpendicular to the xy plane, the flow is two-dimensional, parallel to the xy plane.

It is assumed that no thermal energy is created or destroyed within the solid, that no heat sources or sinks are present there. Then the temperature function T and all its partial derivatives of first and second order are continuous at all points interior to the body. This statement and formula (1) for the flux of heat by conduction are postulates for the mathematical theory of heat conduction, postulates that also apply at interior points where there is a continuous distribution of sources.

189

Consider an interior element of the solid, the element having the shape of a prism of unit length perpendicular to the xy plane, with a rectangular base Δx by Δy in that plane (Fig. 52). The time rate of flow of heat toward the right across the left-hand face is $-K \Delta y\, \partial T/\partial x$. If K is a constant, the difference between that rate and the rate of flow across the right-hand face is

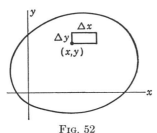

FIG. 52

$$(2) \qquad -K \Delta y\, \frac{\partial^2 T}{\partial x^2}\, \Delta x,$$

which is the resultant rate of loss of heat from the element through those two faces. The expressions here are approximations whose accuracy increases as Δx and Δy are made smaller.

Similarly, the resultant rate of loss from the upper and lower faces of the element is

$$(3) \qquad -K \Delta x\, \frac{\partial^2 T}{\partial y^2}\, \Delta y.$$

Heat enters or leaves the element only through those four faces, and the temperatures within the element are steady. Hence the sum of the resultants (2) and (3) is zero; that is,

$$(4) \qquad \frac{\partial^2 T}{\partial x^2} + \frac{\partial^2 T}{\partial y^2} = 0.$$

Since Δx and Δy can be taken as small as we please, we have a brief demonstration here that the temperature function must satisfy Laplace's equation at each interior point of the solid.

In view of equation (4) and the continuity of the temperature function and its partial derivatives, T *is a harmonic function of* x *and* y in the domain represented by the interior of the solid body.

The surfaces $T(x,y) = c$, where c is any constant, are the *isotherms*. They can also be considered as curves in the xy plane, for $T(x,y)$ can be interpreted as the temperature in a thin sheet of the material in that plane with the faces of the sheet thermally insulated. The isotherms are the level curves of the function T. The gradient of T is perpendicular to the isotherm at each point, and the current of heat, that is, the maximum flux, is in the direction of the gradient. If $S(x,y)$ is a conjugate harmonic of the function $T(x,y)$, then the curves $S(x,y) = c$ have the gradient vectors as their tangents; those curves are the lines of flow.

If the normal derivative dT/dn is zero along any part of the boundary of the solid sheet, the flux of heat across that part is zero. That is, the part is thermally insulated; it is therefore a line of flow.

The function T may also denote the concentration of a substance that is diffusing through a solid. In this case, the constant K is the diffusion constant. The above discussion and derivation apply as well to steady-state diffusion as to the conduction of heat.

83. Steady Temperatures in a Wall. Let us find the formula for the steady temperatures $T(x,y)$ in a semi-infinite slab bounded by the planes $x = \pi/2$, $x = -\pi/2$, and $y = 0$ when the first two boundaries are kept at temperature zero and the last at temperature $T = 1$ (Fig. 53). The function $T(x,y)$ is to be bounded at all points in this region, in particular, as y tends to infinity. This condition is natural if we consider the slab as a limiting case of a slab of finite height whose upper boundary is kept at a fixed temperature as the height is increased.

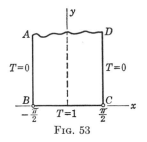

FIG. 53

The problem is also that of finding the temperatures in a plate having the form of a semi-infinite strip, where the faces of the plate are perfectly insulated.

The boundary value problem to be solved here can be written

$$\text{(1)} \qquad \frac{\partial^2 T}{\partial x^2} + \frac{\partial^2 T}{\partial y^2} = 0 \qquad \left(-\frac{\pi}{2} < x < \frac{\pi}{2},\, y > 0 \right),$$

$$\text{(2)} \qquad T\left(-\frac{\pi}{2}, y \right) = T\left(\frac{\pi}{2}, y \right) = 0 \qquad (y > 0),$$

$$\text{(3)} \qquad T(x,0) = 1 \qquad \left(-\frac{\pi}{2} < x < \frac{\pi}{2} \right);$$

also $|T(x,y)| < M$, where M is some constant, a condition that could be replaced by the condition that T is to approach zero as y tends to infinity.

This is a Dirichlet problem for the semi-infinite strip. In fact, the boundary conditions are all of the type $T = c$, a type that is invariant under conformal transformations (Sec. 81). It is difficult to discover an analytic function whose real or imaginary component satisfies the boundary conditions (2) and (3). We therefore use conformal transformations to obtain a region and problem simple enough that such a function is evident.

The transformation $z' = \sin z$ transforms the strip into the upper half of the z' plane, as noted in Fig. 9 of Appendix 2. As indicated in Fig. 54, the image of the base of the strip is the segment of the x' axis between the points $z' = -1$ and $z' = 1$, and the images of the sides are the remaining parts of the x' axis. We note in Fig. 19, Appendix 2, that this half plane is transformed into the infinite strip between the lines $v = 0$ and $v = \pi$

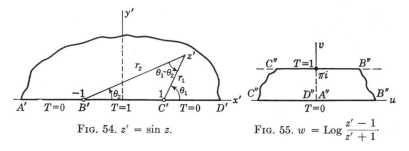

FIG. 54. $z' = \sin z$.   FIG. 55. $w = \operatorname{Log} \dfrac{z' - 1}{z' + 1}$.

by the transformation

$$w = \operatorname{Log} \frac{z' - 1}{z' + 1} = \operatorname{Log} \frac{r_1}{r_2} + i(\theta_1 - \theta_2)$$
$$(0 < \theta_1 < \pi,\ 0 < \theta_2 < \pi).$$

As indicated in Figs. 54 and 55, the segment of the x' axis between $z' = -1$ and $z' = 1$ maps onto the upper side of the strip, and the rest of that axis onto the lower side.

A harmonic function of u and v that is zero on the side $v = 0$ of the strip, unity on the side $v = \pi$, and bounded in the strip is clearly

(4) $$T = \frac{1}{\pi} v,$$

for this is the imaginary coefficient of the analytic function $f(w) = w/\pi$. Changing to the coordinates x' and y' by means of the transformation

(5) $$w = \operatorname{Log} \frac{z' - 1}{z' + 1} = \operatorname{Log} \left| \frac{z' - 1}{z' + 1} \right| + i \arg \frac{z' - 1}{z' + 1},$$

we find that

$$v = \arg \left(\frac{x' - 1 + iy'}{x' + 1 + iy'} \right) = \arg \left[\frac{x'^2 + y'^2 - 1 + 2iy'}{(x' + 1)^2 + y'^2} \right],$$

or

$$v = \arctan \left(\frac{2y'}{x'^2 + y'^2 - 1} \right),$$

where the arctangent function has the range 0 to π since

$$\arg \frac{z' - 1}{z' + 1} = \theta_1 - \theta_2,$$

and the angles here are those indicated in Fig. 54.

The function T given by equation (4) therefore becomes

(6) $$T = \frac{1}{\pi} \arctan \left(\frac{2y'}{x'^2 + y'^2 - 1} \right).$$

The function used in the transformation (5) is analytic in the upper half plane $y' > 0$. Since the function (4) is harmonic in the strip, the function (6) must be a harmonic function in the half plane $y' > 0$. The boundary conditions for the two functions must be the same on corresponding parts of the boundaries. It can, of course, be verified directly that the function (6) satisfies Laplace's equation and approaches the values indicated in Fig. 54 as the point approaches the x' axis from above.

The function represents the steady temperatures in the semi-infinite plate $y' \geq 0$ with a section $(-1 < x' < 1)$ of its boundary $y' = 0$ kept at the temperature $T = 1$ and the rest at temperature zero. The isotherms $T = c$ $(0 < c < 1)$ are the circles

$$x'^2 + y'^2 - \frac{2}{\tan \pi c} y' - 1 = 0$$

with their centers on the y' axis and passing through the points $(\pm 1, 0)$.

We proceed now to the solution of the original problem represented by equations (1) to (3). Under the transformation

(7) $$z' = \sin z,$$

the change of variables can be written

$$x' = \sin x \cosh y, \qquad y' = \cos x \sinh y,$$

and the harmonic function (6) becomes

$$T = \frac{1}{\pi} \arctan\left(\frac{2\cos x \sinh y}{\sin^2 x \cosh^2 y + \cos^2 x \sinh^2 y - 1}\right).$$

The denominator here reduces to $\sinh^2 y - \cos^2 x$, and the fraction can be written

$$\frac{2\cos x \sinh y}{\sinh^2 y - \cos^2 x} = \frac{2\cos x/\sinh y}{1 - (\cos x/\sinh y)^2} = \tan 2\alpha,$$

where $\tan\alpha = \cos x/\sinh y$. Our formula for T therefore reduces to

$$(8) \qquad\qquad T = \frac{2}{\pi} \arctan\left(\frac{\cos x}{\sinh y}\right).$$

The arctangent function here has the range 0 to $\pi/2$, its argument being nonnegative.

Since $\sin z$ is analytic, the transformation (7) ensures that the function (8) will be harmonic in the strip $-\pi/2 < x < \pi/2$, $y > 0$, onto which the half plane maps, and it must satisfy the boundary conditions (2) and (3). Moreover, $|T(x,y)| \leqq 1$ throughout the strip. Formula (8) is therefore the temperature formula sought.

The isotherms $T = c$ are the curves

$$\cos x = \tan\frac{\pi c}{2} \sinh y,$$

each of which passes through the points $(\pm\pi/2, 0)$. If K is the thermal conductivity, the flux of heat into the wall through its base is

$$-K\frac{\partial T}{\partial y}\bigg]_{y=0} = \frac{2K}{\pi \cos x} \qquad \left(-\frac{\pi}{2} < x < \frac{\pi}{2}\right),$$

and the flux outward through the plane $x = \pi/2$ is

$$-K\frac{\partial T}{\partial x}\bigg]_{x=\pi/2} = \frac{2K}{\pi \sinh y} \qquad\qquad (y > 0).$$

The product of a harmonic function by a constant is also harmonic. The function

$$T = \frac{2T_0}{\pi} \arctan\left(\frac{\cos x}{\sinh y}\right)$$

represents the steady temperatures in the above slab when the base is kept at temperature T_0 and the sides at zero.

The boundary value problem given by equations (1) to (3) can also be solved with the aid of Fourier series. That method is more direct, but it gives the solution in the form of an infinite series.[1]

84. Temperatures in a Quadrant with Part of One Boundary Insulated. Let us find the steady temperatures in a plate having

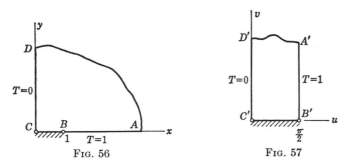

FIG. 56   FIG. 57

the form of a quadrant if a segment at the end of one edge is insulated, if the rest of that edge is kept at a fixed temperature, and if the second edge is kept at another fixed temperature. The faces are insulated so that the problem is two-dimensional.

The temperature scale and the unit of length can be so chosen that the boundary value problem in the temperature function T becomes

(1)
$$\frac{\partial^2 T}{\partial x^2} + \frac{\partial^2 T}{\partial y^2} = 0 \qquad (x > 0,\, y > 0);$$

(2)
$$\frac{\partial T}{\partial y}\bigg]_{y=0} = 0 \qquad (0 < x < 1);$$
$$T(x,0) = 1 \qquad (x > 1);$$

(3)
$$T(0,y) = 0 \qquad (y > 0),$$

where $T(x,y)$ is bounded for all positive x and y. The plate and its boundary conditions are shown in Fig. 56.

Conditions (2) prescribe the value of the normal derivative of

---

[1] See for instance the author's "Fourier Series and Boundary Value Problems," probs. 8 and 9, p. 116, 1941. Also, a short treatment of the uniqueness of solutions of boundary value problems will be found in chap. 7 of that book.

the function T over a part of a boundary line and the value of the function itself over the rest of that line. The Fourier method mentioned above, which would call for the use of a Fourier integral in this case, is not adapted to problems with such different types of conditions on the same boundary line.

As indicated in Fig. 10 of Appendix 2, the transformation

$$(4) \qquad\qquad z = \sin w$$

maps the quadrant $x \geqq 0$, $y \geqq 0$ onto the strip $0 \leqq u \leqq \pi/2$, $v \geqq 0$. The insulated segment of the x axis maps onto the base of the strip and the rest of the boundary onto the sides of the strip, as shown in Fig. 57. The corresponding boundary conditions on the function T of u and v are indicated in that figure. The bounded function T here is clearly

$$(5) \qquad\qquad T = \frac{2}{\pi} u = \Re\left(\frac{2}{\pi} w\right),$$

for this is a harmonic function of u and v such that $T = 0$ when $u = 0$, $T = 1$ when $u = \pi/2$; also $\partial T/\partial v = 0$ everywhere, along the u axis in particular. The required temperature function for the quadrant is obtained by writing T in terms of x and y.

In order to obtain u in terms of x and y, we may first note, according to equation (4), that

$$(6) \qquad x = \sin u \cosh v, \qquad y = \cos u \sinh v;$$

therefore

$$(7) \qquad\qquad \frac{x^2}{\sin^2 u} - \frac{y^2}{\cos^2 u} = 1.$$

In solving for u it is convenient to observe that for each fixed u the point (x,y), which is in the first quadrant, lies on the hyperbola (7) with foci at the points $(\pm 1,0)$ and with a transverse axis of length $2 \sin u$. The difference of its distances from the foci is therefore $2 \sin u$,

$$\sqrt{(x + 1)^2 + y^2} - \sqrt{(x - 1)^2 + y^2} = 2 \sin u.$$

According to equation (5), the required temperature function is therefore

$$(8) \quad T = \frac{2}{\pi} \arcsin \frac{1}{2} [\sqrt{(x+1)^2 + y^2} - \sqrt{(x-1)^2 + y^2}],$$

where the inverse sine has the range from zero to $\pi/2$, the range of u. If we wish to verify that this function satisfies the boundary conditions (2), we must remember that the square roots here are positive, so that $\sqrt{(x-1)^2}$ denotes $x - 1$ when $x > 1$ and $1 - x$ when $x < 1$.

It can be seen from equation (5) that the isotherms $T = c$ are the parts of the confocal hyperbolas (7), where $u = \pi c/2$, which lie in the first quadrant. The lines of flow are quarters of the confocal ellipses obtained by holding v constant in equations (6), since the function $2v/\pi$ is a harmonic conjugate of the function (5). The temperature along the insulated part of the lower edge is

$$T(x,0) = \frac{2}{\pi} \arcsin x.$$

EXERCISES

1. For heat conduction in the semi-infinite plate shown in Fig. 54, note the harmonic conjugate of the temperature function $T(x'y')$ from equation (5), Sec. 83, and find the lines of flow of heat. Show that those lines consist of the upper half of the y' axis and the upper halves of certain circles on either side of that axis, with their centers on the segment $A'B'$ or $C'D'$ of the x' axis.

2. If the function T in Sec. 83 were not required to be bounded, show that the harmonic function (4) of that section could be replaced by the harmonic function

$$T_1 = \mathcal{I} \left(\frac{1}{\pi} w + A \cosh w \right) = \frac{1}{\pi} v + A \sinh u \sin v,$$

where A is an arbitrary real constant, and hence that the solution of the Dirichlet problem for the strip (Fig. 55) is not unique.

3. Suppose that the condition $|T(x,y)| < M$ were omitted from the boundary value problem of temperatures in a semi-infinite slab (Sec. 83, Fig. 53). Show that an infinite number of solutions would then be possible by noting the effect of adding to the solution found there the imaginary coefficient of the function $A \sin z$, where A is an arbitrary real constant.

4. Use the function Log z to find a formula for the bounded steady temperatures in a plate having the form of a quadrant $x \geq 0$, $y \geq 0$, if its flat faces are perfectly insulated and its edges have temperatures $T(x,0) = 0$ and $T(0,y) = 1$ (Fig. 58). Find the isotherms and lines of flow and draw some of them.   *Ans.* $T = (2/\pi) \arctan (y/x)$.

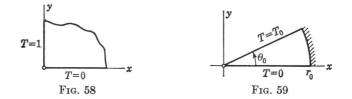

FIG. 58   FIG. 59

5. Find the steady temperatures in a solid in the shape of a long cylindrical wedge if its boundary planes $\theta = 0$ and $\theta = \theta_0$ are kept at constant temperatures zero and T_0, respectively, and its surface $r = r_0$ is perfectly insulated (Fig. 59).   *Ans.* $T = (T_0/\theta_0) \arctan (y/x)$.

6. Find the bounded steady temperatures $T(x,y)$ in the semi-infinite solid $y \geq 0$, if $T = 0$ on the part $x < -1$ of the boundary, $T = 1$ on

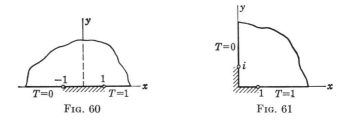

FIG. 60   FIG. 61

the part $x > 1$, and if the strip $-1 < x < 1$ of the boundary is insulated (Fig. 60).

Ans. $T = \dfrac{1}{2} + \dfrac{1}{\pi} \arcsin \dfrac{1}{2} [\sqrt{(x + 1)^2 + y^2} - \sqrt{(x - 1)^2 + y^2}]$

$$\left(-\frac{\pi}{2} \leq \arcsin t \leq \frac{\pi}{2} \right).$$

7. Find the bounded steady temperatures in a quadrant when the boundary planes are kept at fixed temperatures except for strips of equal width at the corner that are insulated, as shown in Fig. 61.

Ans. $T = \dfrac{1}{2} + \dfrac{1}{\pi} \arcsin \dfrac{1}{2} [\sqrt{(x^2 - y^2 + 1)^2 + 4x^2y^2}$

$$- \sqrt{(x^2 - y^2 - 1)^2 + 4x^2y^2}] \qquad \left(-\frac{\pi}{2} \leq \arcsin t \leq \frac{\pi}{2} \right).$$

8. Solve this Dirichlet problem for the semi-infinite strip (Fig. 62):

$$\frac{\partial^2 H}{\partial x^2} + \frac{\partial^2 H}{\partial^2 y} = 0 \qquad \left(0 < x < \frac{\pi}{2}, y > 0\right),$$

$$H(0,y) = 1, \qquad H\left(\frac{\pi}{2},y\right) = 0, \qquad H(x,0) = 0, \qquad 0 \le H(x,y) \le 1.$$

$$Ans. \ H = \frac{2}{\pi} \arctan\left(\frac{\tanh y}{\tan x}\right).$$

9. Derive a formula for the temperatures $T(r,\theta)$ in a half disk $r \le 1$, $0 \le \theta \le \pi$ with insulated flat faces if $T = 1$ along the radial edge $\theta = 0$

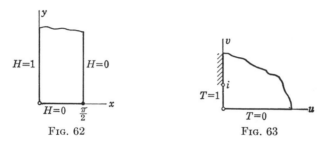

FIG. 62   FIG. 63

and $T = 0$ on the rest of the boundary. (This problem can be transformed into the one in Exercise 8.) Verify that your function does satisfy all three boundary conditions.

10. Apply the transformation $w = i/z$ to the problem on temperatures in a quadrant solved in Sec. 84 (Fig. 56). State the new problem on temperatures in a quadrant of the uv plane and write the temperature formula (see Fig. 63). Then use the transformation $w = \sin z'$ in that new problem and state the resulting problem on temperatures in a semi-infinite strip in the z' plane.

11. The part $x < 0$ of each of the two boundary planes of an infinite slab $0 \le y \le \pi$ is thermally insulated. On the parts $x > 0$ the condi-

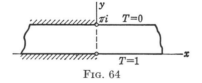

FIG. 64

tions $T(x,0) = 1$ and $T(x,\pi) = 0$ are maintained (Fig. 64). Find the steady temperatures $T(x,y)$ in the slab. (This problem can be transformed into the one in Exercise 6.)

12. In Sec. 54 and Exercise 11, Sec. 55, it was shown that a function u that is harmonic in a domain D must assume its maximum and minimum values on the boundary of D, never at an interior point. By interpreting $u(x,y)$ as a steady-state temperature, state a physical reason why that property of maximum and minimum values should hold true.

85. Electric Potential. The intensity of an electric field of force at a point is the electric force that would be exerted on a unit positive charge placed at the point. The *electrostatic potential* is a function of the coordinates of a point whose directional derivative in each direction is the negative of the component of the intensity of the electric field in that direction.

The electric force of attraction or repulsion between two stationary charged particles in space is inversely proportional to the square of the distance between them and directly proportional to the product of their charges. Starting from this inverse-square law for the force, it can be seen that the potential due to a single particle in space is inversely proportional to the first power of the distance from the point to the particle. The potential due to any distribution of charges, at points in a region that is free from electric charges, can then be shown to satisfy Laplace's equation in the three-dimensional region.

When conditions are such that the potential V is the same in all planes parallel to the xy plane, then in regions free from charges V is a harmonic function of the two variables x and y:

$$\frac{\partial^2 V}{\partial x^2} + \frac{\partial^2 V}{\partial y^2} = 0.$$

The intensity of the electric field of force at each point is then a vector parallel to the xy plane with components $-\partial V/\partial x$ and $-\partial V/\partial y$ parallel to the coordinate axes. Thus the electric intensity is represented by a vector that is the negative of the gradient of V.

A surface along which V is constant is an equipotential surface. The force tangent to a conducting surface is zero in the static case, since charges are free to move on such a surface under an electric force along it. Thus V is constant along the surface of a conductor, and that surface is an equipotential.

If $U(x,y)$ is a harmonic conjugate of $V(x,y)$, the curves $U = c$ in the xy plane are called the *flux lines*. These curves are orthogonal to the equipotential surfaces or curves. The electric intensity has the direction of the flux line at each point.

As in the case of steady temperatures, the methods of complex variables are limited to problems in the two-dimensional potential $V(x,y)$, sometimes called the *logarithmic potential*. Such potentials may arise from a distribution of charges that is uniform along every line perpendicular to the xy plane. The electric force at a point due to a single uniformly charged line turns out to be inversely proportional to the first power of the distance from the point to the line.

Boundary value problems in the potential V are the same mathematical problems as those in steady temperatures T. In fact, the temperature is the potential for the flow of heat by conduction.

The problem in Sec. 83 (Fig. 53), for instance, can be interpreted as the problem of finding the two-dimensional electrostatic potential in the empty space bounded by the conducting planes $x = \pm\pi/2$ and $y = 0$, insulated at their intersections, when the planes at the sides are kept at potential zero and the base at the potential $V = 1$. Problems of this type arise in electronics. If the space charge inside a vacuum tube is small, the space is sometimes considered free of charge, as an approximation; then the potential can be assumed to satisfy Laplace's equation.

The potential in the steady flow of electricity in a plane conducting sheet is also a harmonic function at points free from sources or sinks. Magnetic potential and gravitational potential are further examples of harmonic functions in physics.

86. Potential in a Cylindrical Space. A long circular cylinder is made out of a thin sheet of conducting material, and the cylinder is split along two of its elements to form two equal parts. Those parts are separated by slender strips of insulating material and used as electrodes, one of which is grounded and the other kept at some other fixed potential. We take the coordinate axes and units of length and potential difference as indicated in Fig. 65. The electrostatic potential $V(x,y)$ over any cross section of the enclosed space that is distant from the ends of the cylinder is a harmonic function inside the circle $x^2 + y^2 = 1$; also, $V = 0$ on the upper half of the circle and $V = 1$ on the lower half.

A linear fractional transformation that maps the interior of the unit circle onto the upper half plane, the upper half of the circle onto the positive real axis, and the lower half onto the negative real axis was devised in Exercise 10, Sec. 35. The result is given in Fig. 13 of Appendix 2. We interchange w and z

there to write that transformation as

(1) $$z = \frac{i - w}{i + w}.$$

Under this transformation the new problem for V in the half plane is the one indicated in Fig. 66.

The problem of determining the potential V in this half plane can be reduced to a still simpler one by using the transformation $w = \exp z'$. But the second transformation is unnecessary if we

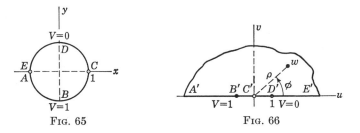

FIG. 65   FIG. 66

observe that the imaginary coefficient of the function

(2) $$\frac{1}{\pi} \log w = \frac{1}{\pi} \text{Log } \rho + \frac{i}{\pi} \phi \qquad (0 \leq \phi \leq \pi)$$

is a bounded function of u and v that assumes the required values on the two parts $\phi = 0$ and $\phi = \pi$ of the u axis. The required harmonic function for the half plane is therefore

(3) $$V = \frac{1}{\pi} \arctan \frac{v}{u}.$$

Equation (1) can be written in the form

(4) $$w = i \frac{1 - z}{1 + z},$$

from which u and v can be seen as functions of x and y. The function (3) then becomes

(5) $$V = \frac{1}{\pi} \arctan \left(\frac{1 - x^2 - y^2}{2y} \right),$$

where $0 \leq \arctan t \leq \pi$ and therefore

$$\lim_{t \to +0} \arctan t = 0, \qquad \lim_{t \to -0} \arctan t = \pi.$$

The function (5) is the potential function for the space enclosed by the cylindrical electrodes, since it must be harmonic in the circle and it must assume the required values on the semicircles, which are the images of the half lines $\phi = 0$ and $\phi = \pi$ in the w plane. A direct verification of all conditions from formula (5) is not difficult.

The equipotentials $V = c$ in the circular region are arcs of the circles

$$x^2 + y^2 + 2y \tan \pi c = 1,$$

each of which passes through the points $(\pm 1,0)$. Also, the segment of the x axis between those points is the equipotential $V = \frac{1}{2}$. The conjugate harmonic U of V is $(1/\pi) \operatorname{Log} \rho$, according to equation (2). In view of equation (4),

$$U = \frac{1}{\pi} \operatorname{Log} \frac{|1 - z|}{|1 + z|}.$$

From this equation it can be seen that the flux lines $U = c$ are arcs of circles with centers on the x axis. The segment of the y axis between the electrodes is also a flux line.

EXERCISES

1. The harmonic function (3) of Sec. 86 is bounded in the half plane $v \geqq 0$ and satisfies the boundary conditions indicated in Fig. 66. Show that if the imaginary coefficient of Ae^w is added to that function, where A is any real constant, the resulting function satisfies all requirements except the boundedness condition. Also show that the resulting function transforms under equation (4), Sec. 86, into a function of x and y that is not bounded in a neighborhood of the point $z = -1$, a point on the circle in Fig. 65 where V is discontinuous.

2. Prove that the transformation (1) of Sec. 86 maps the upper half of the circular region shown in Fig. 65 onto the first quadrant of the w plane and the diameter CE onto the positive v axis. Then find the electrostatic potential V in the space bounded by the upper half of the cylinder $x^2 + y^2 = 1$ and the plane $y = 0$ when $V = 0$ on the cylindrical surface and $V = 1$ on the plane surface (Fig. 67).

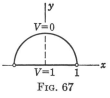

FIG. 67

$$\textit{Ans. } V = \frac{2}{\pi} \arctan \left(\frac{1 - x^2 - y^2}{2y} \right).$$

3. Find the electrostatic potential $V(r,\theta)$ in the space bounded by the half planes $\theta = 0$ and $\theta = \pi/4$ and the portion $0 < \theta < \pi/4$ of the cylindrical surface $r = 1$, when $V = 1$ on the plane boundaries and $V = 0$ on the cylindrical boundary (see Exercise 2). Verify that your function satisfies the boundary conditions.

4. Note that all branches of $\log z$ have the same real component which is harmonic everywhere except at the origin. Then write a formula for the electrostatic potential $V(x,y)$ in the space between two coaxial conducting cylindrical surfaces $x^2 + y^2 = 1$ and $x^2 + y^2 = r_0^2$ if $V = 0$ on the first surface and $V = 1$ on the second.

$$Ans. \; V = \frac{\text{Log}\,(x^2 + y^2)}{2\,\text{Log}\,r_0}.$$

5. Find the bounded electrostatic potential $V(x,y)$ in the space above an infinite conducting plane $y = 0$ one strip $(-a < x < a)$ of which is insulated from the rest and kept at potential $V = 1$, while $V = 0$ on the rest, as indicated in Fig. 68. Verify that your function satisfies the boundary conditions.

$$Ans. \; V = \frac{1}{\pi}\arctan\left(\frac{2ay}{x^2 + y^2 - a^2}\right) \quad (0 \leqq \arctan t \leqq \pi).$$

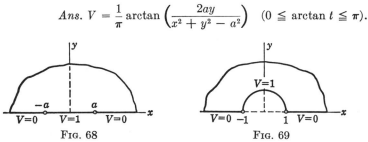

FIG. 68   FIG. 69

6. Derive a formula for the electrostatic potential in the space indicated in Fig. 69, bounded below by two half planes and half a cylinder, if $V = 1$ on the cylinder and $V = 0$ on the planes. Draw some of the equipotential lines.

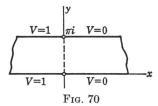

FIG. 70

$$Ans. \; V = \frac{2}{\pi}\arctan\left(\frac{2y}{x^2 + y^2 - 1}\right).$$

7. Find the potential V in the space between the planes $y = 0$ and $y = \pi$ if $V = 0$ on the part $x > 0$ of each of those planes and $V = 1$ on the parts $x < 0$ (Fig. 70). Check your result with the boundary conditions.

$$Ans. \; V = \frac{1}{\pi}\arctan\left(\frac{\sin y}{\sinh x}\right) \quad (0 \leqq \arctan t \leqq \pi).$$

8. Derive a formula for the electrostatic potential V in the space interior to a long cylinder $r = 1$ if $V = 0$ on the quadrant $0 < \theta < \pi/2$

of the cylindrical surface and $V = 1$ on the rest $(\pi/2 < \theta < 2\pi)$ of that surface (see Fig. 21 and Exercise 12, Sec. 35). Show that $V = \frac{3}{4}$ on the axis of the cylinder. Check your formula with the boundary conditions.

9. Find the steady temperatures T in a plate in the form of a segment of a circle (region $ABCE$ in Fig. 20, Appendix 2) with its faces insulated, when $T = 0$ on the circular edge ABC and $T = 1$ on the base DEF. Verify that your formula agrees with the boundary conditions.

10. The Dirichlet problem

$$\frac{\partial^2 V}{\partial x^2} + \frac{\partial^2 V}{\partial y^2} = 0 \quad (0 < x < a, 0 < y < b),$$

$$V(0,y) = V(a,y) = V(x,0) = 0, \qquad V(x,b) = 1$$

for $V(x,y)$ in a rectangle (Fig. 71) can be solved with the aid of the Fourier sine series.[1]   The solution is

$$V = \frac{4}{\pi} \sum_{n=1}^{\infty} \frac{\sinh (m\pi y/a)}{m \sinh (m\pi b/a)} \sin \frac{m\pi x}{a} \quad (m = 2n - 1).$$

Accepting this formula as correct, find the potential $V(r,\theta)$ in the space

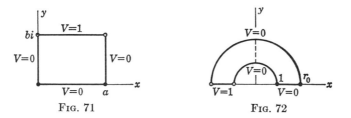

FIG. 71   FIG. 72

$1 \leq r \leq r_0, 0 \leq \theta \leq \pi$, if $V = 1$ on the boundary $\theta = \pi$ and $V = 0$ on the rest of the boundary (Fig. 72).

$$Ans. \ V = \frac{4}{\pi} \sum_{n=1}^{\infty} \frac{\sinh N\theta}{\sinh N\pi} \frac{\sin (N \operatorname{Log} r)}{2n - 1} \quad \left[N = \frac{(2n - 1)\pi}{\operatorname{Log} r_0} \right].$$

11. With the aid of the formula for $V(x,y)$ in a rectangle, given in Exercise 10, find the potential function $V(r,\theta)$ for the region $1 \leq r \leq r_0$,

[1] See the author's book "Fourier Series and Boundary Value Problems," p. 114, 1941.

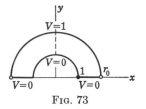

FIG. 73

$0 \leq \theta \leq \pi$, if $V = 1$ on the boundary $r = r_0$ and $V = 0$ on the rest of the boundary (Fig. 73).

$$\text{Ans. } V = \frac{4}{\pi} \sum_{n=1}^{\infty} \frac{r^m - r^{-m}}{r_0{}^m - r_0{}^{-m}} \frac{\sin m\theta}{m} \qquad (m = 2n - 1).$$

12. A plate with insulated faces has the form of the semiellipse shown in Fig. 11, Appendix 2. The temperature of the elliptical part of its boundary is $T = 1$; $T = 0$ on the segment $-1 < x < 1$ of its base, and the rest of its base is insulated. Find the steady-state lines of flow of heat.

87. Two-dimensional Fluid Flow. Harmonic functions play an important role in hydrodynamics and aerodynamics. Again, we consider only the two-dimensional steady-state type of flow. That is, the motion of the fluid is assumed to be the same in all planes parallel to the xy plane, the velocity being parallel to that plane and independent of the time. It is then sufficient to consider the motion of a sheet of the fluid in the xy plane.

Let the vector that represents the complex variable

$$q = q_1 + iq_2$$

denote the velocity of a particle of the fluid at any point (x,y), so that the x and y components of the velocity have the values $q_1(x,y)$ and $q_2(x,y)$. At interior points of a domain of flow in which no sources or sinks of the fluid occur, the real-valued functions q_1 and q_2 and their partial derivatives of the first order are assumed to be continuous. Let C be a given curve, a contour, and let the real-valued function q_t denote the component of the velocity q tangent to C. If s is arc length along C, the value of the line integral

(1) $$\int_C q_t(x,y) \, ds$$

is called the *circulation* of the fluid along C. When the circulation is divided by the length of the curve, the quotient represents a mean velocity of the fluid along the curve.

Suppose that C is a closed contour interior to a simply connected domain in which q_1, q_2, and their derivatives of the first order are continuous. If $x + iy$ denotes points on C, the complex number $dx + i\,dy$ represents a vector tangent to C and of length ds. Now $q_t\,ds$ is the product of the lengths of the vectors q and $dx + i\,dy$ by the cosine of the angle between them; that is, $q_t\,ds$ is the scalar product of those two vectors. It can be written

$$q_t\,ds = q_1\,dx + q_2\,dy.$$

With the aid of Green's theorem, the circulation around C can be written

$$(2) \qquad \int_C (q_1\,dx + q_2\,dy) = \int\int_R \left(\frac{\partial q_2}{\partial x} - \frac{\partial q_1}{\partial y} \right) dx\,dy,$$

where R is the region bounded by C.

In order to see a physical interpretation of the integrand of the last integral, let C be a circle $|z - z_0| = r_0$. The mean velocity v_0 along C is then found by dividing the circulation by $2\pi r_0$, and the mean angular velocity ω_0 of the fluid about the axis of the circle is v_0/r_0; thus

$$\omega_0 = \frac{1}{\pi r_0{}^2} \int\int_R \frac{1}{2} \left(\frac{\partial q_2}{\partial x} - \frac{\partial q_1}{\partial y} \right) dx\,dy.$$

The member on the right represents the mean value of the function

$$(3) \qquad \omega = \frac{1}{2}\left(\frac{\partial q_2}{\partial x} - \frac{\partial q_1}{\partial y} \right)$$

over the circular region R. Its limit as r_0 tends to zero is the value of ω at the point z_0. Hence the function $\omega(x,y)$, called the *rotation* of the fluid, represents the limiting angular velocity of a circular element of the fluid as the circle shrinks to the point (x,y).

If $\omega = 0$ at all points in some domain, the flow is *irrotational* in the domain. We consider only such irrotational flows. We also assume that fluid is *incompressible* and *free from viscosity*.

Let D be a simply connected domain in which the flow is irrotational. If C is any closed contour in D, it follows from equation (2) that the circulation around C is zero,

$$\int_C (q_1\,dx + q_2\,dy) = 0.$$

As a consequence, if (x_0, y_0) is a fixed point in D, the equation

$$(4) \qquad \phi(x,y) = \int_{(x_0, y_0)}^{(x,y)} [q_1(x', y')\, dx' + q_2(x', y')\, dy']$$

defines a function of the point (x,y) in D that is independent of

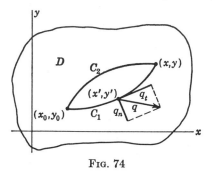

the path of integration between the limits, as long as the path is a contour interior to D, for the integral along one path C_1 (Fig. 74) minus the integral along another path C_2 is the integral along a closed path C, which must be zero.

FIG. 74

Since the line integral (4) is independent of the path, it follows that its integrand is an exact differential, the differential of the function $\phi(x,y)$. Hence

$$(5) \qquad q_1 = \frac{\partial \phi}{\partial x}, \qquad q_2 = \frac{\partial \phi}{\partial y};$$

that is, the vector q is the gradient of ϕ,

$$(6) \qquad q = \frac{\partial \phi}{\partial x} + i\frac{\partial \phi}{\partial y},$$

and the directional derivative of ϕ in any direction represents the component of the velocity of flow in that direction.

The function $\phi(x,y)$ is called the *velocity potential*. It follows from equation (4) that $\phi(x,y)$ changes by an additive constant when the reference point z_0 is changed.

The curves $\phi(x,y) = c$ are called *equipotentials*. They are the level curves of the function ϕ. The velocity vectors at all points are normal to them, since q is the gradient of ϕ.

Just as in the case of the flow of heat, the condition of continuity of the steady-state flow, that is, the condition that the incompressible fluid enters or leaves an element of volume of the domain only by flowing through the boundaries of the element, requires that ϕ must satisfy Laplace's equation

$$(7) \qquad \frac{\partial^2 \phi}{\partial x^2} + \frac{\partial^2 \phi}{\partial y^2} = 0$$

in a domain that is free from sources or sinks of the fluid. In view of equations (5) and the continuity of q_1 and q_2 and their derivatives, the partial derivatives of ϕ up to the second order are continuous in such a domain; thus the velocity potential ϕ *is a harmonic function* in the domain.

88. The Stream Function. If $\psi(x,y)$ is a conjugate harmonic of the function $\phi(x,y)$, then the velocity vectors are tangent to the curves

$$(1) \qquad\qquad \psi(x,y) = c.$$

These curves are called the *streamlines* of the flow; the function ψ is the *stream function*. In particular, a boundary across which fluid cannot flow is a streamline of flow for nonviscous fluids.

The analytic function

$$F(z) = \phi(x,y) + i\psi(x,y)$$

is called the *complex potential* of the flow. Now

$$F'(z) = \frac{\partial \phi}{\partial x} + i\frac{\partial \psi}{\partial x} = \frac{\partial \phi}{\partial x} - i\frac{\partial \phi}{\partial y},$$

since ϕ and ψ satisfy the Cauchy-Riemann conditions. In view of equation (6), Sec. 87, it follows that the conjugate of the derivative of the complex potential function is the velocity,

$$(2) \qquad\qquad q = \overline{F'(z)}.$$

The speed, or magnitude of the velocity, is given by the formula

$$(3) \qquad\qquad |q| = |F'(z)|.$$

According to equation (3), Sec. 78, if ϕ is harmonic in a simply connected domain D, then a harmonic conjugate of ϕ there can be written

$$\psi(x,y) = \int_{(x_0,y_0)}^{(x,y)} \left[-\frac{\partial \phi(x',y')}{\partial y'}\, dx' + \frac{\partial \phi(x',y')}{\partial x'}\, dy' \right].$$

In view of equations (5) of Sec. 87, then

$$(4) \qquad \psi(x,y) = \int_{(x_0,y_0)}^{(x,y)} [-q_2(x',y')\, dx' + q_1(x',y')\, dy'].$$

The path of integration is any contour C_1 interior to D and joining the two points (Fig. 74).

A physical interpretation of the stream function can be seen from equation (4). Since the fluid is incompressible, its density is uniform, and the volume occupied by any part bears a constant ratio to the mass on that part. The integrand in equation. (4) is the scalar product of the vectors q and $-i\,dz'$, where

$$dz' = dx' + i\,dy';$$

also, $-i\,dz'$ is a vector of length ds obtained by rotating the tangent vector dz' through the angle $-\pi/2$. The integrand is therefore the product of the lengths of q and $-i\,dz'$ by the cosine of the angle between those vectors, or $q_n\,ds$, where q_n is the component of q normal to C_1. Thus formula (4) can be written

$$(5) \qquad \psi(x,y) = \int_{C_1} q_n(x',y')\,ds.$$

Physically, then, $\psi(x,y)$ represents the time rate of flow of the fluid across the curve C_1 from (x_0,y_0) to (x,y); more precisely, it is the rate of flow, by volume, across a cylinder of unit height standing perpendicular to the xy plane on the curve C_1.

When the point (x,y) is on the streamline through (x_0,y_0), then

$$\psi(x,y) = 0.$$

Since ϕ and ψ are harmonic functions, the properties established in Secs. 80 and 81 under transformations $z = f(w)$, where f is analytic, apply to those functions. Thus they transform into harmonic functions of u and v which may be interpreted as velocity potential and stream function for a flow in the new region. A streamline or natural boundary $\psi = c$ in one plane transforms into a streamline or natural boundary $\psi = c$ in the other.

Under our assumptions of steady irrotational flow of fluids with uniform density ρ, it can be shown that the fluid pressure $p(x,y)$ satisfies this special case of *Bernoulli's equation:*[1]

$$(6) \qquad \frac{p}{\rho} + \frac{1}{2}\,|q|^2 + V = \text{constant}.$$

Here V is the potential function for any field of forces, such as gravity, that acts on the fluid regardless of its flow. We assume

[1] See, for instance, H. Lamb, "Hydrodynamics," pp. 21ff., 1945; or A. M. Kuethe and J. D. Shetzer, "Foundations of Aerodynamics," p. 55, 1959.

that V is constant, an assumption that is valid in many cases. Then the pressure is greatest where the speed $|q|$ is least.

89. Flow around a Corner.   When the complex potential is the function

$$(1) \qquad\qquad F(z) = Az,$$

where A is a positive real constant, then

$$(2) \qquad\qquad \phi(x,y) = Ax, \qquad \psi(x,y) = Ay.$$

The streamlines $\psi = c$ are the horizontal lines $y = c/A$, and the velocity of the fluid is the vector

$$q = \overline{F'(z)} = A.$$

Here the point (x_0, y_0) at which $\psi = 0$ is any point on the x axis. If it is taken as the origin, then $\psi(x,y)$ is the rate of flow across a

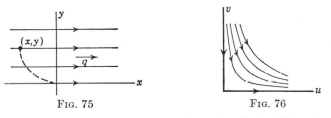

FIG. 75   FIG. 76

contour drawn from the origin to the point (x,y) (Fig. 75).   The flow is a uniform flow to the right.   It can be interpreted as the uniform flow in the upper half plane bounded by the x axis or as the uniform flow between two parallel lines $y = y_1$ and $y = y_2$.

To determine a flow in a quadrant $u \geq 0$, $v \geq 0$, we note that the boundary is mapped onto the entire x axis by the transformation

$$(3) \qquad\qquad z = w^2 = u^2 - v^2 + 2uvi,$$

and the quadrant is mapped onto the upper half of the xy plane. The stream function $\psi = Ay$ for the flow in the half plane transforms into the stream function

$$(4) \qquad\qquad \psi = 2Auv$$

for the flow in the quadrant.   That is, this function ψ must be harmonic in the quadrant and reduce to zero on the boundaries.

The streamlines $\psi = c$ in the quadrant are branches of the rectangular hyperbolas (Fig. 76)

$$2Auv = c.$$

The complex potential is the function $F = Aw^2$, and the velocity of the fluid is

$$q = \overline{F'(w)} = 2A(u - iv).$$

The speed

$$|q| = 2A \sqrt{u^2 + v^2}$$

is directly proportional to the distance of the particle from the origin. The value of the stream function (4) can be interpreted here as the rate of flow across a line segment extending from the origin to the point (u,v).

In such problems it is simplest to write first the complex potential as a function of the complex variable in the new region. The stream function and the velocity can be obtained from that potential function.

The function ψ characterizes a definite flow in the region. The question of whether just one function exists corresponding to a given region, except possibly for a constant factor or an additive constant, cannot be adequately examined here. In some of the examples to follow, in which the velocity is uniform far from the obstruction, or in Chap. 10, where sources and sinks are involved, the physical situation indicates that the flow is uniquely determined by the conditions given in the problem.

It may be noted that a harmonic function is not always uniquely determined, even up to a constant factor, by simply prescribing its values on the boundary of a region. We noted above, for example, that $\psi = Ay$ is harmonic in the half plane $y \geqq 0$ and vanishes on the boundary. The function $\psi_1 = Be^x \sin y$ also satisfies those conditions. However, the streamline $\psi_1 = 0$ consists not only of the line $y = 0$ but also of the lines $y = n\pi$, which are interior to the region. Here the function $F_1 = Be^z$ is the complex potential for the flow in the strip between the lines $y = 0$ and $y = \pi$, both boundaries of which make up the streamline $\psi_1 = 0$; the fluid flows to the right along the lower boundary and to the left along the upper one, if $B > 0$.

90. Flow around a Cylinder. Let a long circular cylinder of unit radius be placed in a large body of fluid flowing with a uniform velocity, with its axis perpendicular to the direction of flow. To determine the steady flow around the cylinder, we can represent the cylinder by the circle $x^2 + y^2 = 1$ and let the flow distant from it be parallel to the x axis (Fig. 77). The symmetry shows that the part of the x axis exterior to the circle may be treated as a boundary, so that we need consider only the upper part of the figure as the region of flow.

The boundary of this region of flow, consisting of the upper semicircle and the two parts of the x axis, is mapped onto the entire u axis by the transformation

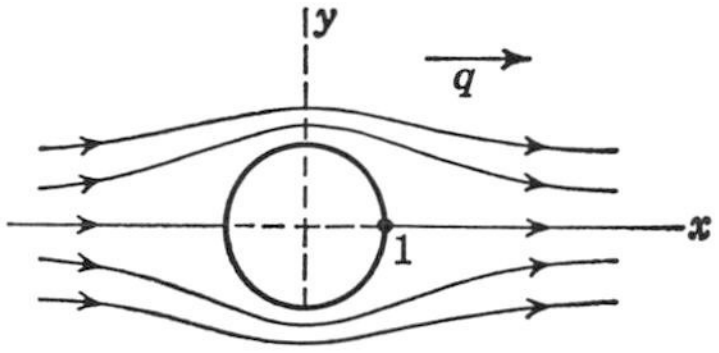

FIG. 77

$$(1) \qquad w = z + \frac{1}{z}.$$

The region is mapped onto the half plane $v \geq 0$ (Fig. 17, Appendix 2). The complex potential for a uniform flow in the half plane is

$$F = Aw,$$

where A is a real constant. Hence the complex potential for the region about the circle is

$$(2) \qquad F = A\left(z + \frac{1}{z}\right).$$

The velocity

$$(3) \qquad q = A\left(1 - \frac{1}{\bar{z}^2}\right)$$

approaches A as $|z|$ increases; that is, the flow is nearly uniform and parallel to the x axis at points distant from the circle. This result also follows by observing that *the derivative of the mapping function* (1) *approaches unity as* $|z|$ *increases*, and hence directions and lengths are only slightly changed by the transformation, at points far from the origin $z = 0$ (Secs. 75 and 76).

From formula (3) we see that $q(\bar{z}) = \overline{q(z)}$; hence the formula also represents velocities of flow in the lower region, with the lower semicircle as a streamline.

According to the formula for F, the stream function is, in polar coordinates,

$$(4) \qquad \psi = A\left(r - \frac{1}{r}\right)\sin\theta.$$

The streamlines

$$A\left(r - \frac{1}{r}\right)\sin\theta = c$$

are symmetric to the y axis and have asymptotes parallel to the x axis. Note that when $c = 0$ the streamline consists of the circle and the x axis.

EXERCISES[1]

1. State why the components of velocity can be obtained from the stream function by the formulas

$$q_1 = \frac{\partial \psi}{\partial y}, \qquad q_2 = -\frac{\partial \psi}{\partial x}.$$

2. At an interior point of a region of flow under the conditions we have assumed, the fluid pressure cannot be less than the pressure at all other points in a neighborhood of that point. Justify this statement with the aid of statements in Secs. 54 and 88.

3. For the flow around a corner described in Sec. 89, at what point of the region $x \geqq 0$, $y \geqq 0$ is the fluid pressure greatest?

4. Show that the speed of the fluid at points on the cylindrical surface in Sec. 90 is $2|A \sin \theta|$ and that the fluid pressure on the cylinder is greatest at the points $z = \pm 1$ and least at the top and bottom of the cylinder.

5. Write the complex potential for the flow around a cylinder $r = r_0$ when the velocity q approaches a real constant A as the point recedes from the cylinder.

6. Obtain the stream function $\psi = Ar^4 \sin 4\theta$ for a flow in the angular region $0 \leqq \theta \leqq \pi/4$ (Fig. 78), and trace one or two of the streamlines inside the region.

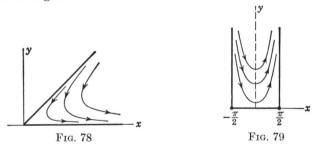

FIG. 78   FIG. 79

7. Obtain the complex potential $F = A \sin z$ for a flow inside the semi-infinite region $-\pi/2 \leqq x \leqq \pi/2$, $y \geqq 0$ (Fig. 79). Write the equations of the streamlines.

[1] Additional problems on fluid flow are presented in Chap. 10. For further examples and problems see, for instance, L. M. Milne-Thomson, "Theoretical Hydrodynamics."

8. If the velocity potential is $\phi = A \operatorname{Log} r$, where $A > 0$, for flow in the region $r \geq r_0$, show that the streamlines are the rays $\theta = c \ (r \geq r_0)$ and that the rate of flow outward through each complete circle about the origin is $2\pi A$, corresponding to a source of that strength at the origin.

9. Obtain the complex potential $F = A(z^2 + z^{-2})$ for a flow in the region $r \geq 1,\ 0 \leq \theta \leq \pi/2$. Write formulas for q and ψ. Note how the speed $|q|$ varies along the boundary of the region, and verify that $\psi = 0$ on the boundary.

10. If the flow at an infinite distance from the cylinder of unit radius in Sec. 90 is uniform in a direction making an angle α with the x axis, that is, if

$$\lim_{|z| \to \infty} q = A \exp(i\alpha) \qquad\qquad (A > 0),$$

find the complex potential.   *Ans.* $F = A[z \exp(-i\alpha) + z^{-1} \exp(i\alpha)]$.

11. The transformation $z = w + 1/w$ maps the circle $|w| = 1$ onto the line segment between the points $z = 2$ and $z = -2$ and maps the domain outside the circle onto the rest of the z plane (see Exercises 13 and 14, Sec. 41). Write

$$z - 2 = r_1 \exp(i\theta_1), \qquad z + 2 = r_2 \exp(i\theta_2),$$

and
$$(z^2 - 4)^{\frac{1}{2}} = \sqrt{r_1}\ \sqrt{r_2} \exp\frac{i\theta_1}{2} \exp\frac{i\theta_2}{2}$$

$$(0 \leq \theta_1 < 2\pi,\ 0 \leq \theta_2 < 2\pi);$$

then the function $(z^2 - 4)^{\frac{1}{2}}$ is single-valued and analytic everywhere except on the branch cut consisting of the segment of the x axis between the points $z = \pm 2$. Show that the inverse of the transformation $z = w + 1/w$, such that $|w| > 1$ for every point z not on the branch cut, can be written

$$w = \frac{1}{2}[z + (z^2 - 4)^{\frac{1}{2}}] = \frac{1}{4}\left(\sqrt{r_1} \exp\frac{i\theta_1}{2} + \sqrt{r_2} \exp\frac{i\theta_2}{2}\right)^2.$$

Thus the transformation and that inverse give a one to one correspondence between points in the two domains.

12. With the aid of the results found in Exercises 10 and 11, derive the formula

$$F(z) = A[z \cos \alpha - i(z^2 - 4)^{\frac{1}{2}} \sin \alpha]$$

for the complex potential for the steady flow around a long plate of width 4, whose cross section is the line segment between the two points $z = \pm 2$ in Fig. 80, when the velocity of the fluid at an infinite distance from the plate is $A \exp(i\alpha)$. The branch $(z^2 - 4)^{\frac{1}{2}}$ is the one described in Exercise 11, and $A > 0$.

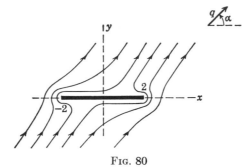

FIG. 80

13. If $\sin \alpha \neq 0$ in Exercise 12, show that the speed of the fluid along the line segment is infinite at the ends $z = \pm 2$ and equal to $A \left| \cos \alpha \right|$ at the mid-point.

14. For the sake of simplicity suppose that $0 < \alpha \leqq \pi/2$ in Exercise 12. Then show that the velocity of the fluid along the upper side of the line segment representing the plate in Fig. 80 is zero at the point $x = 2 \cos \alpha$ and that the velocity along the lower side of the segment is zero at the point $x = -2 \cos \alpha$.

15. A circle with its center at a point x_0 on the x axis, where $0 < x_0 < 1$, and passing through the point $z = -1$, is subjected to the

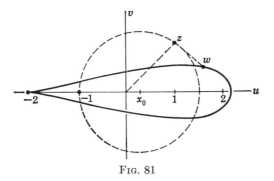

FIG. 81

transformation $w = z + 1/z$. Individual points $z = \exp{(i\theta)}$ can be mapped geometrically by adding the vector $r^{-1} \exp{(-i\theta)}$ to the vector z. Indicate by mapping some points that the image of the circle is a profile of the type shown in Fig. 81 and that points exterior to the circle map into points exterior to the profile. This is a special case of the profile of a *Joukowski airfoil*. (See also Exercises 16 and 17 below.)

16. (a) Show that the mapping of the circle in Exercise 15 is conformal except at the point $z = -1$.   (b) The complex numbers

$$t = \lim_{\Delta z \to 0} \frac{\Delta z}{|\Delta z|}, \qquad \tau = \lim_{\Delta z \to 0} \frac{\Delta w}{|\Delta w|}$$

represent unit tangent vectors to a directed curve at $z = -1$ and its image under the transformation $w = z + 1/z$. Show that $\tau = -t^2$ and hence that the above Joukowski profile has a cusp at the point $w = -2$, and that the angle between the tangents at the cusp is zero.

17. The inverse of the transformation $w = z + 1/z$ used in Exercise 15 is given, with w and z interchanged, in Exercise 11. Find the complex potential for the flow around the airfoil introduced in Exercise 15 when the velocity q of the fluid at an infinite distance from the origin is A, where the constant A is real.

18. Note that, under the transformation

$$w = e^z + z,$$

both the positive and negative parts of the line $y = \pi$ are mapped upon the half line $v = \pi$, $u \leqq -1$. Similarly, $y = -\pi$ maps onto $v = -\pi$,

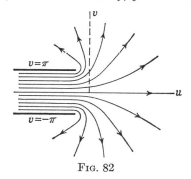

Fig. 82

$u \leqq -1$, and the strip $-\pi \leqq y \leqq \pi$ maps onto the w plane. Also note that the change of directions, arg (dw/dz), under this transformation approaches zero as $x \to -\infty$. Show that the streamlines of a fluid flowing through the open channel formed by the half lines in the w plane (Fig. 82) are the images of the lines $y = c$ in the strip. These streamlines also represent the equipotentials of the electrostatic field near the edge of a parallel-plate capacitor.

CHAPTER 10

THE SCHWARZ-CHRISTOFFEL TRANSFORMATION

91. Mapping the Real Axis onto a Polygon. We represent the unit tangent vector to a smooth directed arc C at a point z_0 by the complex number t. Let the number τ denote the unit tangent vector at the corresponding point w_0 of the image S of C under a transformation $w = f(z)$, where f is analytic at z_0 and $f'(z_0) \neq 0$. In Sec. 75 we found that

$$
\text{(1)} \qquad\qquad \arg \tau = \arg t + \arg f'(z_0).
$$

In particular, if C is a segment of the x axis with positive sense to the right, then at each of its points $z_0 = x$ it is true that $t = 1$ and $\arg t = 0$, and equation (1) can be written

$$
\text{(2)} \qquad\qquad \arg \tau = \arg f'(x).
$$

In case $f'(z)$ has a constant argument along that segment, it follows that $\arg \tau$ is constant; that is, the image S of that segment is also a segment of a straight line.

Let us now construct a transformation $w = f(z)$ that maps the whole x axis onto a polygon of n sides, where $x_1, x_2, \ldots, x_{n-1}$ and $z = \infty$ are the points on that axis whose images are to be the vertices of the polygon and where

$$
x_1 < x_2 < \cdots < x_{n-1}.
$$

The vertices are the points $w_j = f(x_j)$ $(j = 1, 2, \ldots, n-1)$ and $w_n = f(\infty)$. The function f should be such that $\arg f'(z)$ jumps from one constant value to another at points $z = x_j$ as the point z traces the x axis.

If f is chosen as a function such that

$$
\text{(3)} \quad f'(z) = A(z - x_1)^{-k_1}(z - x_2)^{-k_2} \cdots (z - x_{n-1})^{-k_{n-1}},
$$

where A is a complex constant and each k_j is a real constant, the

218

argument of $f'(z)$ changes in the prescribed manner as z describes
the real axis; for the argument of the function (3) can be written

(4) $\arg f'(z) = \arg A - k_1 \arg (z - x_1) - k_2 \arg (z - x_2)$
$$- \cdots - k_{n-1} \arg (z - x_{n-1}).$$

When $z = x$ and $x < x_1$,

$\arg (z - x_1) = \arg (z - x_2) = \cdots = \arg (z - x_{n-1}) = \pi$.

When $x_1 < x < x_2$, $\arg (z - x_1) = 0$ here, and each of the other
arguments is π. According to equation (4), then, $\arg f'(z)$

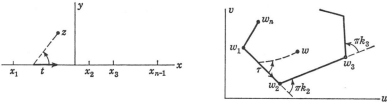

Fig. 83

increases abruptly by the angle $k_1\pi$ as z moves to the right
through the point $z = x_1$. It again jumps in value, by the
amount $k_2\pi$, as z passes through the point x_2, etc.

In view of equation (2), the unit vector τ is constant in direction as z moves from x_{j-1} to x_j, so that w moves in that fixed direction along a straight line. But the direction of τ changes
abruptly, by the angle $k_j\pi$, at the image point w_j of x_j (Fig. 83).
Those angles $k_j\pi$ are the exterior angles of the polygon described
by the point w.

The exterior angles can be limited to angles between $-\pi$ and π;
then $-1 < k_j < 1$. We assume that the sides of the polygon
never cross one another. Then the sum of the exterior angles of a
closed polygon is 2π, and the exterior angle at the vertex w_n, the
image of the point $z = \infty$, can be written

$$k_n\pi = 2\pi - (k_1 + k_2 + \cdots + k_{n-1})\pi.$$

Thus the numbers k_j must necessarily satisfy the conditions

(5) $k_1 + k_2 + \cdots + k_{n-1} + k_n = 2,$ $-1 < k_j < 1$
$$(j = 1, 2, \ldots, n).$$

Note that $k_n = 0$ in case

(6) $k_1 + k_2 + \cdots + k_{n-1} = 2;$

then the directions of the first and last sides of the polygon coincide, and w_n is not a vertex. It is a point on the first side, and the polygon has $n - 1$ sides.

The existence of a mapping function f whose derivative is given by formula (3) will now be established.

92. The Schwarz-Christoffel Transformation. In our formula

$$(1) \qquad f'(z) = A(z - x_1)^{-k_1}(z - x_2)^{-k_2} \cdots (z - x_{n-1})^{-k_{n-1}}$$

for the derivative of a function that is to map the x axis onto a polygon, let the factors represent branches of the power functions with their branch cuts extending below that axis. To be specific, we write

$$(2) \qquad (z - x_j)^{-k_j} = |z - x_j|^{-k_j} \exp(-ik_j\theta_j) \qquad \left(-\frac{\pi}{2} < \theta_j < \frac{3\pi}{2}\right)$$

where $\theta_j = \arg(z - x_j)$ and $j = 1, 2, \ldots, n - 1$. Then f' is analytic in the half plane $y \geq 0$ except for the $n - 1$ branch points x_j.

If z_0 is a point in that region of analyticity, the function

$$(3) \qquad F(z) = \int_{z_0}^{z} f'(\varsigma)\, d\varsigma$$

is single-valued and analytic when $y \geq 0$ and $z \neq x_j$, provided the path of integration from z_0 to z is any contour in that half plane that does not pass through a point x_j. Moreover, $F'(z) = f'(z)$.

To show that the function F is continuous at the point $z = x_1$, we note that $(z - x_1)^{-k_1}$ is the only one of the factors in the expression (1) for $f'(z)$ that is not analytic at x_1. If $\phi(z)$ denotes the product of the rest of those factors, then

$$f'(z) = (z - x_1)^{-k_1}\phi(z) = \phi(x_1)(z - x_1)^{-k_1} + \phi'(x_1)(z - x_1)^{1-k_1} + \cdots$$

in a neighborhood of x_1; that is,

$$(4) \qquad f'(z) = \phi(x_1)(z - x_1)^{-k_1} + (z - x_1)^{1-k_1}\psi(z),$$

where ψ is analytic in the neighborhood. Since $1 - k_1 > 0$, the last term represents a continuous function of z in the upper half $y \geq 0$ of the neighborhood; thus its integral from Z_1 to z, where Z_1 is a point of that half neighborhood, is a continuous function of z at $z = x_1$. Also, the integral

$$\int_{Z_1}^{z} (\zeta - x_1)^{-k_1}\, d\zeta = \frac{1}{1 - k_1}\, [(z - x_1)^{1-k_1} - (Z_1 - x_1)^{1-k_1}]$$

represents a continuous function of z at x_1 if we define its value there as its limit as z approaches x_1 in the half neighborhood. The integral of the function (4) from Z_1 to z is therefore continuous at $z = x_1$, and so is the integral (3), since it can be written as the integral from z_0 to Z_1 plus the integral from Z_1 to z.

The argument applies to each of the $n - 1$ points x_j to show that F is continuous up to those boundary points of the region $y \geqq 0$.

From equation (1) we can show that for a sufficiently large positive number R, a positive constant M exists such that

$$(5) \qquad\qquad |f'(z)| < \frac{M}{|z|^{2-k_n}} \qquad \text{when } |z| > R \text{ and } y \geqq 0.$$

Since $2 - k_n > 1$, this order property of the integrand in equation (3) ensures the existence of the limit of the integral as z tends to infinity; that is, a number W_n exists such that

$$(6) \qquad\qquad \lim_{z \to \infty} F(z) = W_n \qquad\qquad (y \geqq 0).$$

Details of the argument are left to Exercise 7, Sec. 95.

Our mapping function whose derivative is given by formula (1) can be written $f = F + B$, where B is a complex constant. The resulting transformation

$$(7) \quad w = A \int_{z_0}^{z} (\zeta - x_1)^{-k_1}(\zeta - x_2)^{-k_2} \cdots (\zeta - x_{n-1})^{-k_{n-1}}\, d\zeta + B$$

is the *Schwarz-Christoffel transformation*, named in honor of the two German mathematicians, H. A. Schwarz (1843–1921) and E. B. Christoffel (1829–1900), who discovered it independently.

The transformation (7) is continuous throughout the half plane $y \geqq 0$; it is conformal there except at the points x_j. We have assumed that the numbers k_j satisfy conditions (5), Sec. 91. In addition, we suppose that the constants x_j and k_j are such that the sides of the polygon do not cross, so that the polygon is a closed contour. Then, according to Sec. 91, as the point z describes the x axis in the positive direction, its image w describes the polygon P in the positive sense, and there is a one to one correspondence between points on that axis and points on P.

According to condition (6), the image w_n of the point $z = \infty$ does exist, and $w_n = W_n + B$.

If z is an interior point of the half plane ($y > 0$) and x_0 is any point other than x_j on the x axis, then the angle from the vector t to the vector $z - x_0$ is positive and less than π (Fig. 83). At the image w_0 of x_0, the angle from the vector τ to the image of the vector $z - x_0$ has that same value. Thus the images of points of the half plane lie on the left of all vectors τ on the sides of the polygon. A proof that the transformation gives a one to one correspondence between points in the half plane and the interior of the polygon is left to the exercises.

Given a definite polygon P, let us examine the number of constants in the Schwarz-Christoffel transformation that must be determined in order to map P onto the x axis. For this purpose we may write $z_0 = 0$, $A = 1$, and $B = 0$, and simply require that some polygon P' similar to P is to map onto that axis. The size, orientation, and position of P' can then be adjusted to match those of P by introducing the appropriate constants A and B.

The numbers k_j are all determined from the exterior angles at the vertices of P. The $n - 1$ constants x_j remain. The image of the x axis is some polygon P' which has the same angles as P; but if P' is to be similar to P, then $n - 2$ of its sides must have a common ratio to the corresponding sides of P, a condition that is expressed by means of $n - 3$ equations in the $n - 1$ real constants x_j. Thus *two of the numbers x_j, or two relations between them, can be chosen arbitrarily*, provided those $n - 3$ equations in the remaining $n - 3$ constants have real-valued solutions.

When a finite point $z = x_n$ on the x axis, instead of the infinite point, represents the image of the vertex w_n, then it follows from the preceding section that the Schwarz-Christoffel transformation takes the form

$$(8) \quad w = A \int_{z_0}^{z} (z' - x_1)^{-k_1}(z' - x_2)^{-k_2} \cdots (z' - x_n)^{-k_n} \, dz' + B,$$

where $k_1 + k_2 + \cdots + k_n = 2$. The exponents k_j are determined from the exterior angles of the polygon. But in this case there are n real constants x_j which must satisfy the $n - 3$ equations noted above. Thus *three of the numbers x_j, or three conditions on those n numbers, can be chosen arbitrarily* in the transformation (8) of a given polygon onto the x axis.

93. Triangles and Rectangles. The Schwarz-Christoffel transformation is written in terms of the *images* x_j of the vertices of the polygon, not in terms of the vertices themselves. Not more than three of those images can be chosen arbitrarily, so that when the given polygon has more than three sides, some of the images must be determined in order to make the given polygon, or any polygon congruent to it, map onto the real axis. The selection

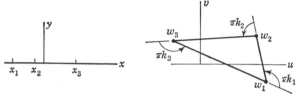

Fɪɢ. 84

of conditions for the determination of those constants, conditions that are convenient to use, often requires ingenuity.

Another limitation in using the transformation, however, arises because of the integration that is involved. In most cases, the integral cannot be evaluated in terms of a finite number of elementary functions. In such cases, the transformation may still be highly useful, but the solution of problems by means of it can become quite involved.

If the polygon is a triangle with vertices at the points w_1, w_2, and w_3 (Fig. 84), the transformation can be written

$$(1) \quad w = A \int_{z_0}^{z} (z' - x_1)^{-k_1}(z' - x_2)^{-k_2}(z' - x_3)^{-k_3} \, dz' + B,$$

where $k_1 + k_2 + k_3 = 2$. In terms of the interior angles θ_j,

$$k_j = 1 - \frac{1}{\pi}\,\theta_j \qquad\qquad (j = 1, 2, 3).$$

Here we have taken all three images x_j as finite points on the x axis. Arbitrary values can be assigned to each of the three constants x_j. The complex constants A and B, associated with the size and position of the triangle, can be determined so that the given triangular region maps onto the upper half plane.

If we take the image of the vertex w_3 as the infinite point, the transformation of the triangle becomes

$$(2) \qquad w = A \int_{z_0}^{z} (z' - x_1)^{-k_1}(z' - x_2)^{-k_2} \, dz' + B,$$

where arbitrary real values can be assigned to x_1 and x_2.

The integrals in equations (1) and (2) do not represent elementary functions unless the triangle is degenerate, that is, unless one or two of its vertices are at infinity. The integral in equation (2) becomes an elliptic integral when the triangle is equilateral and when it is a right triangle with one of its angles equal to either $\pi/3$ or $\pi/4$. In these cases z is an elliptic function of w, but for other nondegenerate triangles the process of solving for z as a function of w involves further complications.

For an equilateral triangle $k_1 = k_2 = k_3 = \frac{2}{3}$. It is convenient to write $x_1 = -1$, $x_2 = 1$, and $x_3 = \infty$ and to use equation (2) where $z_0 = 1$, $A = 1$, and $B = 0$. Then the transformation becomes

$$(3) \qquad w = \int_1^z (z' + 1)^{-\frac{2}{3}}(z' - 1)^{-\frac{2}{3}}\, dz'.$$

The image of the point $z = 1$ is clearly $w = 0$; that is, $w_2 = 0$. When $z = -1$ in the integral, we write $z' = x$; then $-1 < x < 1$

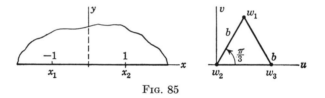

FIG. 85

and $x + 1 > 0$ and $\arg (x + 1) = 0$, while $|x - 1| = 1 - x$ and $\arg (x - 1) = \pi$. Therefore

$$(4) \quad w_1 = \int_1^{-1} (x + 1)^{-\frac{2}{3}} \exp\left(-\tfrac{2}{3}\pi i\right)(1 - x)^{-\frac{2}{3}}\, dx$$

$$= \exp\left(\frac{\pi i}{3}\right) \int_{-1}^1 \frac{dx}{(1 - x^2)^{\frac{2}{3}}}.$$

The last integral reduces to the one used in defining the beta function (Exercise 9, Sec. 74). Let b denote its value $(b > 0)$:

$$(5) \qquad b = 2 \int_0^1 \frac{dx}{(1 - x^2)^{\frac{2}{3}}} = B\left(\frac{1}{2}, \frac{1}{3}\right).$$

The vertex w_1 is therefore the point (Fig. 85)

$$(6) \qquad\qquad w_1 = b \exp \frac{\pi i}{3}.$$

The vertex w_3 is on the positive u axis, because

$$w_3 = \int_1^\infty (x+1)^{-\frac{2}{3}}(x-1)^{-\frac{2}{3}}\, dx = \int_1^\infty \frac{dx}{(x^2-1)^{\frac{2}{3}}}.$$

But the value of w_3 is also represented by the integral (3) when z tends to infinity along the negative x axis; that is,

$$w_3 = \int_1^{-\infty} (x+1)^{-\frac{2}{3}}(x-1)^{-\frac{2}{3}}\, dx.$$

In view of equation (4), then,

$$w_3 = w_1 + \exp\left(-\tfrac{4}{3}\pi i\right)\int_{-1}^{-\infty} (|x+1|\,|x-1|)^{-\frac{2}{3}}\, dx$$
$$= b\exp\frac{\pi i}{3} + \exp\left(-\frac{\pi i}{3}\right)\int_1^\infty \frac{dx}{(x^2-1)^{\frac{2}{3}}}$$

or $\qquad w_3 = b\exp\dfrac{\pi i}{3} + w_3\exp\left(-\dfrac{\pi i}{3}\right).$

Solving for w_3, we find that

(7) $$w_3 = b.$$

Thus we have verified that the image of the x axis is the equilateral triangle of side b, shown in Fig. 85. We can see also that $w = \frac{1}{2}b\exp(\pi i/3)$ when $z = 0$.

When the polygon is a rectangle, $k_j = \frac{1}{2}$. If we choose points ± 1 and $\pm a$ as the images x_j of the four vertices and write

(8) $$g(z) = (z+a)^{-\frac{1}{2}}(z+1)^{-\frac{1}{2}}(z-1)^{-\frac{1}{2}}(z-a)^{-\frac{1}{2}},$$

where $0 \leqq \arg(z-x_j) \leqq \pi$, the transformation can be written

(9) $$w = -\int_0^z g(z')\, dz'$$

except for a transformation $W = Aw + B$ to adjust the size, orientation, and position of the rectangle. The integral (9) is a constant times the elliptic integral

$$\int_0^z (1-z'^2)^{-\frac{1}{2}}(1-k^2z'^2)^{-\frac{1}{2}}\, dz' \qquad \left(k = \frac{1}{a}\right);$$

but form (8) of the integrand indicates more clearly the appropriate branches of the irrational functions.

Let us locate the vertices of the rectangle when $a > 1$. Then, as shown in Fig. 86, $x_1 = -a$, $x_2 = -1$, $x_3 = 1$, and $x_4 = a$.

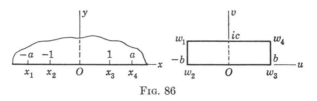

FIG. 86

All four vertices can be described in terms of two positive numbers b and c which depend on the value of a in this manner:

$$(10) \qquad b = \int_0^1 |g(x)|\, dx = \int_0^1 \frac{dx}{\sqrt{(1 - x^2)(a^2 - x^2)}},$$

$$(11) \qquad c = \int_1^a |g(x)|\, dx = \int_1^a \frac{dx}{\sqrt{(x^2 - 1)(a^2 - x^2)}}.$$

When $-1 < x < 0$, then $\arg (x + a) = \arg (x + 1) = 0$ while $\arg (x - 1) = \arg (x - a) = \pi$; hence

$$g(x) = [\exp (-\tfrac{1}{2}\pi i)]^2 |g(x)| = -|g(x)|.$$

When $-a < x < -1$, then $g(x) = [\exp (-\tfrac{1}{2}\pi i)]^3 |g(x)| = i|g(x)|$. Therefore

$$w_1 = -\int_0^{-a} g(x)\, dx = -\int_0^{-1} g(x)\, dx - \int_{-1}^{-a} g(x)\, dx$$

$$= \int_0^{-1} |g(x)|\, dx - i \int_{-1}^{-a} |g(x)|\, dx = -b + ic.$$

It is left to the exercises to show that

$$(12) \qquad w_2 = -b, \qquad w_3 = b, \qquad w_4 = b + ic.$$

The position and dimensions of the rectangle are shown in Fig. 86.

94. Degenerate Polygons. We shall now apply the Schwarz-Christoffel transformation to some degenerate polygons for which the integrals represent elementary functions. For the purpose of illustration, we begin with some known transformations.

As our first example, let us map the semi-infinite strip

$$-\frac{\pi}{2} \leq u \leq \frac{\pi}{2}, \qquad v \geq 0$$

onto the half plane $y \geq 0$. We consider this strip as the limiting form of a triangle with vertices w_1, w_2, and w_3 (Fig. 87) as the imaginary part of w_3 tends to infinity.

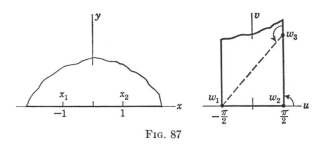

FIG. 87

The limiting values of the exterior angles are

$$\pi k_1 = \pi k_2 = \frac{\pi}{2}, \qquad \pi k_3 = \pi.$$

We choose the points $x_1 = -1$, $x_2 = 1$, and $x_3 = \infty$ as the images of the vertices. Then the derivative of the mapping function can be written

$$\frac{dw}{dz} = A(z + 1)^{-\frac{1}{2}}(z - 1)^{-\frac{1}{2}} = A'(1 - z^2)^{-\frac{1}{2}}.$$

Thus $w = A' \sin^{-1} z + B$, or, if we write $A' = 1/a$ and $B = b/a$, then

$$z = \sin (aw - b).$$

This transformation satisfies the conditions that $z = -1$ when $w = -\pi/2$ and $z = 1$ when $w = \pi/2$ if its coefficients are assigned the values $a = 1$ and $b = 0$. The resulting transformation is

$$z = \sin w,$$

which we verified in Sec. 39 as one that maps the strip onto the half plane.

95. The Infinite Strip. Consider the strip $0 < v < \pi$ as the limiting form of a rhombus with vertices at the points $w_1 = \pi i$, w_2, $w_3 = 0$, and w_4, as points w_2 and w_4 are moved infinitely far to the left and right, respectively (Fig. 88). In the limit the exterior angles become

$$\pi k_1 = 0, \qquad \pi k_2 = \pi, \qquad \pi k_3 = 0, \qquad \pi k_4 = \pi.$$

We leave x_1 to be determined and choose the values $x_2 = 0$, $x_3 = 1$, and $x_4 = \infty$. The derivative of the Schwarz-Christoffel mapping function then becomes

$$\frac{dw}{dz} = A(z - x_1)^0 z^{-1}(z - 1)^0 = \frac{A}{z};$$

thus $\qquad\qquad w = A \operatorname{Log} z + B.$

Now $B = 0$ because $w = 0$ when $z = 1$. The constant A must be real because the point w lies on the real axis when $z = x$ and

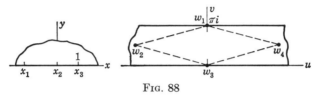

FIG. 88

$x > 0$. The image of the point $w = \pi i$ is the point $z = x_1$, where x_1 is a negative number; therefore

$$\pi i = A \operatorname{Log} x_1 = A \operatorname{Log} |x_1| + A\pi i.$$

By identifying real and imaginary coefficients here, we see that $|x_1| = 1$ and $A = 1$. Hence the transformation becomes

$$w = \operatorname{Log} z;$$

also $x_1 = -1$. In Sec. 38 we verified that this transformation maps the strip onto the half plane.

The procedure used here and in the preceding section is not rigorously sound, because limiting values of angles and coordinates were not introduced in an orderly way. Limiting values were used whenever it seemed expedient to do so. But if we verify the mapping obtained, it is not essential that we justify the steps in our derivation of the mapping function. The formal method used here is shorter and less tedious than rigorous methods.

EXERCISES

1. In the transformation (1) of Sec. 93 write $B = z_0 = 0$ and

$$A = \exp\frac{3\pi i}{4}, \qquad x_1 = -1, \qquad x_2 = 0, \qquad x_3 = 1,$$

$$k_1 = \tfrac{3}{4}, \qquad k_2 = \tfrac{1}{2}, \qquad k_3 = \tfrac{3}{4}.$$

to map the x axis onto an *isosceles right triangle*.   In terms of the positive constant b, where

$$b = \int_0^1 (1 - x^2)^{-\frac{1}{2}} x^{-\frac{1}{2}} \, dx,$$

show that the vertices of the triangle are the points

$$w_1 = bi, \qquad w_2 = 0, \qquad w_3 = b.$$

Also show that $2b = B(\frac{1}{4}, \frac{1}{4})$, where B is the beta function.

2. Obtain the formulas (12) in Sec. 93 for the rest of the vertices of the rectangle shown in Fig. 86.

3. When $0 < a < 1$ in formulas (8) and (9), Sec. 93, show that the vertices of the rectangle are those shown in Fig. 86 if b and c now have the values

$$b = \int_0^a |g(x)| \, dx, \qquad c = \int_a^1 |g(x)| \, dx.$$

4. Show that the special case

$$w = i \int_0^z (\zeta + 1)^{-\frac{1}{2}} (\zeta - 1)^{-\frac{1}{2}} \zeta^{-\frac{1}{2}} \, d\zeta$$

of the Schwarz-Christoffel transformation (7), Sec. 92, maps the x axis onto the *square* with vertices

$$w_1 = bi, \qquad w_2 = 0, \qquad w_3 = b, \qquad w_4 = b + ib,$$

where the positive number b is given in terms of the beta function by the formula

$$b = \tfrac{1}{2} B(\tfrac{1}{4}, \tfrac{1}{2}).$$

5. Use the Schwarz-Christoffel transformation to arrive at the transformation $w = z^m$, which maps the angular region $0 \leq \arg w \leq m\pi$ onto the half plane $y \geq 0$ and the point $w = 1$ into the point $z = 1$.   Consider the angular region as the limiting case of the triangle shown in Fig. 89 as the angle α tends to zero.

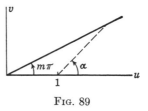

6. Refer to Fig. 26, Appendix 2.   In traversing the boundary of the region in the w plane, a point w moves through A' and B', then through C' to D' and from D'

FIG. 89

through E'.   This path might be considered as a degenerate triangle; at least the point is moving in the same direction on the right of E' as it is on the left of A', and the infinite ends of those parts of the path might be considered as a single point on the same side of the triangle.   Proceed formally with the Schwarz-Christoffel transformation to obtain the mapping function given with the figure.

7. In Sec. 92, use condition (5) and conditions for the existence of improper integrals of real-valued functions to show that $F(x)$ has some limit W_n as $x \rightarrow \infty$, where $F(z)$ is defined by equation (3) of that section. Also show that the integral of $f'(z)$ over each arc of a semicircle $|z| = R$, $y \geq 0$, tends to zero as $R \rightarrow \infty$. Then deduce that $F(z)$ has the limit W_n as $z \rightarrow \infty$ $(y \geq 0)$, as stated in equation (6).

8. A special case of the linear fractional transformation (6), Sec. 35, that maps the unit disk $|Z| \leq 1$ conformally onto the half plane $y \geq 0$ is

$$Z = -\frac{z - i}{z + i}.$$

Let Z_j be the images of the points $z = x_j$ under that transformation, where x_j $(j = 1, 2, \ldots, n)$ are the points used in the Schwarz-Christoffel transformation (8), Sec. 92. Show formally (without determining the branches of the irrational functions) that

$$\frac{dw}{dZ} = A'(Z - Z_1)^{-k_1}(Z - Z_2)^{-k_2} \cdots (Z - Z_n)^{-k_n},$$

where $|Z_j| = 1$ and A' is a constant, and hence that the transformation

$$w = A' \int_0^Z (\zeta - Z_1)^{-k_1}(\zeta - Z_2)^{-k_2} \cdots (\zeta - Z_n)^{-k_n} \, d\zeta + B$$

maps the *interior of the circle* $|Z| = 1$ *onto the interior of a polygon*, the points Z_j on the circle being the images of the vertices of the polygon.

9. Use residues to prove the following extension of the property of the logarithmic derivative given in Exercise 10, Sec. 69. *Let g be an analytic function in a simply connected domain D in which $g'(z) \neq 0$. Let C denote a closed contour in D, described in the positive sense, such that $g(z) \neq 0$ at any point on C. Then the number of zeros of g interior to C is given by the formula*

$$N = \frac{1}{2\pi i} \int_C \frac{g'(z)}{g(z)} \, dz.$$

10. In the formula for N in Exercise 9 write $g(z) = w(z) - w_0$, where w is the Schwarz-Christoffel mapping function (7), Sec. 92, and the point w_0 is either interior to or exterior to the polygon P that is the image of the x axis; thus $w(x) \neq w_0$. Let the contour C consist of the upper half of a circle $|z| = R$ and a segment $-R < x < R$ of the x axis that contains all $n - 1$ points x_j, except that a small segment about each point x_j is replaced by the upper half of a circle $|z - x_j| = r_j$ with that segment as its diameter. Then the number of points z interior to C

where $w(z) = w_0$ is

$$N_c = \frac{1}{2\pi i} \int_C \frac{w'(z)}{w(z) - w_0}\, dz.$$

Let r_j tend to zero and prove that the number of points in the upper half of the z plane at which $w(z) = w_0$ is

$$N = \frac{1}{2\pi i} \lim_{R \to \infty} \int_{-R}^{R} \frac{w'(x)}{w(x) - w_0}\, dx.$$

Since

$$\int_P \frac{dw}{w - w_0} = \lim_{R \to \infty} \int_{-R}^{R} \frac{w'(x)}{w(x) - w_0}\, dx,$$

deduce that $N = 1$ if w_0 is interior to P and that $N = 0$ if w_0 is exterior to P and hence that the mapping of the half plane $y > 0$ onto the interior of P is one to one.

96. Fluid Flow in a Channel through a Slit.   Let us present a further example of the idealized steady flow treated in Chap. 9, an example that will help to show how sources and sinks can be accounted for in problems of the flow of a fluid.

Consider the two-dimensional steady flow of fluid between two parallel planes $y = 0$ and $y = \pi$, when the fluid is entering through a narrow slit along the line $x = 0$ in the first plane (Fig. 90).   Let the rate of flow of fluid into the channel through

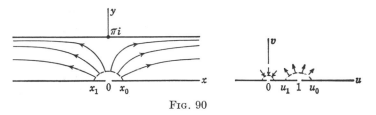

Fig. 90

the slit be Q units of volume per unit time for each unit of depth of the channel, where the depth is measured perpendicular to the xy plane.   Then the rate of flow out at either end is $\frac{1}{2}Q$.

We transform the strip into the upper half of the w plane by means of the transformation $z = \text{Log } w$, derived in the preceding section; then

(1) $$w = e^z = e^x e^{iy}.$$

The image of the x axis is the positive half of the u axis, and the image of the line $y = \pi$ is the negative half of the u axis.   Thus the boundary of the cross section of the channel transforms into the boundary of the half plane.

The image of the point $z = 0$ is the point $w = 1$. The image of a point $z = x_0$ such that $x_0 > 0$ is a point $w = u_0$ where $u_0 > 1$. The rate of flow of fluid across a curve joining the point $z = x_0$ to a point (x,y) within the strip is a stream function $\psi(x,y)$ for the flow (Sec. 88). If x_1 is a negative real number, then the rate of flow into the channel through the slit can be written

$$\psi(x_1,0) = Q.$$

Now, under a conformal transformation, the function ψ is a function of u and v that represents the stream function for the flow in the region in the w plane; that is, the rate of flow is the same across corresponding curves in the two planes. Since the image of the point $z = x_1$ is a point $w = u_1$ where $0 < u_1 < 1$, the rate of flow across any curve connecting the points $w = u_0$ and $w = u_1$ and lying in the upper half of the w plane is also equal to Q. Thus there is a source at the point $w = 1$ equal to the source at $z = 0$.

The above argument applies in general to show that, *under a conformal transformation, a source or sink at a given point corresponds to an equal source or sink at the image of that point.*

As $x \to -\infty$, the image of the point z approaches the point $w = 0$. A sink of strength $\frac{1}{2}Q$ at the latter point corresponds to the sink infinitely far to the left in the strip. To apply the above argument in this case, we consider the rate of flow across a curve connecting the boundaries $y = 0$ and $y = \pi$ of the left-hand part of the strip and the flow across the image of that curve in the w plane.

The sink at the right-hand end of the strip transforms into a sink at infinity in the w plane.

The stream function ψ for the flow in the upper half of the w plane in this case must be a function that has a constant value along each of the three parts of the u axis. Moreover, its value must increase by Q when the point w moves around the point $w = 1$ from the position $w = u_0$ to the position $w = u_1$, and its value must decrease by $\frac{1}{2}Q$ when w moves about the origin in the corresponding manner. In terms of the polar coordinate angles

θ_1 and θ_2 ranging from zero to π, where

$$w = r_1 \exp \theta_1, \qquad w - 1 = r_2 \exp \theta_2,$$

we see that the function

$$\psi = \frac{Q}{\pi}\left(\theta_2 - \frac{1}{2}\theta_1\right)$$

satisfies those requirements.   Furthermore, this function is harmonic because it is the imaginary coefficient of the function

$$F = \frac{Q}{\pi}\left[\operatorname{Log}(w - 1) - \frac{1}{2}\operatorname{Log} w\right]$$

$$= \frac{Q}{\pi}\operatorname{Log}(w^{\frac{1}{2}} - w^{-\frac{1}{2}}).$$

The function F is a complex potential for the flow in the w plane.   Since $w = \exp z$, a complex potential for the flow in the channel is

$$F(z) = \frac{Q}{\pi}\operatorname{Log}(e^{z/2} - e^{-z/2}).$$

By dropping an additive constant, the potential can be written

(2) $$F(z) = \frac{Q}{\pi}\operatorname{Log}\sinh\frac{z}{2}.$$

The velocity vector $\overline{F'(z)}$ is given by the formula

(3) $$q = \frac{Q}{2\pi}\coth\frac{\bar{z}}{2}.$$

From this formula it can be seen that

$$\lim_{|x|\to\infty} q = \frac{Q}{2\pi}.$$

Also, the point $z = \pi i$ is a *stagnation point;* that is, the velocity is zero there.   Hence the fluid pressure along the wall $y = \pi$ of the channel is greatest at points opposite the slit.

The stream function $\psi(x,y)$ for the channel is the imaginary coefficient of the function $F(z)$ given by equation (2).   The streamlines $\psi(x,y) = c$ are therefore curves

$$\frac{Q}{2\pi}\arg\left(\sinh\frac{z}{2}\right) = c,$$

an equation that reduces to

(4) $$\tan \frac{y}{2} = k \tanh \frac{x}{2},$$

where k is any real constant.   Some of these streamlines are indicated in Fig. 90.

97. Flow in a Channel with an Offset.   As a further example of the use of the Schwarz-Christoffel transformation, let us find the complex potential for the flow of a fluid in a channel with an abrupt change in its breadth (Fig. 91).   We take our unit of

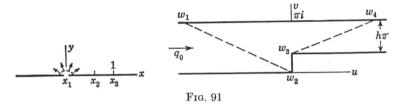

FIG. 91

length such that the breadth of the wide part of the channel is π units; then $h\pi$ represents the breadth of the narrow part, where $0 < h < 1$.   Let the real constant q_0 denote the velocity of the fluid far from the offset in the wide part; more precisely,

$$\lim_{u \to -\infty} q = q_0,$$

where the complex variable q represents the velocity vector. The rate of flow per unit depth through the channel, or the strength of the source on the left and of the sink on the right, is then

(1) $$Q = \pi q_0.$$

The cross section of the channel can be considered as the limiting case of the quadrilateral with the vertices w_1, w_2, w_3, and w_4 shown in the figure, as the first and last of these vertices are moved infinitely far to the left and to the right, respectively. In the limit the exterior angles become

$$\pi k_1 = \pi, \qquad \pi k_2 = \frac{\pi}{2}, \qquad \pi k_3 = -\frac{\pi}{2}, \qquad \pi k_4 = \pi.$$

If we write $x_1 = 0, x_3 = 1, x_4 = \infty$ and leave x_2 to be determined, where $0 < x_2 < 1$, the derivative of the mapping function becomes

(2) $$\frac{dw}{dz} = Az^{-1}(z - x_2)^{-\frac{1}{2}}(z - 1)^{\frac{1}{2}}.$$

In order to simplify the determination of the constants A and x_2 here, let us proceed at once to the use of the complex potential of the flow. The source of the flow in the channel infinitely far to the left is transformed into an equal source at $z = 0$ (Sec. 96). The entire boundary of the cross section of the channel has the x axis as its image. In view of equation (1), then, the complex potential for the flow in the channel is transformed into the function

(3) $$F = q_0 \operatorname{Log} z = q_0 \operatorname{Log} r + iq_0\theta,$$

since this is the potential for the flow in the upper half of the z plane with the required source at the origin. Note that the sink on the right of the channel must transform into a sink at infinity in the z plane.

The complex conjugate of the velocity q in the w plane can be written

$$\overline{q(w)} = \frac{dF}{dw} = \frac{dF}{dz}\frac{dz}{dw}.$$

Thus, by referring to equations (2) and (3), we can write

(4) $$\overline{q(w)} = \frac{q_0}{A}\left(\frac{z - x_2}{z - 1}\right)^{\frac{1}{2}}.$$

At the limiting position of the point w_1, which corresponds to $z = 0$, the velocity is the real constant q_0. Consequently, it follows from equation (4) that

$$q_0 = \frac{q_0}{A}\sqrt{x_2}.$$

At the limiting position of w_4, which corresponds to $z = \infty$, let the real number q_4 denote the velocity. Now it seems plausible that q approaches q_4, at all points of a vertical line segment that spans the narrow part of the channel, as the segment is moved infinitely far to the right. We could establish this conjecture as a fact by first finding w as a function of z from equation (2); but to shorten our discussion, we assume that this conjecture is true here.   Then, since the flow is steady,

$$\pi h q_4 = \pi q_0 = Q,$$

or $q_4 = q_0/h$.   Letting z tend to infinity in equation (4), we therefore find that

$$\frac{q_0}{h} = \frac{q_0}{A}.$$

Thus

(5) $A = h, \qquad x_2 = h^2,$

and

(6) $\overline{q(w)} = \frac{q_0}{h}\left(\frac{z - h^2}{z - 1}\right)^{\frac{1}{2}}.$

From equation (6) we can see that the magnitude $|q|$ of the velocity becomes infinite at the corner w_3 of the offset, since the image of that point is the point $z = 1$.   Also, the corner w_2 is a stagnation point, a point where $q = 0$.   Along the boundary of the channel, the fluid pressure is therefore greatest at w_2 and least at w_3.

In order to write the relation between the potential and the variable w, we must integrate equation (2), which can now be written

(7) $\frac{dw}{dz} = \frac{h}{z}\left(\frac{z - 1}{z - h^2}\right)^{\frac{1}{2}}.$

By substituting a new variable s here, where

$$\frac{z - h^2}{z - 1} = s^2,$$

we can show that equation (7) reduces to the equation

$$\frac{dw}{ds} = 2h\left(\frac{1}{1 - s^2} - \frac{1}{h^2 - s^2}\right).$$

Therefore

(8) $w = h \operatorname{Log}\frac{1 + s}{1 - s} - \operatorname{Log}\frac{h + s}{h - s},$

where the constant of integration is zero, because when $z = h^2$, that is, when $s = 0$, $w = 0$.

In terms of s the potential (3) becomes

$$F = q_0 \operatorname{Log} \frac{h^2 - s^2}{1 - s^2};$$

consequently,

(9)
$$s^2 = \frac{\exp (F/q_0) - h^2}{\exp (F/q_0) - 1}.$$

By substituting s from this equation into equation (8), we get an implicit relation between the potential $F(w)$ and w.

98. Electrostatic Potential about an Edge of a Conducting Plate.   Two parallel conducting plates of infinite extent are kept at the electrostatic potential $V = 0$, and a parallel semi-infinite plate, placed midway between them, is kept at the potential $V = 1$.   The coordinate system and the unit of length are chosen so that the plates lie in the planes $v = 0$, $v = \pi$, and $v = \pi/2$ (Fig. 92).   Let us determine the potential function $V(u,v)$ in the region between those plates.

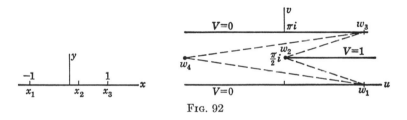

FIG. 92

The region has the limiting form of the quadrilateral bounded by the broken lines in the figure, as the points w_1 and w_3 move out to the right and w_4 to the left.   In applying the Schwarz-Christoffel transformation here, we let the image x_4 of the vertex w_4 be infinity.   We choose the images $x_1 = -1$, $x_3 = 1$ and leave x_2 to be determined.   The limiting values of the exterior angles of the quadrilateral are

$$\pi k_1 = \pi, \qquad \pi k_2 = -\pi, \qquad \pi k_3 = \pi k_4 = \pi.$$

Thus
$$\frac{dw}{dz} = A (z + 1)^{-1}(z - x_2)(z - 1)^{-1}$$

$$= A \frac{z - x_2}{z^2 - 1} = \frac{A}{2} \left(\frac{1 + x_2}{z + 1} + \frac{1 - x_2}{z - 1} \right),$$

so that the transformation of the divided strip in the w plane into the upper half of the z plane has the form

$$(1) \quad w = \frac{A}{2}\left[(1 + x_2) \operatorname{Log}(z + 1) + (1 - x_2) \operatorname{Log}(z - 1)\right] + B.$$

Let A_1, A_2 and B_1, B_2 denote the real and imaginary components of the constants A and B. When $z = x$, the point w lies on the boundary of the divided strip, and, according to equation (1),

$$(2) \quad \begin{aligned} u + iv = {\tfrac{1}{2}}(A_1 + iA_2)\{&(1 + x_2)[\operatorname{Log}|x + 1| \\ &+ i \arg(x + 1)] + (1 - x_2)[\operatorname{Log}|x - 1| \\ &+ i \arg(x - 1)]\} + B_1 + iB_2. \end{aligned}$$

In order to determine the constants here, we first note that the limiting position of the line joining the points w_1 and w_4 is the u axis. The image of that line is the part of the x axis to the left of the point $x_1 = -1$, because the part $x > 1$ is the image of the line joining w_3 and w_4, and the remaining two segments of the x axis are the images of the other two sides of the quadrilateral. Hence, when $v = 0$ and u tends to infinity through positive values, the image point x approaches the point $z = -1$ from the left; thus

$$\arg(x + 1) = \pi, \qquad \arg(x - 1) = \pi, \qquad \operatorname{Log}|x + 1| \to -\infty,$$

and since $-1 < x_2 < 1$, the real part of the quantity inside the braces in equation (2) tends to negative infinity. Since $v = 0$, it follows that $A_2 = 0$; otherwise the coefficient of the imaginary part on the right would become infinite. By equating imaginary coefficients on the two sides, we now see that

$$0 = {\tfrac{1}{2}}A_1[(1 + x_2)\pi + (1 - x_2)\pi] + B_2.$$

Hence

$$(3) \qquad\qquad -\pi A_1 = B_2, \qquad A_2 = 0.$$

The limiting position of the line joining the points w_1 and w_2 is the half line $v = \pi/2$, $u \geqq 0$. The images of points on that half line are the points $z = x$, where $-1 < x \leqq x_2$, and therefore

$$\arg(x + 1) = 0, \qquad \arg(x - 1) = \pi.$$

Identifying the imaginary parts of the two members of equation

(2) for those points, we see that

(4)
$$\frac{\pi}{2} = \frac{A_1}{2} (1 - x_2)\pi + B_2.$$

Finally, the limiting positions of points on the line joining w_3 to w_4 are the points $u + \pi i$, and their images are the points x where $x > 1$. By identifying the imaginary parts in equation (2) for those points, we find that

$$\pi = B_2.$$

Then, in view of equations (3) and (4),

$$A_1 = -1, \qquad x_2 = 0.$$

Thus $x = 0$ when $w = \pi i/2$, and upon substituting these values into equation (2) and identifying real parts, we see that $B_1 = 0$.

The transformation (1) now becomes

(5)
$$w = -\tfrac{1}{2} [\text{Log} \, (z + 1) + \text{Log} \, (z - 1)] + \pi i,$$

or

(6)
$$z^2 = 1 + e^{-2w}.$$

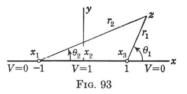

Fig. 93

Under this transformation, the required harmonic function $V(u,v)$ becomes a harmonic function of x and y in the region $y > 0$, which satisfies the boundary conditions indicated in Fig. 93. Note that $x_2 = 0$ now. The harmonic function in that half plane that assumes those values on the boundary is the imaginary coefficient of the analytic function

$$F(z) = \frac{1}{\pi} \text{Log} \, \frac{z-1}{z+1} = \frac{1}{\pi} \text{Log} \, \frac{r_1}{r_2} + \frac{i}{\pi} (\theta_1 - \theta_2),$$

where θ_1 and θ_2 range from zero to π. Writing the tangents of these angles as functions of x and y and simplifying, we find that the function V satisfies the equation

(7)
$$\tan \pi V = \tan (\theta_1 - \theta_2) = \frac{2y}{x^2 + y^2 - 1}.$$

Equation (6) furnishes expressions for $|z|^2$ (or $x^2 + y^2$) and $x^2 - y^2$ in terms of u and v. Then from formula (7) we find that the relation between the potential V and the coordinates u and v can be written

$$(8) \qquad\qquad \tan \pi V = \frac{1}{s} \sqrt{e^{-4u} - s^2},$$

where $\qquad s = -1 + \sqrt{1 + 2e^{-2u} \cos 2v + e^{-4u}}.$

EXERCISES

1. Use the Schwarz-Christoffel transformation to obtain formally the mapping function given with Fig. 22, Appendix 2, for the mapping shown there.

2. Point out why the solution of the problem of flow in a channel with a semi-infinite rectangular obstruction (Fig. 94) is included in the solution of the problem treated in Sec. 97.

3. Let $T(u,v)$ denote the steady temperatures in the strip with an offset shown in Fig. 91, when $T(u,\pi) = 1$ and $T = 0$ on the rest of the boundary. The faces of the strip parallel to the uv plane are insulated. Write $h = e^{-H}$, where $H > 0$. When $s = \exp(-H - i\alpha)$, where $0 < \alpha < \pi/2$ and s is the auxiliary variable used in Sec. 97, show that the point z, where $z = (s^2 - h^2)/(s^2 - 1)$, lies in the upper half plane. In terms of the parameter α, show that the image of the point z in the w plane is the point

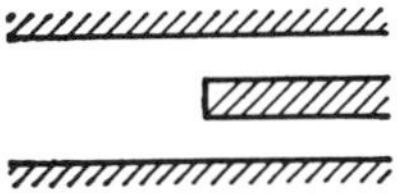

Fig. 94

$$w = \frac{e^{-H}}{2} \operatorname{Log} \frac{\cosh H + \cos \alpha}{\cosh H - \cos \alpha} + \operatorname{Log} \tan \frac{\alpha}{2}$$

$$+ i \left(\frac{\pi}{2} - e^{-H} \arctan \frac{\sin \alpha}{\sinh H} \right)$$

and that the temperature at that point w is

$$T(u,v) = \frac{1}{\pi} \arctan \frac{\tanh H}{\tan \alpha} \qquad \left(0 < \alpha < \frac{\pi}{2}, H > 0 \right),$$

where the inverse tangents have values between zero and $\pi/2$. When α varies from zero to $\pi/2$, those two formulas therefore give the temperatures at all points w on a certain curve interior to the strip.

4. In Fig. 29 of Appendix 2 consider the boundary of the shaded region in the w plane as a degenerate triangle with exterior angles $-\pi/2$, $\pi/2$, and 2π at B', C', and infinity, respectively, and derive formally the mapping function given there. Verify that the transformation, written in the form

$$w = \frac{h}{\pi} \{(z + 1)^{\frac{1}{2}} (z - 1)^{\frac{1}{2}} + \operatorname{Log} [z + (z + 1)^{\frac{1}{2}} (z - 1)^{\frac{1}{2}}]\},$$

where $0 \leq \arg (z \pm 1) \leq \pi$, does map the boundary in the manner indicated in the figure.

5. Let $T(u,v)$ denote the bounded steady-state temperatures in the shaded region of the w plane in Fig. 29 of Appendix 2, if $T(u,h) = 1$ when $u < 0$ and $T = 0$ on the rest $(B'C'D')$ of the boundary.   In terms of the real parameter α $(0 < \alpha < \pi/2)$, show that the image of each point $z = i \tan \alpha$ of the positive y axis is the point

$$w = \frac{h}{\pi}\left[\operatorname{Log}\,(\tan \alpha + \sec \alpha) + i\left(\frac{\pi}{2} + \sec \alpha\right)\right]$$

(see Exercise 4) and that the temperature at that point w is

$$T(u,v) = \frac{\alpha}{\pi} \qquad\qquad \left(0 < \alpha < \frac{\pi}{2}\right).$$

6. Let $F(w)$ denote the complex potential for the flow of a fluid over a step in the bed of a deep stream represented by the shaded region of the w plane in Fig. 29 of Appendix 2, if the fluid velocity q approaches a real constant q_0 as $|w|$ tends to infinity in that region.   The single-valued mapping function w that maps the region onto the upper half of the z plane is noted in Exercise 4.   Since $F'(w) = F'(z)/(dw/dz)$, show that

$$\overline{q(w)} = q_0(z - 1)^{\frac{1}{2}}(z + 1)^{-\frac{1}{2}}$$

and that at points along the bed of the stream

$$|q| = |q_0|\,\sqrt{\left|\frac{x - 1}{x + 1}\right|},$$

in terms of the images $z = x$ of those points.   Thus note that the speed increases from $|q_0|$ along $A'B'$ until $|q| = \infty$ at B', then diminishes to zero at C', and increases toward $|q_0|$ from C' to D'; also that the speed is $|q_0|$ at the point $w = ih(\frac{1}{2} + 1/\pi)$ between B' and C'.

CHAPTER 11

INTEGRAL FORMULAS OF POISSON TYPE

99. Poisson's Integral Formula. Cauchy's integral formula

$$(1) \qquad f(z) = \frac{1}{2\pi i} \int_{C_0} \frac{f(z')}{z' - z}\, dz'$$

gives the values of an analytic function f at points z interior to a closed contour C_0 in terms of the values of f at points z' on C_0.

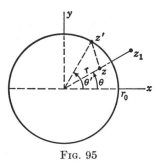

FIG. 95

When C_0 is a circle, we can obtain a corresponding formula for a harmonic function, that is, a formula that solves the Dirichlet problem for the circle. Identification of real components in equation (1), however, where $f = u + iv$, gives u at points inside C_0 in terms of both u and v at points on C_0; thus some modification of that procedure is needed.

Let the equation of the circle C_0 be $z' = r_0 \exp(i\theta')$ and write $z = r \exp(i\theta)$, where $r < r_0$ (Fig. 95). The inverse z_1 of the point z with respect to the circle can be written

$$(2) \qquad z_1 = \frac{r_0{}^2}{r} \exp(i\theta) = \frac{r_0{}^2}{\bar{z}} = \frac{z'\bar{z}'}{\bar{z}}.$$

When a function f *is analytic everywhere within and on the circle*, formula (1) gives $f(z)$; but the value of the integral there is zero when z is replaced by z_1. Upon replacing dz' by $iz'\, d\theta'$, we can therefore write

$$f(z) = \frac{1}{2\pi} \int_0^{2\pi} \left(\frac{z'}{z' - z} - \frac{z'}{z' - z_1} \right) f(z')\, d\theta',$$

assuming for the moment that $z \neq 0$. The factor of the integrand inside the parentheses is real, for in view of the final expression (2) for z_1, that factor can be written in the forms

(3) $$\frac{z'}{z' - z} - \frac{1}{1 - \bar{z}'/\bar{z}} = \frac{z'}{z' - z} + \frac{\bar{z}}{\bar{z}' - \bar{z}} = \frac{r_0{}^2 - r^2}{|z' - z|^2}.$$

An alternate form of the Cauchy integral formula is therefore

(4) $$f(re^{i\theta}) = \frac{r_0{}^2 - r^2}{2\pi} \int_0^{2\pi} \frac{f(r_0 e^{i\theta'})}{|z' - z|^2} \, d\theta' \qquad (r < r_0).$$

We note that $|z' - z|$ is the distance between points z' and z,

(5) $$|z' - z|^2 = r_0{}^2 - 2r_0 r \cos (\theta' - \theta) + r^2 > 0;$$

also that formula (4) is valid in case $z = 0$, because in that case it reduces to the Cauchy integral formula (1) for $f(0)$.

If u is the real component of f, then, according to formula (4),

(6) $$u(r,\theta) = \frac{1}{2\pi} \int_0^{2\pi} \frac{(r_0{}^2 - r^2)u(r_0, \theta')}{r_0{}^2 - 2r_0 r \cos (\theta' - \theta) + r^2} \, d\theta' \qquad (r < r_0).$$

This is *Poisson's integral formula* for the harmonic function u in the circle.

The integral in the formula represents a linear integral transformation of $u(r_0, \theta')$, with parameters r and θ, which transforms the function $u(r_0, \theta')$ into $2\pi u(r,\theta)$. The kernel of that integral transformation, the function represented by the expressions (3), is the positive real-valued function

(7) $$P(r_0, r, \theta' - \theta) = \frac{r_0{}^2 - r^2}{r_0{}^2 - 2r_0 r \cos (\theta' - \theta) + r^2} = \frac{r_0{}^2 - r^2}{|z' - z|^2}.$$

It is called the *Poisson kernel*. Since $\bar{z}/(\bar{z}' - \bar{z})$ and its complex conjugate $z/(z' - z)$ have the same real components, we find from equations (3) that

(8) $$P(r_0, r, \theta' - \theta) = \Re \left(\frac{z'}{z' - z} + \frac{z}{z' - z} \right) = \Re \left(\frac{z' + z}{z' - z} \right);$$

thus P *is a harmonic function* of (r,θ) interior to C_0 for each fixed z' on C_0. From equation (7) we see that P is an *even periodic* function of $\theta' - \theta$, with period 2π, and that $P = 1$ when $r = 0$.

Poisson's integral formula (6) can now be written

(9) $$u(r,\theta) = \frac{1}{2\pi} \int_0^{2\pi} P(r_0, r, \theta' - \theta)u(r_0, \theta') \, d\theta' \qquad (r < r_0).$$

From the special case $f = u = 1$ we see that P has the property

$$(10) \qquad \frac{1}{2\pi} \int_0^{2\pi} P(r_0, r, \theta' - \theta) \, d\theta' = 1 \qquad (r < r_0).$$

We assumed here that f is analytic not only interior to C_0 but on C_0 itself and therefore that u is harmonic in a domain that includes all points on the circle. In particular, u is continuous on C_0. The conditions will now be relaxed.

100. A Dirichlet Problem for the Circle. Let F be a given sectionally continuous function of θ $(0 < \theta < 2\pi)$. Then the function u defined by the Poisson integral transformation of F, namely,

$$(1) \qquad u(r,\theta) = \frac{1}{2\pi} \int_0^{2\pi} P(r_0, r, \theta' - \theta) F(\theta') \, d\theta' \qquad (r < r_0),$$

satisfies these conditions: *u is harmonic throughout the interior of the circle* $r = r_0$ *and, for each fixed θ where F is continuous,*

$$(2) \qquad \lim_{r \to r_0} u(r,\theta) = F(\theta) \qquad (r < r_0).$$

Thus u is a solution of the Dirichlet problem for the circle in the sense that the boundary value $F(\theta)$ is approached by $u(r,\theta)$ when the point (r,θ) approaches (r_0,θ) along a radius of the circle, except at the finite number of points (r_0,θ) where F may have jumps.

Before proving the above statement, let us apply it to find the potential $V(r,\theta)$ interior to a cylinder $r = 1$ when $V = 0$ on the upper half of the cylinder and $V = 1$ on the lower half (Fig. 65). That problem was solved by conformal mapping in Sec. 86. In formula (1) we write V for u, $F(\theta) = 0$ when $0 < \theta < \pi$ and $F(\theta) = 1$ when $\pi < \theta < 2\pi$ to get the equation

$$V(r,\theta) = \frac{1}{2\pi} \int_\pi^{2\pi} P(1, r, \theta' - \theta) \, d\theta'$$

$$= \frac{1}{2\pi} \int_\pi^{2\pi} \frac{(1 - r^2) \, d\theta'}{1 + r^2 - 2r \cos (\theta' - \theta)}.$$

An indefinite integral of P can be written as

$$(3) \qquad \int P(1,r,\phi) \, d\phi = 2 \arctan \left(\frac{1 + r}{1 - r} \tan \frac{\phi}{2} \right),$$

and the inverse tangent function here can be described as a con--

tinuous function of $\phi/2$ which ranges from $-\pi$ to π as $\phi/2$ ranges from $-\pi$ to π. Then

$$\pi V(r,\theta) = \arctan\left(\frac{1+r}{1-r} \tan\frac{2\pi - \theta}{2}\right) - \arctan\left(\frac{1+r}{1-r} \tan\frac{\pi - \theta}{2}\right)$$

and, by simplifying the expression for $\tan(\pi V)$, we find that

$$(4) \qquad\qquad V(r,\theta) = \frac{1}{\pi} \arctan\frac{1 - r^2}{2r \sin\theta} \qquad (0 \leqq \arctan t \leqq \pi).$$

That formula (1) defines a harmonic function u interior to the circle $r = r_0$ follows from the fact that P is harmonic there. Since F is sectionally continuous, the integral (1) can be written as a sum of a finite number of definite integrals each of which has an integrand that is continuous in r, θ, and θ'. The partial derivatives of those integrands with respect to r and θ are likewise continuous. Since P satisfies Laplace's equation in polar coordinates, it follows that u satisfies that equation.

To establish condition (2), we show that corresponding to each positive number ϵ there is a number δ such that

$$(5) \qquad\qquad |u(r,\theta) - F(\theta)| < 2\epsilon \qquad \text{whenever } 0 < r_0 - r < \delta.$$

In view of property (10), Sec. 99, of P, the first inequality here can be written

$$(6) \qquad \frac{1}{2\pi}\left| \int_0^{2\pi} P(r_0, r, \theta' - \theta)[F(\theta') - F(\theta)] \, d\theta' \right| < 2\epsilon.$$

The integrand is periodic in θ and θ' if we consider F periodic.

Since F is continuous at the fixed point θ, there is a number σ corresponding to the given number ϵ such that

$$|F(\theta') - F(\theta)| < \epsilon \qquad \text{when } |\theta' - \theta| < \sigma.$$

Let us write

$$I_1(r,\sigma) = \frac{1}{2\pi} \int_{\theta-\sigma}^{\theta+\sigma} P(r_0, r, \theta' - \theta)[F(\theta') - F(\theta)] \, d\theta',$$

$$I_2(r,\sigma) = \frac{1}{2\pi} \int_{\theta+\sigma}^{2\pi+\theta-\sigma} P(r_0, r, \theta' - \theta)[F(\theta') - F(\theta)] \, d\theta'.$$

Then $u(r,\theta) - F(\theta) = I_1 + I_2$. Since $P > 0$,

$$|I_1| \leqq \frac{1}{2\pi} \int_{\theta-\sigma}^{\theta+\sigma} |F(\theta') - F(\theta)| \, P \, d\theta' < \frac{\epsilon}{2\pi} \int_0^{2\pi} P \, d\theta' = \epsilon.$$

Recalling that $P = (r_0{}^2 - r^2)/|z' - z|^2$, we see from Fig. 95 that the function $|z' - z|^2$ has a positive minimum value $m(\sigma)$ as θ', the argument of z', varies from $\theta + \sigma$ up to $2\pi + (\theta - \sigma)$. If M denotes an upper bound of $|F(\theta') - F(\theta)|$ for all values of θ and θ', then

$$|I_2| < \frac{2\pi M}{2\pi m(\sigma)} (r_0{}^2 - r^2) \leqq \frac{2Mr_0}{m(\sigma)} (r_0 - r) < \epsilon$$

when $r_0 - r < m(\sigma)\epsilon/(2Mr_0)$. Therefore $|I_1| + |I_2| < 2\epsilon$ when $r_0 - r < \delta$, where

$$\delta = \frac{m(\sigma)\epsilon}{2Mr_0}.$$

This is a number δ such that condition (5) is satisfied.

When $r = 0$, formula (1) reduces to

$$(7) \qquad u(0,\theta) = \frac{1}{2\pi} \int_0^{2\pi} F(\theta')\, d\theta'.$$

Thus *the value of a harmonic function at the center of the circle is the average of its boundary values on the circle.*

It is left to the exercises below to prove that P and u can be represented by series of the elementary harmonic functions $r^n \sin n\theta$ and $r^n \cos n\theta$ as follows:

$$(8) \quad P(r_0, r, \theta' - \theta) = 1 + 2 \sum_{n=1}^{\infty} \left(\frac{r}{r_0}\right)^n \cos n(\theta' - \theta) \qquad (r < r_0);$$

$$(9) \quad u(r,\theta) = \frac{1}{2} a_0 + \sum_{n=1}^{\infty} \left(\frac{r}{r_0}\right)^n (a_n \cos n\theta + b_n \sin n\theta) \qquad (r < r_0),$$

where

$$(10) \quad a_n = \frac{1}{\pi} \int_0^{2\pi} F(\theta') \cos n\theta'\, d\theta', \qquad b_n = \frac{1}{\pi} \int_0^{2\pi} F(\theta') \sin n\theta'\, d\theta'.$$

101. Related Boundary Value Problems. Details of proofs of results given below are left to the exercises. The functions F and G that represent boundary values are assumed to be sectionally continuous.

In case F is an odd function of the coordinate y on the circle $r = r_0$, that is, $F(2\pi - \theta) = -F(\theta)$, the Poisson integral formula

(1) of Sec. 100 can be written

$$(1) \quad u(r,\theta) = \frac{1}{2\pi} \int_0^\pi [P(r_0, r, \theta' - \theta) - P(r_0, r, \theta' + \theta)]F(\theta')\,d\theta'.$$

This function u vanishes on the diameter ($\theta = 0$ or $\theta = \pi$) of the circle, as we expect when we interpret u as a steady temperature. Formula (1) therefore solves *the Dirichlet problem for the semi-*

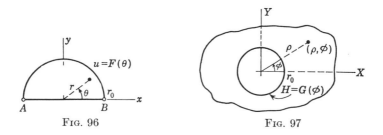

FIG. 96   FIG. 97

circular region $r < r_0$, $0 \leq \theta \leq \pi$ (Fig. 96) *in which* $u = 0$ *on the diameter* AB *and,* at each point θ where F is continuous,

$$(2) \qquad\qquad \lim_{r \to r_0} u(r,\theta) = F(\theta) \qquad (0 < \theta < \pi, r < r_0).$$

If F is an even function of y, $F(2\pi - \theta) = F(\theta)$, then

$$(3) \quad u(r,\theta) = \frac{1}{2\pi} \int_0^\pi [P(r_0, r, \theta' - \theta) + P(r_0, r, \theta' + \theta)]F(\theta')\,d\theta'$$

and $\partial u/\partial \theta = 0$ when $\theta = 0$ or $\theta = \pi$. Formula (3) therefore represents a function u that is *harmonic in the semicircular region* $0 \leq \theta \leq \pi, r < r_0$ (Fig. 96) *and satisfies condition* (2) *and the condition that its normal derivative on the diameter* AB *vanishes.*

The conformal transformation $z = r_0^2/Z$ maps the circle $|z| = r_0$ onto the circle $|Z| = r_0$ in the Z plane and the interior of the first circle onto the exterior of the second. We write $Z = \rho \exp(i\phi)$ as indicated in Fig. 97; then $r = r_0^2/\rho$ and $\theta = 2\pi - \phi$. When $G(\theta) = F(2\pi - \theta)$, the harmonic function u represented by formula (1) of Sec. 100 becomes a harmonic function $H(\rho,\phi)$ in the domain $\rho > r_0$, and the formula reduces to the form

$$(4) \quad H(\rho,\phi) = -\frac{1}{2\pi} \int_0^{2\pi} P(r_0, \rho, \phi' - \phi)G(\phi')\,d\phi' \qquad (\rho > r_0).$$

For each fixed ϕ where G is continuous we find from condition (2), Sec. 100, that

(5) $$\lim_{\rho \to r_0} H(\rho,\phi) = G(\phi) \qquad\qquad (\rho > r_0).$$

Thus formula (4) solves *the Dirichlet problem for the region exterior to the circle* $\rho = r_0$. We note that $P < 0$ here; also,

(6) $$\frac{1}{2\pi} \int_0^{2\pi} P(r_0, \rho, \phi' - \phi) \, d\phi' = -1 \qquad\qquad (\rho > r_0),$$

(7) $$\lim_{\rho \to \infty} H(\rho,\phi) = \frac{1}{2\pi} \int_0^{2\pi} G(\phi') \, d\phi'.$$

EXERCISES

1. Use the Poisson integral formula (1), Sec. 100, to derive the formula

$$V(x,y) = \frac{1}{\pi} \arctan \frac{1 - x^2 - y^2}{(x - 1)^2 + (y - 1)^2 - 1} \qquad (0 \leqq \arctan t \leqq \pi)$$

for the electrostatic potential interior to a cylinder $x^2 + y^2 = 1$ if $V = 1$ on the first quadrant ($x > 0$, $y > 0$) of the cylinder and $V = 0$ on the rest of that surface. Also note that $1 - V$ is the solution of Exercise 8, Sec. 86.

2. Let T denote the steady temperatures in a disk $r \leqq 1$ with insulated faces when $T = 1$ on the sector $0 < \theta < 2\theta_0$ of the edge $r = 1$ and $T = 0$ on the rest of the edge, where $0 < \theta_0 < \pi/2$. Use the Poisson integral formula to show that

$$T(x,y) = \frac{1}{\pi} \arctan \frac{(1 - x^2 - y^2)y_0}{(x - 1)^2 + (y - y_0)^2 - y_0{}^2},$$

where $y_0 = \tan \theta_0$ and $0 \leqq \arctan t \leqq \pi$. Verify that this function T satisfies the boundary conditions.

3. Let I denote this *finite unit impulse function:*

$$I(h, \theta - \theta_0) = \frac{1}{h} \qquad \text{when } \theta_0 < \theta < \theta_0 + h,$$
$$= 0 \qquad \text{when } 0 \leqq \theta < \theta_0 \text{ or } \theta_0 + h < \theta < 2\pi,$$

where h is a positive constant and $0 \leqq \theta_0 < 2\pi$. Note that $\int_0^{2\pi} I \, d\theta = 1$. With the aid of a mean-value theorem for integrals, show that

$$\lim_{h \to 0} \int_0^{2\pi} P(r_0, r, \theta' - \theta)I(h, \theta' - \theta_0) \, d\theta' = P(r_0, r, \theta - \theta_0)$$
$$(r < r_0).$$

Thus the Poisson kernel $P(r_0, r, \theta - \theta_0)$ is the limit, as $h \to 0$, of the harmonic function inside the circle $r = r_0$ whose boundary values are represented by the impulse function $2\pi I$.

4. Show that the formula in Exercise 11, Sec. 65, for the sum of a series of cosines can be written

$$1 + 2 \sum_{n=1}^{\infty} k^n \cos n\theta = \frac{1 - k^2}{1 + k^2 - 2k \cos \theta} \qquad (-1 < k < 1),$$

and consequently that the Poisson kernel has the series representation (8), Sec. 100.

5. In Sec. 100, show that the series in formula (8) converges uniformly with respect to θ'; then obtain from formula (1) the series representation (9) for u, when F is sectionally continuous.

6. Use formulas (9) and (10) of Sec. 100 to find the steady temperatures $T(r,\theta)$ in a solid cylinder $r < r_0$ of infinite length if $T(r_0,\theta) = A \cos \theta$. Show that no heat flows across the plane $y = 0$.

$$Ans. \ T = A(r/r_0) \cos \theta = Ax/r_0.$$

7. As special cases of formula (4), Sec. 101, obtain formulas

(a) $H(\rho,\phi) = \dfrac{1}{2\pi} \displaystyle\int_0^\pi [P(r_0, \rho, \phi + \phi') - P(r_0, \rho, \phi - \phi')]G(\phi')\, d\phi',$

(b) $H(\rho,\phi) = -\dfrac{1}{2\pi} \displaystyle\int_0^\pi [P(r_0, \rho, \phi' + \phi) + P(r_0, \rho, \phi' - \phi)]G(\phi')\, d\phi'$

for the harmonic functions in the unbounded region $\rho > r_0$, $0 \leq \phi \leq \pi$, shown in Fig. 98, if each of the functions satisfies the boundary condition

$$\lim_{\rho \to r_0} H(\rho,\phi) = G(\phi) \qquad (\rho > r_0, 0 < \phi < \pi)$$

on the semicircle and if the function (a) vanishes on the rays BA and DE while the normal derivative of the function (b) vanishes on those rays.

8. Give the details in establishing formula (1) of Sec. 101 as a solution of the Dirichlet problem stated there for the region shown in Fig. 96.

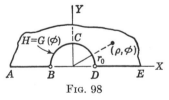

9. Give the details in establishing formula (3) of Sec. 101 as a solution of the boundary value problem stated there.

FIG. 98

10. Obtain formula (4), Sec. 101, as a solution of the Dirichlet problem for the domain exterior to a circle (Fig. 97).

11. State why formula (6), Sec. 101, is valid.

12. Establish equation (7) of Sec. 101.

102. Integral Formulas for the Half Plane. Let f be an analytic function of z throughout the half plane $y \geq 0$ such that, for some positive constants k and M, f satisfies the order property

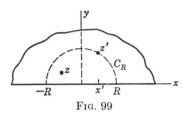

FIG. 99

$$(1) \quad |z^k f(z)| < M \qquad (y \geq 0, k > 0).$$

For a fixed point z above the x axis let C_R denote a semicircle $z' = R \exp(i\theta')$, where $R > |z|$ and θ' ranges from zero to π (Fig. 99). Then, according to the Cauchy integral formula,

$$(2) \quad 2\pi i f(z) = \int_{C_R} \frac{f(z')\,dz'}{z' - z} + \int_{-R}^{R} \frac{f(x')\,dx'}{x' - z}.$$

We find that the first of these integrals vanishes as R tends to infinity because $|f(z')| < M/R^k$; therefore

$$(3) \quad f(z) = \frac{1}{2\pi i} \int_{-\infty}^{\infty} \frac{f(x')}{x' - z}\,dx' \qquad (y > 0).$$

Because of condition (1) the improper integral here exists, and it is therefore the same as its principal value.

The representation (3) is a *Cauchy integral formula for the half plane.*

In case the point z lies below the x axis, the right-hand member of equation (2), and therefore the integral (3), vanishes. Consequently, when z is above the x axis, for each constant c we have this alternate formula:

$$(4) \quad f(z) = \frac{1}{2\pi i} \int_{-\infty}^{\infty} \left(\frac{1}{x' - z} + \frac{c}{x' - \bar{z}} \right) f(x')\,dx' \qquad (y > 0).$$

In the two cases $c = -1$ and $c = 1$ this formula reduces, respectively, to

$$(5) \quad f(z) = \frac{1}{\pi} \int_{-\infty}^{\infty} \frac{yf(x')}{|x' - z|^2}\,dx' \qquad (y > 0),$$

$$(6) \quad f(z) = \frac{1}{\pi i} \int_{-\infty}^{\infty} \frac{(x' - x)f(x')}{|x' - z|^2}\,dx' \qquad (y > 0).$$

If $f = u + iv$, it follows from formulas (5) and (6) that the conjugate harmonic functions u and v are represented in the half plane $y > 0$ in terms of the boundary values of u by the formulas

$$(7) \quad u(x,y) = \frac{1}{\pi} \int_{-\infty}^{\infty} \frac{yu(x',0)}{|x' - z|^2} \, dx' = \frac{y}{\pi} \int_{-\infty}^{\infty} \frac{u(x',0) \, dx'}{(x' - x)^2 + y^2}$$
$$(y > 0),$$

$$(8) \qquad v(x,y) = \frac{1}{\pi} \int_{-\infty}^{\infty} \frac{(x - x')u(x',0)}{|x' - z|^2} \, dx' \qquad (y > 0).$$

Equation (7) is known as the *Poisson integral formula for the half plane*, or the *Schwarz integral formula*. We now relax the conditions for the validity of formulas (7) and (8).

103. A Dirichlet Problem for the Half Plane. Let F denote a real-valued function of x that is bounded for all x and continuous except for at most a finite number of finite jumps. When $y \geqq \epsilon$ and $|x| \leqq 1/\epsilon$, where ϵ is any positive constant, the integral

$$I(x,y) = \int_{-\infty}^{\infty} \frac{F(x') \, dx'}{(x' - x)^2 + y^2} = \int_{-\infty}^{\infty} \frac{F(x + t) \, dt}{t^2 + y^2}$$

converges uniformly with respect to x and y, as do the integrals of the partial derivatives of the integrand with respect to x and y. Also, each integral is the sum of a finite number of improper or definite integrals over intervals where F is continuous, so that the integrand of each component integral is a continuous function of x', x, and y when $y \geqq \epsilon$. Consequently each partial derivative of $I(x,y)$ is represented by the integral of the corresponding derivative of the integrand whenever $y > 0$.

We write $U = yI/\pi$. Thus U is the Schwarz integral transformation (7), Sec. 102, of F:

$$(1) \qquad U(x,y) = \frac{1}{\pi} \int_{-\infty}^{\infty} \frac{yF(x')}{(x' - x)^2 + y^2} \, dx' \qquad (y > 0).$$

The kernel $y|x' - z|^{-2}$ here is the imaginary component of the function $1/(x' - z)$, which is analytic in z when $y > 0$. Hence the kernel is harmonic, so that it satisfies Laplace's equation in x and y. Because the order of differentiation and integration can be interchanged, the function (1) satisfies that equation. Consequently U *is harmonic when* $y > 0$.

To prove that, for each fixed x for which F is continuous,

$$(2) \qquad \lim_{y \to 0} U(x,y) = F(x) \qquad (y > 0),$$

we substitute $x' - x = y \tan \tau$ to write formula (1) as

$$(3) \qquad U(x,y) = \frac{1}{\pi} \int_{-\pi/2}^{\pi/2} F(x + y \tan \tau) \, d\tau \qquad (y > 0).$$

If $\Delta F = F(x + y \tan \tau) - F(x)$, then

$$(4) \qquad \pi[U(x,y) - F(x)] = \int_{-\pi/2}^{\pi/2} \Delta F \, d\tau = I_1 + I_2 + I_3,$$

where, if σ is a small positive constant,

$$I_1 = \int_{-\pi/2}^{-(\pi/2)+\sigma} \Delta F \, d\tau, \qquad I_2 = \int_{-(\pi/2)+\sigma}^{(\pi/2)-\sigma} \Delta F \, d\tau,$$

$$I_3 = \int_{(\pi/2)-\sigma}^{\pi/2} \Delta F \, d\tau.$$

If M denotes an upper bound of $|F|$, then $|\Delta F| \leqq 2M$. For a given positive number ϵ we select σ so that $6M\sigma < \epsilon$; then

$$|I_1| \leqq 2M\sigma < \frac{\epsilon}{3} \qquad \text{and} \qquad |I_3| < \frac{\epsilon}{3}.$$

We shall now show that corresponding to ϵ there is a number δ such that

$$|I_2| < \frac{\epsilon}{3} \qquad\qquad \text{when } 0 < y < \delta;$$

then condition (2) follows from equation (4). Since $F(x)$ is continuous at x, there is a number δ' such that

$$|F(x + y \tan \tau) - F(x)| < \frac{\epsilon}{3\pi} \qquad \text{when } y|\tan \tau| < \delta',$$

and the latter condition is satisfied for all τ involved in I_2 if the maximum value, $\tan (\frac{1}{2}\pi - \sigma) = \cot \sigma$, of $|\tan \tau|$ is used, that is, if $y < \delta' \tan \sigma$. Then

$$|I_2| < (\pi - 2\sigma) \frac{\epsilon}{3\pi} < \frac{\epsilon}{3} \qquad \text{when } 0 < y < \delta,$$

where $\delta = \delta' \tan \sigma$. Thus condition (2) is established.

The Schwarz formula (1) or (3) therefore solves the *Dirichlet problem for the half plane* $y > 0$ with the boundary condition (2). It also shows that U is bounded, $|U(x,y)| \leqq M$ in the half plane, where M is an upper bound of $|F(x)|$. We note that $U = F_0$, a constant, when $F(x) = F_0$.

According to formula (8) of the preceding section, under certain conditions on F, the function

$$(5) \qquad V(x,y) = \frac{1}{\pi} \int_{-\infty}^{\infty} \frac{(x - x')F(x')}{(x' - x)^2 + y^2}\, dx' \qquad (y > 0)$$

is a harmonic conjugate of the function U given by formula (1). Actually, *formula (5) represents a harmonic conjugate of U if F is everywhere continuous, except for at most a finite number of finite jumps, and if F satisfies an order property* $|x^k F(x)| < M$, *where* $k > 0$. For under those conditions we find that U and V satisfy the Cauchy-Riemann conditions when $y > 0$.

Special cases of formula (1) when F is an odd or even function are left to the exercises.

104. Neumann Problems for Circular Regions. As in Sec. 99 and Fig. 95, we write $z' = r_0 \exp (i\theta')$ and $z = r \exp (i\theta)$, where $r < r_0$. When z' is fixed, the function

$$(1) \quad Q = -2r_0 \operatorname{Log} |z' - z|$$
$$= -r_0 \operatorname{Log} [r_0^2 - 2r_0 r \cos (\theta' - \theta) + r^2]$$

is harmonic interior to the circle $|z| = r_0$, because it is the real component of $-2r_0 \log (z - z')$, where the branch cut of $\log (z - z')$ is an outward ray from the point z'. Moreover, if P is the Poisson kernel (7), Sec. 99, then

$$(2) \quad \frac{\partial Q}{\partial r} = -\frac{r_0}{r} \frac{2r^2 - 2r_0 r \cos (\theta' - \theta)}{r_0^2 - 2r_0 r \cos (\theta' - \theta) + r^2}$$
$$= \frac{r_0}{r} [P(r_0, r, \theta' - \theta) - 1].$$

Those observations suggest that Q may be used as a kernel in an integral formula that will represent a harmonic function u whose normal derivative $\partial u / \partial r$ on the circle $r = r_0$ assumes prescribed values $g(\theta)$.

If g is sectionally continuous and u_0 is an arbitrary constant, the function

$$(3) \qquad u(r,\theta) = \frac{1}{2\pi} \int_0^{2\pi} Q(r_0, r, \theta' - \theta)g(\theta')\, d\theta' + u_0 \qquad (r < r_0)$$

is harmonic because the integrand is a harmonic function of

(r,θ). If the mean value of g over the circle is zero, that is, if

(4) $$\int_0^{2\pi} g(\theta')\, d\theta' = 0,$$

then in view of equation (2),

$$\frac{\partial u}{\partial r} = \frac{r_0}{2\pi r} \int_0^{2\pi} (P-1)g\, d\theta' = \frac{r_0}{r}\frac{1}{2\pi}\int_0^{2\pi} P(r_0, r, \theta' - \theta)g(\theta')\, d\theta'.$$

According to equations (1) and (2) of Sec. 100, it follows that

(5) $$\lim_{r \to r_0} \frac{\partial u}{\partial r} = g(\theta) \qquad\qquad (r < r_0)$$

for each value of θ where g is continuous.

Since Q is a constant when $r = 0$, it follows from equations (3) and (4) that u_0 is the value of u at the center of the circle:

(6) $$u_0 = u(0,\theta).$$

When g is sectionally continuous and satisfies condition (4), the formula

(7) $$u(r,\theta) = -\frac{r_0}{2\pi}\int_0^{2\pi} \text{Log } [r_0{}^2 - 2r_0 r \cos (\theta' - \theta)$$
$$+ r^2]g(\theta')\, d\theta' + u_0,$$

where $r < r_0$, therefore solves *the Neumann problem for the region interior to the circle* where $g(\theta)$ is the normal derivative of this harmonic function u at the boundary in the sense of condition (5).

The values $u(r,\theta)$ may represent steady temperatures in a disk $r < r_0$ with insulated faces. Then condition (5) states that the flux of heat into the disk at its edge is proportional to $g(\theta)$. Condition (4) is the natural physical requirement that the total rate of flow of heat into the disk must be zero, since temperatures do not vary with time.

A corresponding formula for a harmonic function H in the domain *exterior* to a circle can be written in terms of the kernel Q as

(8) $$H(\rho,\phi) = -\frac{1}{2\pi}\int_0^{2\pi} Q(r_0, \rho, \phi' - \phi)G(\phi')\, d\phi' + A$$
$$(\rho > r_0),$$

where A is a constant. We assume that G is sectionally continuous and that

$$(9) \qquad\qquad \int_0^{2\pi} G(\phi')\, d\phi' = 0.$$

Then $A = H(\infty,\phi)$ and, for each ϕ where H is continuous,

$$(10) \qquad\qquad \lim_{\rho \to r_0} \frac{\partial H}{\partial \rho} = G(\phi) \qquad\qquad (\rho > r_0).$$

The verification of formula (8), and the special cases of formula (3) that apply to semicircular regions, are left to the exercises.

105. A Neumann Problem for the Half Plane. Let $g(x)$ be continuous for all real x, except for at most a finite number of finite jumps, and let it satisfy an order property

$$(1) \qquad\qquad |x^k g(x)| < M \qquad (k > 1, \ -\infty < x < \infty).$$

If $z = x + iy$, for each fixed x' the function $\mathrm{Log}\,|z - x'|$ is harmonic in the half plane $y > 0$. Consequently the function

$$
\begin{aligned}
(2) \quad U(x,y) &= \frac{1}{\pi} \int_{-\infty}^{\infty} \mathrm{Log}\,|z - x'| g(x')\, dx' + B \\
&= \frac{1}{2\pi} \int_{-\infty}^{\infty} \mathrm{Log}\,[(x' - x)^2 + y^2] g(x')\, dx' + B
\end{aligned}
$$
$$(y > 0),$$

where B is a real constant, is harmonic in that half plane.

Formula (2) was written with the Schwarz formula (1) of Sec. 103 in mind, because it follows from (2) that

$$(3) \qquad\qquad \frac{\partial U}{\partial y} = \frac{1}{\pi} \int_{-\infty}^{\infty} \frac{y g(x')}{(x' - x)^2 + y^2}\, dx' \qquad (y > 0).$$

According to equations (1) and (2), Sec. 103, therefore,

$$(4) \qquad\qquad \lim_{y \to 0} \frac{\partial U}{\partial y} = g(x) \qquad\qquad (y > 0)$$

at each point x where g is continuous.

The integral formula (2) therefore solves a *Neumann problem for the half plane $y > 0$* with boundary condition (4). But we have not presented conditions on g that are sufficient to make the harmonic function U bounded as $|z|$ increases.

When g is an odd function, formula (2) can be written

$$(5) \qquad U(x,y) = \frac{1}{2\pi} \int_0^\infty \text{Log} \, \frac{(x' - x)^2 + y^2}{(x' + x)^2 + y^2} \, g(x') \, dx'$$

$$(x \geqq 0, \, y > 0).$$

This represents a harmonic function in the first *quadrant* that satisfies the conditions

$$(6) \qquad\qquad\qquad U(0,y) = 0 \qquad\qquad\qquad (y > 0),$$

$$(7) \qquad\qquad\qquad \lim_{y \to 0} \frac{\partial U}{\partial y} = g(x) \qquad\qquad (x > 0, \, y > 0).$$

The kernels of all the integral formulas for harmonic functions presented in this chapter can be described in terms of a single real-valued function of x, y, x', and y', namely,

$$(8) \qquad\qquad\qquad R(z,z') = \text{Log} \, |z - z'| \qquad\qquad (z \neq z').$$

This is *Green's function* for the logarithmic potential in the z plane. The function is symmetric: $R(z',z) = R(z,z')$. Expressions for kernels used earlier, in terms of R and its derivatives, are given in the exercises.

EXERCISES

1. As a special case of formula (1), Sec. 103, obtain the formula

$$U(x,y) = \frac{y}{\pi} \int_0^\infty \left[\frac{1}{(x' - x)^2 + y^2} - \frac{1}{(x' + x)^2 + y^2} \right] F(x') \, dx'$$

$$(x \geqq 0, \, y > 0)$$

for a bounded harmonic function U in the first *quadrant* that satisfies the boundary conditions

$$U(0,y) = 0 \qquad\qquad\qquad (y > 0),$$
$$U(x,+0) = F(x) \qquad\qquad (x > 0, \, x \neq x_n),$$

where F is bounded for all positive x and continuous except for at most a finite number of finite jumps at points x_n.

2. As a special case of formula (1), Sec. 103, obtain the formula

$$U(x,y) = \frac{y}{\pi} \int_0^\infty \left[\frac{1}{(x' - x)^2 + y^2} + \frac{1}{(x' + x)^2 + y^2} \right] F(x') \, dx'$$

$$(x \geqq 0, \, y > 0)$$

for a bounded harmonic function U in the first *quadrant* that satisfies the boundary conditions

$$\frac{\partial U}{\partial x} = 0 \qquad \text{when } x = 0 \text{ and } y > 0,$$

$$U(x,+0) = F(x) \qquad (x > 0,\ x \neq x_n),$$

where F is bounded for all positive x and continuous except possibly for finite jumps at a finite number of points $x = x_n$.

3. In order to use principal values $-\pi/2 \leqq \arctan t \leqq \pi/2$ of inverse tangents, interchange the x and y axes in Sec. 103 to write the solution

$$U(x,y) = \frac{1}{\pi} \int_{-\infty}^{\infty} \frac{xF(y')}{(y' - y)^2 + x^2}\, dy' \qquad (x > 0)$$

of the Dirichlet problem for the half plane $x > 0$.   If

$$\lim_{x \to 0} U(x,y) = 1 \qquad \text{when } -1 < y < 1,$$

$$= 0 \qquad \text{when } |y| > 1,$$

where $x > 0$, obtain these formulas for U and its harmonic conjugate V:

$$U(x,y) = \frac{1}{\pi}\left(\arctan \frac{y+1}{x} - \arctan \frac{y-1}{x}\right),$$

$$V(x,y) = \frac{1}{2\pi} \operatorname{Log} \frac{x^2 + (y+1)^2}{x^2 + (y-1)^2}.$$

Also, show that $\pi(V + iU) = \operatorname{Log}(z + i) - \operatorname{Log}(z - i)$.

4. Let $T(x,y)$ denote the bounded steady temperatures in a plate $x > 0$, $y > 0$, with insulated faces when $T \to F(x)$ as $y \to 0$ and $T \to G(y)$ as $x \to 0$ (Fig. 100), where F and G are bounded, and continuous except for at most a finite number of finite jumps. If $x + iy = z$, show with the aid of the formula in Exercise 1 that

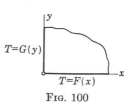

Fig. 100

$$T(x,y) = T_1(x,y) + T_2(x,y) \qquad (x > 0,\ y > 0),$$

where

$$T_1(x,y) = \frac{y}{\pi} \int_0^{\infty} \left(\frac{1}{|x' - z|^2} - \frac{1}{|x' + z|^2}\right) F(x')\, dx',$$

$$T_2(x,y) = \frac{x}{\pi} \int_0^{\infty} \left(\frac{1}{|iy' - z|^2} - \frac{1}{|iy' + z|^2}\right) G(y')\, dy'.$$

5. Establish formula (8) of Sec. 104 as a solution of the Neumann problem for the domain exterior to a circle, with the aid of earlier results found in that section.

6. As a special case of formula (3), Sec. 104, obtain the formula

$$u(r,\theta) = \frac{1}{2\pi} \int_0^\pi [Q(r_0, r, \theta' - \theta) - Q(r_0, r, \theta' + \theta)]g(\theta')\, d\theta'$$

for the harmonic function u in the *semicircular region* $r < r_0,\, 0 \leq \theta \leq \pi$, such that $u = 0$ on the bounding diameter and

$$\lim_{r \to r_0} \frac{\partial u}{\partial r} = g(\theta) \qquad (r < r_0,\, 0 < \theta < \pi).$$

7. As a special case of formula (3), Sec. 104, obtain the formula

$$u(r,\theta) = \frac{1}{2\pi} \int_0^\pi [Q(r_0, \theta' - \theta) + Q(r_0, r, \theta' + \theta)]\, g(\theta')\, d\theta' + u_0$$

for the harmonic function u in the *semicircular region* $r < r_0,\, 0 \leq \theta \leq \pi$, if $\partial u/\partial \theta = 0$ on the bounding diameter and $\partial u/\partial r \to g(\theta)$ as $r \to r_0$, where $\int_0^\pi g(\theta)\, d\theta = 0$.

8. Let $T(x,y)$ denote the steady temperatures in a plate $x > 0$, $y > 0$. The faces of the plate are insulated, and $T = 0$ on the edge $x = 0$. The flux of heat into the plate along the segment $0 < x < 1$ of the edge $y = 0$ is a constant A, and the rest of that edge ($x > 1$) is insulated. Use formula (5) of Sec. 105 to show that the flux out of the plate along the edge $x = 0$ is

$$\frac{A}{\pi} \operatorname{Log}\left(1 + \frac{1}{y^2}\right).$$

9. Show that the Poisson kernel is given in terms of Green's function

$$R(z,z') = \operatorname{Log}|z - z'| = \tfrac{1}{2} \operatorname{Log}[r_0^2 - 2r_0 r \cos(\theta' - \theta) + r^2],$$

when $z' = r_0 \exp(i\theta')$, by the equation

$$P(r_0, r, \theta' - \theta) = 2r_0 \frac{\partial R}{\partial r_0} - 1.$$

10. Show that the kernel used in Sec. 102 to represent u in the half plane $y > 0$ can be written in terms of Green's function $R(z,z')$ in the forms

$$\frac{y}{|x' - z|^2} = \frac{\partial}{\partial y} R(z,x') = -\frac{\partial}{\partial y'} R(z,z')\bigg]_{y'=0}.$$

CHAPTER 12

FURTHER THEORY OF FUNCTIONS

The theory of analytic functions presented in several of the foregoing chapters is intended to be introductory but self-contained. Many topics not essential to the continuity of the presentation were omitted, although several of them deserve a place in an introductory course because of their general interest. We present a few of them in this chapter.

A. ANALYTIC CONTINUATION

106. Conditions under Which $f(z) \equiv 0$. In Sec. 65 we proved that the zeros of an analytic function are isolated unless the function is identically zero. That is, if a function f is analytic at z_0, then there is a neighborhood N of z_0 such that either $f(z) \equiv 0$ in N or else f has no zeros in N, except possibly at the point z_0 itself.

Suppose there is some infinite set of points with z_0 as a limit point, such that $f(z) = 0$ whenever z belongs to that set. Then every neighborhood of z_0 contains zeros of the function f, and if f is analytic at z_0, it follows that there is some neighborhood of z_0 throughout which f vanishes. All coefficients $f(z_0)$, $f^{(n)}(z_0)/n!$ in Taylor's series for $f(z)$ in powers of $z - z_0$ therefore vanish. Thus $f(z) = 0$ at all points interior to the circle $|z - z_0| = r_0$ if f is analytic interior to that circle. Here r_0 is not necessarily small.

In particular, if f vanishes at all points of some *arc* containing point z_0, or at all points of some *domain* that contains z_0, and if f is analytic when $|z - z_0| < r_0$, then f is identically zero in the neighborhood $|z - z_0| < r_0$.

We now consider domains other than neighborhoods.

Theorem. *If a function f is analytic throughout a domain D and vanishes over a domain D_0 interior to D, then $f(z) = 0$ at every point of D.*

Let the complex numbers t_0 and t_n represent any two points of the domain D. Since a domain is a connected open region, there is a continuous chain C of segments of straight lines interior to D that connects the points t_0 and t_n (Fig. 101), where the number

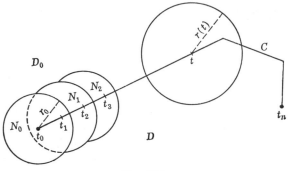

FIG. 101

of segments is finite. Since the function f is analytic at each point $z = t$ of C, its expansion in Taylor's series about the point t has some positive radius of convergence $r(t)$. Let us agree that $r(t)$ is to be replaced by unity whenever the radius of convergence is greater than unity; thus $0 < r(t) \leq 1$. Note that the circle of convergence $|z - t| = r(t)$ may extend beyond D.

To prove that r is a continuous function of t, let $t + h$ denote another point on C, where $|h| < r(t)$, and consider the circle of convergence $|z - (t + h)| = r(t + h)$ of Taylor's series for f about the point $t + h$. Now f is analytic when

$$|z - (t + h)| < r(t) - |h|,$$

because this neighborhood is interior to the circle about t (Fig. 102). Therefore $r(t + h) \geq r(t) - |h|$; that is,

FIG. 102

$$(1) \qquad r(t + h) - r(t) \geq - |h|,$$

a condition that is trivial when $r(t + h) \geq r(t)$. In case

$$r(t + h) < r(t),$$

condition (1) can be written

$$(2) \qquad |r(t + h) - r(t)| \leq |h|.$$

In case $r(t + h) \geqq r(t)$, then f is analytic in the neighborhood

$$|z - t| < r(t + h) - |h|$$

which is interior to the circle of convergence about $t + h$; hence $r(t) \geqq r(t + h) - |h|$, and again condition (2) is satisfied.

For each small positive number ϵ the member on the left of inequality (2) is less than ϵ when $|h| < \epsilon$. Thus r is a continuous function of t on C. It is also a continuous function of the real variable s, the arc length along C from t_0 to t. Since r is continuous and positive for all s on a finite closed interval, it must have some positive minimum value r_0 for all points of C.

Now let t_0 be some point of the domain D_0, and let t_n be any point of D that does not belong to D_0. Since f is identically zero in D_0, it vanishes throughout some neighborhood of t_0. In fact f must vanish throughout the neighborhood $|z - t_0| < r_0$ denoted by the symbol N_0, because f is analytic in N_0 and vanishes over a domain that contains t_0.

Consider a sequence of points $t_0, t_1, \ldots, t_n$ on C such that

$$\tfrac{1}{2}r_0 \leqq |t_j - t_{j-1}| < r_0 \quad (j = 1, 2, \ldots, n),$$

and a neighborhood N_j of each point t_j, of radius r_0, as indicated in Fig. 101. Since the center t_1 of N_1 lies in N_0 where f is identically zero, then $f(z) = 0$ throughout N_1. Likewise, the center of N_2 lies in N_1, so that f vanishes throughout N_2, etc., until we reach N_n. Thus $f(t_n) = 0$, and the proof of the theorem is complete.

107. Permanence of Forms of Functional Identities. As noted above, if a function is analytic in a domain D and vanishes along an arc in D, it vanishes over a neighborhood of each point of the arc. According to the foregoing theorem, the function therefore vanishes throughout D.

If two functions f_1 and f_2 have a domain of analyticity in common and if $f_1(z) = f_2(z)$ at each point of some arc in that domain, then their difference $f = f_1 - f_2$ is analytic there and vanishes along the arc. Thus throughout the domain it is true that $f = 0$, that is, $f_1 = f_2$. This result can be stated as follows.

Theorem 1. *A function that is analytic in a domain D is uniquely determined over D by its values along an arc, or over a domain, interior to D.*

As an illustration, the function exp z is the only entire function that can assume the values e^x along a segment of the real axis. Moreover, given that $e^x e^{-x} = 1$ whenever x is real and that exp z and exp $(-z)$ are entire functions, then

$$\exp z \exp (-z) - 1$$

is an entire function that vanishes along the real axis and therefore everywhere. Thus the identity exp $(-z) = 1/\exp z$ for all complex z follows from the identity when z is real and from the analyticity of the functions.

In like manner the identity $\sin^2 z + \cos^2 z = 1$ can be deduced from the identity $\sin^2 x + \cos^2 x = 1$. Such permanence of forms of other identities between functions, in passing from real to complex variables, is established in the same way. We limit our attention in the theorem below to the important class of identities that involve only polynomials in the functions.

Theorem 2. *Let $P(f_1, f_2, \ldots, f_n)$ be a polynomial in the n variables f_j, where f_j are analytic functions of z in a domain that contains some interval $a < x < b$ of the x axis. If on that interval those functions satisfy an identity*

(1) $$P[f_1(x), f_2(x), \ldots, f_n(x)] = 0 \qquad (a < x < b)$$

then for all z in the domain it is true that

(2) $$P[f_1(z), f_2(z), \ldots, f_n(z)] = 0.$$

The left-hand member of equation (2) is an analytic function of z in the given domain, and it vanishes over an arc in that domain, according to condition (1). Hence (2) is an identity throughout the domain.

108. Uniqueness of Analytic Continuation. The *intersection* of two domains D_1 and D_2 is the domain $D_1 D_2$ consisting of all points that are common to both domains. If the two domains intersect (overlap), then the totality of points that lie in either one also constitutes a domain. That domain is called the *union*, $D_1 + D_2$, of D_1 and D_2.

Given two intersecting domains D_1 and D_2 (Fig. 103) and a function f_1 that is analytic over D_1, a function f_2 *may* exist which is analytic over D_2 and equal to f_1 at each point of the intersection $D_1 D_2$. If so, then f_2 is called *the analytic continuation of f_1 into the domain D_2.*

Whenever that analytic continuation f_2 exists, it is unique, according to Theorem 1 of the preceding section, because not more than one function can be analytic in D_2 and assume the value $f_1(z)$ at each point z of the domain D_1D_2 interior to D_2. However, if there is an analytic continuation f_3 of f_2 from D_2 into a domain D_3 which intersects D_1, as indicated in the figure, it is not necessarily true that $f_3 = f_1$ in D_1D_3. In the following section we illustrate the fact that a chain of continuations of a given function from a domain D_1 may lead to a different function defined over D_1.

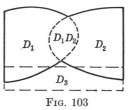

Fig. 103

If f_2 is the analytic continuation of f_1 from a domain D_1 into an intersecting domain D_2, then the function F, where

$$F(z) = f_1(z) \qquad \text{when } z \text{ is in } D_1,$$
$$= f_2(z) \qquad \text{when } z \text{ is in } D_2,$$

is analytic in the union $D_1 + D_2$. The functions f_1 and f_2 are called *elements* of F, and F is the analytic continuation into $D_1 + D_2$ of either f_1 or f_2.

109. Examples. Consider first the function f_1 defined by the equation

$$(1) \qquad f_1(z) = \sum_{n=0}^{\infty} z^n.$$

The power series here converges if and only if $|z| < 1$. It is the Maclaurin series expansion of the function $(1 - z)^{-1}$; thus

$$f_1(z) = \frac{1}{1 - z} \qquad \text{when } |z| < 1,$$

but f_1 is not defined when $|z| \geqq 1$. Now the function

$$(2) \qquad F(z) = \frac{1}{1 - z} \qquad (z \neq 1)$$

is defined and analytic everywhere except at the point $z = 1$. Since it is identical to f_1 in the interior of the circle $|z| = 1$, it represents the analytic continuation of f_1 outside that region whenever $|z| \geqq 1$ and $z \neq 1$. This is the only possible analytic continuation of f_1 beyond the unit circle, according to the results established in the preceding section.   In this case f_1 is an element of the function F defined by equation (2).

It is of interest to note that, if we begin with the information that the power series

$$\sum_{n=0}^{\infty} z^n$$

converges and represents an analytic function of z when $|z| < 1$ and that its sum is $(1 - x)^{-1}$ when $z = x$, then we can conclude that its sum is $(1 - z)^{-1}$ whenever $|z| < 1$, because the function $(1 - z)^{-1}$ is the analytic function interior to the circle that assumes the values $(1 - x)^{-1}$ along the segment of the x axis inside the circle.

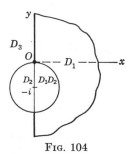

Fig. 104

As another illustration of analytic continuation, consider the function

$$(3) \qquad g_1(z) = \int_0^\infty e^{-zt}\, dt.$$

Since $-z^{-1} \exp(-zt)$ is an indefinite integral of the integrand,

$$(4) \qquad g_1(z) = \left. -\frac{1}{z}\, e^{-zt} \right]_{t=0}^{\infty} = \frac{1}{z} \qquad \text{when } x > 0.$$

Thus g_1 is defined only in the domain $x > 0$ denoted by D_1 in Fig. 104.   It is analytic there.   Let g_2 be defined by this geometric series:

$$(5) \qquad g_2(z) = i \sum_{n=0}^{\infty} \left(\frac{z + i}{i}\right)^n \qquad (|z + i| < 1).$$

Within its circle of convergence, the unit circle about the point $z = -i$, the series converges to $1/z$:

$$(6) \qquad g_2(z) = i\, \frac{1}{1 - (z + i)/i} = \frac{1}{z}$$

when z is in D_2, where D_2 is the domain $|z + i| < 1$.   Thus $g_2 = g_1$ in the intersection $D_1 D_2$, and g_2 is the analytic continuation of g_1 into D_2.

The function $G(z) = 1/z$ $(z \neq 0)$ is the analytic continuation of both g_1 and g_2 into the domain D_3 consisting of all points of the z plane except the origin. The functions g_1 and g_2 are elements of G.

Finally, consider this branch of $z^{\frac{1}{2}}$:

$$h_1(z) = \sqrt{r}\, \exp \frac{i\theta}{2} \qquad (r > 0, 0 < \theta < \pi).$$

Its analytic continuation h_2 across the negative x axis into the lower half plane can be written

$$h_2(z) = \sqrt{r}\, \exp \frac{i\theta}{2} \qquad \left(r > 0, \frac{\pi}{2} < \theta < 2\pi\right).$$

The analytic continuation of h_2 across the positive x axis into the first quadrant is described by the conditions

$$h_3(z) = \sqrt{r}\, \exp \frac{i\theta}{2} \qquad \left(r > 0, \pi < \theta < \frac{5\pi}{2}\right).$$

Thus $h_3 \neq h_1$ in the first quadrant; in fact $h_3(z) = -h_1(z)$ there.

110. The Principle of Reflection. In Chap. 3 we noted that some elementary functions $w = f(z)$ possess the property that $\bar{w} = f(\bar{z})$, and others do not. As examples of those that do, we can cite the functions

$$z, \qquad z^2 + 1, \qquad e^z, \qquad \sin z,$$

for when z is replaced by its conjugate, the value of each of these functions changes to the conjugate of the original value. On the other hand, the functions

$$iz, \qquad z^2 + i, \qquad e^{iz}, \qquad (1 + i)\sin z$$

do not satisfy the property that the reflection of z in the real axis corresponds to the reflection of w in the real axis.

The following theorem shows that an analytic function satisfies this *reflection principle* if and only if the function is real when z is real.

Theorem. *Let a function f be analytic in some domain D that includes a segment of the x axis and is symmetric to the x axis. If $f(x)$ is real whenever x is a point of that segment, then*

$$(1) \qquad\qquad f(\bar{z}) = \overline{f(z)}$$

whenever z is a point in D.   Conversely, if the condition (1) *is satisfied then f(x) is real.*

Equation (1) represents the same condition on f as the equation

$$(2) \qquad \overline{f(\bar{z})} = f(z),$$

where, if $f = u + iv$,

$$(3) \qquad \overline{f(\bar{z})} = u(x,-y) - iv(x,-y).$$

When condition (2) is satisfied at a point on the real axis, then

$$f(x) = u(x,0) + iv(x,0) = u(x,0) - iv(x,0);$$

consequently $v(x,0) = 0$, and $f(x)$ is real.   The converse statement in the theorem is therefore true.

In order to prove the direct statement in the theorem, let us first show that the function $\overline{f(\bar{z})}$ is analytic throughout the domain D.   We write

$$F(z) = \overline{f(\bar{z})} = U(x,y) + iV(x,y).$$

Then, according to equation (3),

$$(4) \quad U(x,y) = u(x,\eta), \qquad V(x,y) = -v(x,\eta), \qquad \text{where } \eta = -y.$$

Since $f(x + i\eta)$ is an analytic function of $x + i\eta$ in D, the functions $u(x,\eta)$, $v(x,\eta)$ and their partial derivatives are continuous and satisfy the Cauchy-Riemann conditions

$$\frac{\partial u}{\partial x} = \frac{\partial v}{\partial \eta}, \qquad \frac{\partial u}{\partial \eta} = -\frac{\partial v}{\partial x}$$

throughout D.   Now, in view of equations (4), we see that

$$\frac{\partial U}{\partial x} = \frac{\partial u}{\partial x}, \qquad \frac{\partial V}{\partial y} = -\frac{\partial v}{\partial \eta}\frac{\partial \eta}{\partial y} = \frac{\partial v}{\partial \eta},$$

and therefore $\partial U/\partial x = \partial V/\partial y$.   Similarly, we find that

$$\frac{\partial U}{\partial y} = -\frac{\partial V}{\partial x},$$

and it follows that the function F is analytic in the domain D.

Since $f(x)$ is real, $v(x,0) = 0$, and therefore

$$F(x) = U(x,0) + iV(x,0) = u(x,0);$$

that is, $F(z) = f(z)$ when the point z is on the segment of the

x axis within the domain.   It follows from Theorem 1 of Sec. 107 that $F(z) = f(z)$ at each point z of D, since both functions are analytic there.   Thus condition (2) is established and the proof of the theorem is complete.

EXERCISES

1. Given that the exponential function, the hyperbolic sine and cosine functions, and the sine and cosine functions are all entire, use Theorem 2 of Sec. 107 to deduce each of these identities for all complex z from the corresponding identities when z is real:

(a) $\sinh z + \cosh z = e^z$;   (b) $\sin 2z = 2 \sin z \cos z$;

(c) $\cosh^2 z - \sinh^2 z = 1$;   (d) $\sin \left(\dfrac{\pi}{2} - z\right) = \cos z.$

2. Show that the function

$$f_2(z) = \frac{1}{z^2 + 1} \qquad\qquad (z \neq i, z \neq -i)$$

is the analytic continuation of the function

$$f_1(z) = \sum_{n=0}^{\infty} (-1)^n z^{2n}$$

into the region beyond the interior of the unit circle $|z| = 1$.

3. Show that the function z^{-2} represents the analytic continuation of the function defined by the series

$$\sum_{n=0}^{\infty} (n+1)(z+1)^n$$

into the region beyond the interior of the circle $|z + 1| = 1$.

4. State why the analytic continuation of the function (Sec. 109)

$$h_1(z) = \sqrt{r}\, \exp \frac{i\theta}{2} \qquad (r > 0, 0 < \theta < \pi)$$

across the positive x axis into the lower half plane is this function: $\sqrt{r} \exp (i\theta/2)$, where $r > 0$ and $-\pi < \theta < \pi$.

5. Find the analytic continuation of Log z from the upper half plane $y > 0$ into the lower half plane across the negative x axis.   Note that this analytic continuation is different from Log z in the lower half plane.

Ans. Log $r + i\theta$ $(r > 0, 0 < \theta < 2\pi)$.

6. Find the analytic continuation of the function

$$f(z) = \int_0^\infty te^{-zt}\, dt$$

into the region on the left of the half plane $x > 0$.   *Ans.* z^{-2}.

7. If k is a real constant, show that the analytic continuation of the function

$$f(z) = \int_0^\infty e^{-zt} \sin kt\, dt \qquad\qquad (x > 0)$$

has simple poles at the points $z = \pm ik$.

8. In the theorem of Sec. 110, show that, if the condition that $f(x)$ be real is replaced by the condition that $f(x)$ have pure imaginary values, the conclusion is changed to $\overline{f(z)} = -f(\bar{z})$.

9. Let S denote a set of points in a domain D such that the set has a limit point in D. Generalize Theorem 1 of Sec. 107 by proving that a function which is analytic over D is uniquely determined by its values on the set S.

B. SINGULAR POINTS AND ZEROS

We now make a further examination of the behavior of functions near their singular points.

111. Poles and Zeros. It was pointed out in Sec. 68 that, if z_0 is a pole of any order of a function f, then

$$(1) \qquad\qquad \lim_{z \to z_0} |f(z)| = \infty\,;$$

that is, given any real number M a positive number δ_M exists such that

$$(2) \qquad\qquad |f(z)| > M \qquad \text{whenever } 0 < |z - z_0| < \delta_M.$$

As a consequence, some neighborhood of each pole is free from zeros of the function f.

Since poles are isolated singular points, it follows that *some neighborhood of each pole z_0 contains neither a zero nor a singular point other than z_0 itself.*

According to Exercise 9, Sec. 69, if z_0 is a zero of order m of a function f, then z_0 is a pole of order m of the reciprocal function $1/f$. A converse is easily established. For if z_0 is a pole of order m of a function g, then the function $(z - z_0)^m g(z)$ has a removable singular point at z_0; in fact, the value of the latter function can be defined at z_0 as some number *other than zero*, so that it is analytic there.   Let ϕ denote that function:

$$(3) \qquad \phi(z) = (z - z_0)^m g(z) \qquad \text{when } 0 < |z - z_0| < r_0,$$
$$= \phi(z_0) \neq 0 \qquad \text{when } z = z_0.$$

Then $1/\phi$ is analytic at z_0, and for some positive number r_1 it is represented by Taylor's series

$$\frac{1}{\phi(z)} = \sum_{n=0}^{\infty} a_n (z - z_0)^n \qquad (|z - z_0| < r_1),$$

where $r_1 \leqq r_0$ and $a_0 = 1/\phi(z_0) \neq 0$.   It follows from equation (3) that

$$(4) \qquad \frac{1}{g(z)} = (z - z_0)^m \sum_{n=0}^{\infty} a_n (z - z_0)^n \qquad (|z - z_0| < r_1).$$

Therefore, *if z_0 is a pole of order m of a function g, then it is a zero of order m of the reciprocal function $1/g$.*

In contrast to condition (2), suppose f is bounded and analytic when $0 < |z - z_0| < r_0$.   Then the following theorem due to Riemann applies.

Theorem.   *Given that a function f is analytic throughout a domain $0 < |z - z_0| < r_0$ and bounded there, that is, for some constant M,*

$$|f(z)| < M \qquad (0 < |z - z_0| < r_0),$$

then either f is analytic at z_0 or else z_0 is a removable singular point of the function.

The function is represented by its Laurent series in the domain about z_0.   If C denotes a circle $|z - z_0| = r_1$, where $r_1 < r_0$, the coefficients A_{-n} of $(z - z_0)^{-n}$ in that series are (Sec. 58)

$$A_{-n} = \frac{1}{2\pi i} \int_C \frac{f(z)\, dz}{(z - z_0)^{-n+1}} = \frac{r_1^n}{2\pi} \int_0^{2\pi} f(z_0 + r_1 e^{i\theta}) e^{in\theta}\, d\theta,$$

where $n = 1, 2, \ldots$ Hence

$$|A_{-n}| < M r_1^n \qquad (r_1 < r_0).$$

But the coefficients are constants and, since r_1 can be chosen arbitrarily small, $A_{-n} = 0$ when $n = 1, 2, \ldots$ Thus Laurent's series reduces to Taylor's series and

$$f(z) = \sum_{n=0}^{\infty} A_n(z - z_0)^n \qquad (0 < |z - z_0| < r_0).$$

If $f(z_0)$ is defined to be the number A_0, then f is analytic at z_0. This proves the theorem.

112. Essential Singular Points.   The behavior of a function near an essential singular point is quite irregular, as shown by the following theorem of Weierstrass.

Theorem. *Let z_0 be an essential singular point of a function f and let c be any given complex number.   Then for each positive number ϵ, however small, the inequality*

$$(1) \qquad\qquad\qquad |f(z) - c| < \epsilon$$

is satisfied at some point z $(z \neq z_0)$ in each neighborhood of z_0.

The theorem shows that the value of f is arbitrarily close to any prescribed number c at points arbitrarily near an essential singular point.   An examination of the function $\exp(1/z)$, which has an essential singular point at the origin, indicates such a behavior as the point z approaches the origin along different rays (see also Exercise 1, Sec. 113).

To prove the theorem, suppose that condition (1) is not satisfied at any point in a neighborhood $|z - z_0| < r_0$, where r_0 is small enough that f is analytic in the domain $0 < |z - z_0| < r_0$. Then $|f(z) - c| \geqq \epsilon$ for all points of that domain, and the function

$$(2) \qquad\qquad\qquad g(z) = \frac{1}{f(z) - c} \qquad (0 < |z - z_0| < r_0)$$

is **analytic** and bounded.   According to Riemann's theorem (Sec. 111), z_0 is a removable singular point of g.   Let $g(z_0)$ be so defined that g is analytic at z_0.   Since f cannot be a constant, g is not a constant and, according to Taylor's series, either $g(z_0) \neq 0$ or else g has a zero of some finite order at z_0.   Therefore its reciprocal

$$\frac{1}{g(z)} = f(z) - c$$

is either analytic at z_0 or else it has a pole there.   But this contradicts the hypothesis that z_0 is an essential singular point of f. Hence condition (1) must be satisfied at some point.

113. The Number of Zeros and Poles. The properties of the logarithmic derivative found in Exercises 10, Sec. 69, and 9, Sec. 95, can be generalized.

Let a function f be analytic inside and on a closed contour C except for at most a finite number of poles interior to C. Also, let f have no zeros on C and at most a finite number of zeros interior to C. Then, if C is described in the positive sense, it is true that

$$(1) \qquad \frac{1}{2\pi i} \int_C \frac{f'(z)}{f(z)} \, dz = N_0 - N_p,$$

where N_0 is the total number of zeros of f inside C, a zero of order m_0 being counted m_0 times, and N_p is the total number of poles of f inside C if a pole of order m_p is counted m_p times.

To prove that statement, we show that the integer $N_0 - N_p$ is the sum of the residues of the function f'/f at the singular points inside the closed contour. Those points consist of the zeros and poles of f interior to C.

If z_0 is a zero of f, then in some neighborhood of z_0

$$(2) \qquad f(z) = (z - z_0)^{m_0} g(z) \qquad\qquad [g(z_0) \neq 0],$$

where m_0 is the order of that zero and g is an analytic function in the neighborhood. Therefore

$$f'(z) = m_0(z - z_0)^{m_0-1} g(z) + (z - z_0)^{m_0} g'(z)$$

and
$$\frac{f'(z)}{f(z)} = \frac{m_0}{z - z_0} + \frac{g'(z)}{g(z)}.$$

Since g'/g is analytic at z_0, the function f'/f has a simple pole at z_0 with residue m_0. The sum of the residues of f'/f at all the zeros of f inside C is therefore the integer N_0.

If z_p is a pole of f, of order m_p, the function

$$(3) \qquad h(z) = (z - z_p)^{m_p} f(z)$$

can be defined at z_p so that h is analytic there; moreover, that defining number $h(z_p)$ is different from zero. Thus in some neighborhood of z_p, except at the point $z = z_p$ itself,

$$(4) \qquad f(z) = (z - z_p)^{-m_p} h(z), \qquad \text{where } h(z_p) \neq 0,$$

and $\quad f'(z) = -m_p(z - z_p)^{-m_p-1} h(z) + (z - z_p)^{-m_p} h'(z).$

Therefore $\qquad \dfrac{f'(z)}{f(z)} = -\dfrac{m_p}{z - z_p} + \dfrac{h'(z)}{h(z)},$

and we see that f'/f has a simple pole at z_p with residue $-m_p$. Hence the sum of the residues of f'/f at all the poles of f inside C is the integer $-N_p$, and formula (1) is established.

The Bolzano-Weierstrass theorem can be stated as follows. *A set of infinitely many points each of which lies in a closed bounded region has at least one limit point in that region.* The proof can be made by selecting any infinite sequence $z_1, z_2, \ldots$ of points from the set and applying to that sequence a process of subdividing squares, a procedure used in Exercise 13, Sec. 50.

In view of that theorem, the conditions used in proving formula (1) can be relaxed. For the number of zeros and poles within the closed contour must necessarily be finite if the function f is to be analytic within and on C, except possibly for poles within C, because zeros and poles are isolated. The argument in full is left as an exercise.

The function $\log f$ is an indefinite integral of f'/f. Since $\text{Log }|f(z)|$ returns to its initial value when the point z makes a cycle around the closed contour C, it turns out that the value of the integral in formula (1) is determined by the change in value of $i\phi$, where $\phi = \arg f(z)$, as follows:

$$(5) \qquad \int_C \frac{f'(z)}{f(z)} \, dz = i \, \Delta_C \phi,$$

where $\Delta_C \phi$ is the change in the number of radians in the continuous angle ϕ as point z makes a cycle about C in the positive sense. Thus formula (1) can be stated in this form, known as the *argument principle:*

$$(6) \qquad \frac{1}{2\pi} \Delta_C[\arg f(z)] = N_0 - N_p.$$

EXERCISES

1. Let $c_0 \exp(i\gamma)$, where $c_0 > 0$, denote any fixed complex number c other than zero. Show that the function $\exp(1/z)$, which has an essential singular point at $z = 0$, takes on that value c at points $z = r \exp(i\theta)$, where r and θ satisfy the equations

$$r^2 = \frac{1}{\gamma^2 + (\text{Log } c_0)^2},$$

$$\sin\theta = \frac{-\gamma}{\sqrt{\gamma^2 + (\text{Log } c_0)^2}}, \qquad \cos\theta = \frac{\text{Log } c_0}{\sqrt{\gamma^2 + (\text{Log } c_0)^2}}.$$

Note that r can be made arbitrarily small by adding multiples of 2π to the angle γ, leaving c unaltered.

2. *If a function f is analytic when $0 < |z - z_0| < r_0$ for some positive number r_0 and if z_0 is a limit point of zeros of the function, then z_0 is an essential singular point of f, unless f is identically zero.* Prove this theorem with the aid of results found in Sec. 111.

3. Examine the set of zeros of the function $z^2 \sin (1/z)$ and apply the theorem stated in Exercise 2 to show that the origin is an essential singular point of the function. Note that this conclusion also follows from the nature of the Laurent series, in powers of z, that represents this function in the domain $|z| > 0$.

4. Let C be a closed contour described in the positive sense and let w_0 be a given complex number. If a function g is analytic within and on C and $g'(z) \neq 0$ at any point interior to C, and if $g(z) \neq w_0$ at any point on C, then

$$\frac{1}{2\pi i} \int_C \frac{g'(z)}{g(z) - w_0} \, dz = N,$$

where the integer N is the number of points interior to C at which $g(z) = w_0$. Show how this result follows from those given in Sec. 113. (Compare the result with those found in Exercises 9 and 10, Sec. 95.)

5. Complete the argument (Sec. 113), based on the Bolzano-Weierstrass theorem, that if a function f is analytic within and on a closed contour C, except possibly for poles inside C, and if f does not vanish at any point on C, then the poles and zeros of f inside C are finite in number and formula (1) is true.

C. RIEMANN SURFACES

A Riemann surface is a generalization of the z plane to a surface of more than one sheet such that a multiple-valued function has only one value corresponding to each point on that surface. Once such a surface is devised for a given function, the function is single-valued on the surface, and the theory of single-valued functions applies there. Complexities arising because the function is multiple-valued are thus relieved by a geometrical device. However, the description of those surfaces and the arrangement of proper connections between the sheets can become quite involved. We limit our attention to fairly simple examples.

114. A Surface for the Function log z. Corresponding to each point other than the origin in the z plane, the function

$$\log z = \text{Log } r + i\theta$$

has infinitely many values.   In order to describe this function as
a single-valued function of a point, we may replace the z plane by
a surface on which a new point is represented whenever the argument of the point z is increased or decreased by 2π.

Consider the z plane as a thin sheet R_0, which is cut along the
positive half of the x axis.   On that sheet let θ range from zero to
2π.   Let a second sheet R_1 be cut in the same way and placed in
front of the sheet R_0.   The lower edge of the slit in R_0 is then
joined to the upper edge of the slit in R_1.   On R_1 the angle θ
ranges from 2π to 4π, so that when z represents a point on R_1,
the imaginary coefficient of log z has a value between 2π and 4π.

A sheet R_2 is then cut in the same way and placed in front of R_1,
and the lower edge of the slit in R_1 is joined to the upper edge of
the slit in this new sheet, and similarly for sheets R_3, R_4, ...
A sheet R_{-1} on which θ varies from zero to -2π is cut and placed
behind R_0, with the lower edge of its slit connected to the upper
edge of the slit in R_0; similarly for the sheet R_{-2}, etc.   The
coordinates r and θ of a point on any sheet can be taken as the
polar coordinates of the projection of the point on the original
z plane, except that the angular coordinate θ is restricted to a
definite range of 2π radians on each sheet.   The origin is a point
common to all the sheets.

Consider any continuous curve on this connected surface of
infinitely many sheets, a curve that does not pass through the
origin.   As a point z moves over that
curve, the values of the function log z
vary continuously, since θ varies continuously, and the function assumes
just one value corresponding to each
point on the curve.   As the point
makes a complete cycle around the
origin in the sheet R_0, for example,
over the path indicated in Fig. 105, the
angle changes from zero to 2π.   As it
moves across the line $\theta = 2\pi$, the point
passes to the sheet R_1 of the surface.   As the point completes a
cycle in R_1, the angle θ varies from 2π to 4π, and as it crosses the
line $\theta = 4\pi$, the point passes to the sheet R_2.

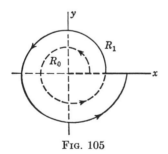

Fig. 105

The surface described here is a Riemann surface for the function log z, a connected surface of infinitely many sheets so

arranged that this function is a single-valued function of points on that surface.

The transformation $w = \log z$ maps the whole Riemann surface, except for the branch point $z = 0$, in a one to one manner onto the entire w plane. The image of the sheet R_0 is the strip $0 \leqq v \leqq 2\pi$. As point z moves into the sheet R_1 over the arc shown in Fig. 106, its image w moves upward across the line $v = 2\pi$, as indicated in the figure.

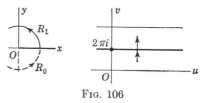

FIG. 106

Note that the function w in the strip $2\pi \leqq v < 4\pi$ represents the analytic continuation of the single-valued analytic function

$$\text{Log } r + i\theta \qquad (0 < \theta < 2\pi)$$

upward across the positive x axis. In this sense, the function w is not only a single-valued function of all points z on the Riemann surface but also an *analytic* function at all points except the origin.

The sheets could, of course, be cut along the negative x axis, or along any other half line starting at the origin, and properly joined along the slits to form other Riemann surfaces for the function $\log z$.

115. A Surface for the Function $z^{\frac{1}{2}}$. The function

$$z^{\frac{1}{2}} = \sqrt{r}\left(\cos\frac{\theta}{2} + i\sin\frac{\theta}{2}\right)$$

has two values corresponding to each point, except the origin, in the z plane. Let the plane be replaced by two sheets R_0 and R_1, each of which is cut along the positive x axis, with R_1 placed in front of R_0. Join the lower edge of the slit in R_0 to the upper edge of the slit in R_1, and the lower edge of the slit in R_1 to the upper edge of the slit in R_0. The two sheets therefore cross each other at the cut.

As the point z describes a continuous circuit (Fig. 107) about the origin on that surface, the angle θ grows from zero to 2π, and then the point passes from the sheet R_0 to the sheet R_1, where θ grows from 2π to 4π. As the point moves still farther, it passes back to the sheet R_0, where the values of θ vary either from 4π to

6π or from zero to 2π, a choice that does not affect the value of the function $z^{\frac{1}{2}}$, etc.   The function is a single-valued function of points on this surface, except that some more artificial device is needed to distinguish between points of the two sheets along the cut.

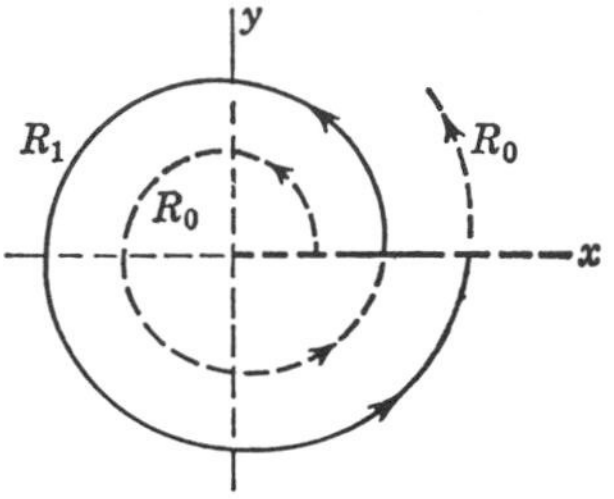

Fig. 107

The image of the sheet R_0 of this Riemann surface for the function $z^{\frac{1}{2}}$ is the upper half of the w plane, since

$$w = \rho e^{i\phi} = \sqrt{r}\, e^{i\theta/2},$$

and $0 \leq \theta/2 \leq \pi$ on R_0.   The image of the sheet R_1 is the lower half of the w plane.   As defined on either sheet, the function is the analytic continuation, across the cut, of the function defined on the other sheet.   In this respect, this single-valued function $z^{\frac{1}{2}}$ of points on the Riemann surface is analytic at all points except the origin.

116. Surfaces for Other Irrational Functions.   Let us describe a Riemann surface for the double-valued function

(1) $$f(z) = (z^2 - 1)^{\frac{1}{2}} = \sqrt{r_1 r_2} \exp\left(i\, \frac{\theta_1 + \theta_2}{2}\right),$$

where $z - 1 = r_1 \exp(i\theta_1)$ and $z + 1 = r_2 \exp(i\theta_2)$, as shown in Fig. 23.   A branch of this function, with the line segment P_1P_2 between the branch points $z = \pm 1$ as a branch cut, was described in Sec. 37.   That branch is given by formula (1) when both θ_1 and θ_2 range from zero to 2π.   It is discontinuous on the segment P_1P_2.

The Riemann surface for the double-valued function (1) must consist of two sheets R_0 and R_1.   Let both be cut along the segment P_1P_2, and let the lower edge of the slit in R_0 be joined to the upper edge of the slit in R_1, and the lower edge in R_1 to the upper edge in R_0.   The two sheets of the "continuous" surface so formed cross each other along that segment.   A point on the surface can move from one sheet to the other only by crossing that line segment.

Let the sheet R_0 be the one on which each of the angles θ_1 and θ_2 may have values Θ_1 and Θ_2 ranging from zero to 2π.   However, at any point on R_0 the value of both angles may be increased or decreased by 2π because the function f will have the same value as before. That change in the angles corresponds to a movement of the point z from its original position around any curve enclosing the entire segment P_1P_2 and back to its original position. Likewise, the value of either θ_1 or θ_2 can be changed by $\pm 4\pi$ if the other angle is not changed, without altering the value of f, a change that corresponds to moving the point z over a curve twice around just one of the branch points and back to its original position. Thus for each point on R_0 the angles θ_1 and θ_2 have the values

$$\theta_1 = \Theta_1 + 2\pi n_1, \qquad \theta_2 = \Theta_2 + 2\pi n_2 \qquad (0 \leqq \Theta_j \leqq 2\pi, j = 1, 2),$$

where the integers n_1 and n_2 (positive, negative, or zero) are both even or both odd, so that their sum is even. Here zero is to be included among the even integers.

If one of the integers n_1 or n_2 is even and the other odd, the angles

$$\theta_1 = \Theta_1 + 2\pi n_1, \qquad \theta_2 = \Theta_2 + 2\pi n_2$$

are coordinates of points on the sheet R_1. The point that has the coordinates $\theta_1 = 5\pi/2$, $\theta_2 = \pi/4$, for example, is on R_1.

The function (1) has just one value corresponding to each point of the Riemann surface consisting of the two sheets R_0 and R_1, except for points on the segment P_1P_2. Since the positions of all points on R_0 can be described with angles θ_1 and θ_2 ranging

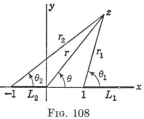

Fig. 108

from zero to 2π, the argument $(\theta_1 + \theta_2)/2$ of $f(z)$ ranges from zero to 2π. The transformation $w = f(z)$ maps the sheet R_0 onto the entire w plane. It also maps R_1 onto the entire w plane.

As another example, consider the double-valued function

$$(2) \qquad g(z) = [z(z^2 - 1)]^{\frac{1}{2}} = \sqrt{rr_1r_2} \exp\left(i\,\frac{\theta + \theta_1 + \theta_2}{2}\right)$$

(Fig. 108). The points $z = 0$, $z = \pm 1$ are branch points of this function. We note that, if the point z describes a circuit that includes all three of those points, the argument of $g(z)$ changes by the angle 3π, and hence the value of the function changes. Therefore, a branch cut must be run from one of those branch points to infinity in order to describe a single-valued branch of g.   Thus the infinite point is a branch point, as we can show also by writing $z = 1/Z$ and noting that $g(1/Z)$ has a branch point at $Z = 0$.

Let two sheets be cut along the line segment L_2 from $z = -1$ to $z = 0$ and along the part L_1 of the real axis on the right of the point $z = 1$.   On the sheet R_0 we specify that each of the three angles θ, θ_1, and θ_2 may range from zero to 2π, and on R_1 from 2π to 4π; but we add the specification that the angles corresponding to a point on either sheet may be increased or diminished by multiples of 2π in such a way the sum of the three angles changes by a multiple of 4π, so that the value of the function g is not altered.

If we connect the edges of the slits along L_1 and L_2 crosswise, that is, if along L_1 we join the lower edge in R_0 to the upper edge in R_1, etc., so that whenever a point crosses either L_1 or L_2 it moves from one sheet to the other, a Riemann surface for the function g is formed.   The reader can verify with the aid of Fig. 108 that one branch of the function is represented by its values at points on R_0 and the other branch at points on R_1 and that the values change to those of the other branch when and only when the point crosses either L_1 or L_2.

EXERCISES

1. Describe a Riemann surface for the triple-valued function

$$w = (z - 1)^{\frac{1}{3}},$$

and point out which third of the w plane represents the image of each sheet of the surface.

2. Describe the image, on a Riemann surface, of the entire circle $|w| = 1$ under the transformation $w = z^{\frac{1}{2}}$.

3. It was pointed out in the preceding section that, although a single value of the function

$$w = (z^2 - 1)^{\frac{1}{2}}$$

corresponds to each point z on the Riemann surface, there are two points z corresponding to each value of w, in general.   Show in another way why this is so.

4. Corresponding to each point on the Riemann surface described in the preceding section for the function $w = g(z)$, there is just one value of w. Show that corresponding to each value of w there are in general three points on the surface.

5. Describe a Riemann surface for the function

$$w = \left(\frac{z-1}{z}\right)^{\frac{1}{2}}.$$

6. Let C denote the circle $|z - 2| = 1$ on the Riemann surface described in Sec. 115 for the function $z^{\frac{1}{2}}$, where the upper half of that circle lies in the sheet R_0 and the lower half in R_1. For all points on C note that we can write

$$z^{\frac{1}{2}} = \sqrt{r} \exp\frac{i\theta}{2}, \qquad \text{where } 4\pi - \frac{\pi}{2} < \theta < 4\pi + \frac{\pi}{2}.$$

State why it follows that

$$\int_C z^{\frac{1}{2}}\, dz = 0.$$

Generalize this result to fit the case of other closed curves that cross from one sheet to another without enclosing the branch points, and generalize to other functions, thus extending the Cauchy-Goursat theorem to integrals of multiple-valued functions.

7. Note that the Riemann surface described in Sec. 116 for the function $(z^2 - 1)^{\frac{1}{2}}$ is also a Riemann surface for the function w of z defined by either of the equations

$$w = z + (z^2 - 1)^{\frac{1}{2}}, \qquad z = \frac{1}{2}\left(w + \frac{1}{w}\right).$$

If f_0 denotes the branch of $(z^2 - 1)^{\frac{1}{2}}$ defined on the sheet R_0, show that the branches w_0 and w_1 of w on the two sheets are given by the equations

$$w_0 = \frac{1}{w_1} = z + f_0(z).$$

8. In Exercise 7, the branch f_0 of $(z^2 - 1)^{\frac{1}{2}}$ can be described by the equation

$$f_0(z) = \sqrt{r_1 r_2} \exp\frac{i\theta_1}{2} \exp\frac{i\theta_2}{2},$$

where θ_1 and θ_2 range from zero to 2π and

$$z - 1 = r_1 \exp(i\theta_1), \qquad z + 1 = r_2 \exp(i\theta_2).$$

Since $2z = r_1 \exp(i\theta_1) + r_2 \exp(i\theta_2)$, show that the branch w_0 of the function $w = z + (z^2 - 1)^{\frac{1}{2}}$ can be written in the form

$$w_0(z) = \frac{1}{2} \left(\sqrt{r_1} \exp \frac{i\theta_1}{2} + \sqrt{r_2} \exp \frac{i\theta_2}{2} \right)^2.$$

Find $w_0 \bar{w}_0$ and note that $r_1 + r_2 \geqq 2$ and $\cos \frac{1}{2}(\theta_1 - \theta_2) \geqq 0$, for all z, to prove that $|w_0(z)| \geqq 1$. Then show that, under the transformation $z = \frac{1}{2}(w + 1/w)$, the sheet R_0 of the Riemann z surface maps onto the region $|w| \geqq 1$, the sheet R_1 onto the region $|w| \leqq 1$, and the branch cut between the points $z = \pm 1$ onto the circle $|w| = 1$ (compare Exercise 14, Sec. 41).

APPENDIX 1

BIBLIOGRAPHY

The following list of books, for supplementary study of the theory of functions of a complex variable and applications of the theory, is far from exhaustive. Further references can be found in several of the books listed here.

THEORY

Ahlfors, L. V.: "Complex Analysis," McGraw-Hill Book Company, Inc., New York, 1953.

Bieberbach, L.: "Conformal Mapping," Chelsea Publishing Company, New York, 1953.

————: "Lehrbuch der Funktionentheorie," vols. 1 and 2, B. G. Teubner, Berlin, 1934.

Caratheodory, C.: "Conformal Representation," Cambridge University Press, London, 1952.

————: "Theory of Functions of a Complex Variable," vols. 1 and 2, Chelsea Publishing Company, New York, 1954.

Copson, E. T.: "Theory of Functions of a Complex Variable," Oxford University Press, London, 1957.

Dienes, P.: "The Taylor Series: An Introduction to the Theory of Functions of a Complex Variable," Dover Publications, New York, 1957.

Evans, G. C.: "The Logarithmic Potential," American Mathematical Society, Providence, R.I., 1927.

Forsyth, A. R.: "Theory of Functions of a Complex Variable," Cambridge University Press, London, 1918.

Hille, E.: "Analytic Function Theory," vol. 1, Ginn & Company, Boston, 1959.

Hurwitz, A., and R. Courant: "Vorlesungen über allgemeine Funktionentheorie und elliptische Funktionen," Interscience Publishers, Inc., New York, 1944.

Kellogg, O. D.: "Foundations of Potential Theory," Springer-Verlag OHG, Berlin, 1929.

Knopp, K.: "Elements of the Theory of Functions," Dover Publications, New York, 1952.

MacRobert, T. M.: "Functions of a Complex Variable," Macmillan & Co., Ltd., London, 1954.

Nehari, Z.: "Conformal Mapping," McGraw-Hill Book Company, Inc., New York, 1952.

Springer, G.: "Introduction to Riemann Surfaces," Addison-Wesley Publishing Company, Reading, Mass., 1957.

Sternberg, W. J., and T. L. Smith: "Theory of Potential and Spherical Harmonics," University of Toronto Press, Toronto, 1944.

Titchmarsh, E. C.: "Theory of Functions," Oxford University Press, London, 1939.

Whittaker, E. T., and G. N. Watson: "Modern Analysis," Cambridge University Press, London, 1950.

APPLICATIONS

Bowman, F.: "Introduction to Elliptic Functions, with Applications," English Universities Press, London, 1953.

Churchill, R. V.: "Operational Mathematics," 2d ed., McGraw-Hill Book Company, Inc., New York, 1958.

Glauert, H.: "The Elements of Aerofoil and Airscrew Theory," Cambridge University Press, London, 1948.

Green, S. L.: "Hydro- and Aero-dynamics," Sir Isaac Pitman & Sons, Ltd., London, 1937.

Guillemin, E. A.: "The Mathematics of Circuit Analysis," John Wiley & Sons, Inc., New York, 1951.

Jeans, J. H.: "Mathematical Theory of Electricity and Magnetism," Cambridge University Press, London, 1925.

Kober, H.: "Dictionary of Conformal Representations," Dover Publications, New York, 1952.

Lamb, H.: "Hydrodynamics," Dover Publications, New York, 1945.

Love, A. E. H.: "Elasticity," Dover Publications, New York, 1944.

Milne-Thomson, L. M.: "Theoretical Hydrodynamics," Macmillan & Co., Ltd., London, 1955.

Muskhelishvili, N. I.: "Some Basic Problems of the Mathematical Theory of Elasticity," P. Noordhoff, N. V., Groningen, Netherlands, 1953.

Oberhettinger, F., and W. Magnus: "Anwendung der elliptischen Funktionen in Physik und Technik," Springer-Verlag OHG, Berlin, 1949.

Rothe, R., F. Ollendorff, and K. Pohlhausen: "Theory of Functions as

Applied to Engineering Problems," Technology Press, Massachusetts Institute of Technology, Cambridge, Mass., 1948.

Smythe, W. R.: "Static and Dynamic Electricity," 2d ed., McGraw-Hill Book Company, Inc., New York, 1950.

Sokolnikoff, I. S.: "Mathematical Theory of Elasticity," 2d ed., McGraw-Hill Book Company, Inc., New York, 1956.

Walker, M.: "Conjugate Functions for Engineers," Oxford University Press, London, 1933.

TABLE OF TRANSFORMATIONS OF REGIONS
(See Sec. 41)

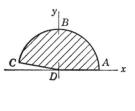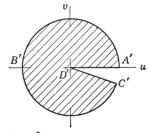

Fig. 1. $w = z^2$.

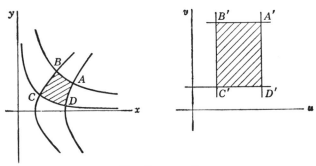

Fig. 2. $w = z^2$.

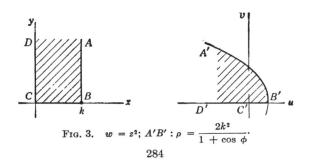

Fig. 3. $w = z^2$; $A'B' : \rho = \dfrac{2k^2}{1 + \cos \phi}$.

284

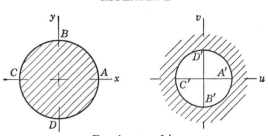

FIG. 4. $w = 1/z$.

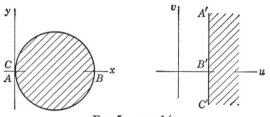

FIG. 5. $w = 1/z$.

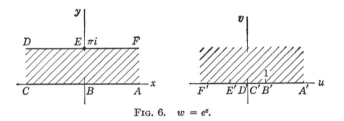

FIG. 6. $w = e^z$.

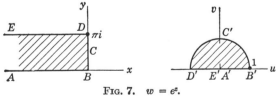

FIG. 7. $w = e^z$.

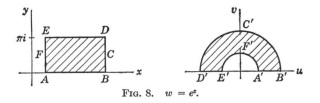

FIG. 8. $w = e^z$.

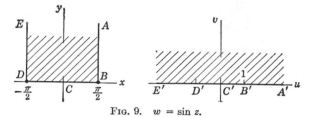

FIG. 9. $w = \sin z$.

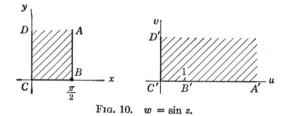

FIG. 10. $w = \sin z$.

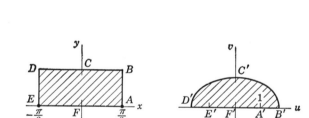

FIG. 11. $w = \sin z$; $BCD: y = k$, $B'C'D': \left(\dfrac{u}{\cosh k}\right)^{2} + \left(\dfrac{v}{\sinh k}\right)^{2} = 1.$

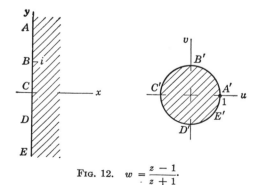

FIG. 12. $w = \dfrac{z - 1}{z + 1}.$

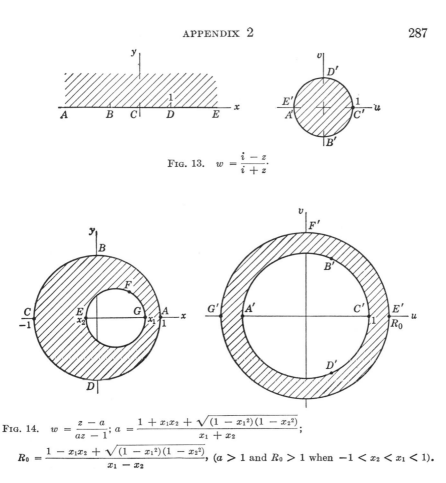

FIG. 13. $w = \dfrac{i - z}{i + z}$.

FIG. 14. $w = \dfrac{z - a}{az - 1}; \; a = \dfrac{1 + x_1 x_2 + \sqrt{(1 - x_1{}^2)(1 - x_2{}^2)}}{x_1 + x_2};$

$R_0 = \dfrac{1 - x_1 x_2 + \sqrt{(1 - x_1{}^2)(1 - x_2{}^2)}}{x_1 - x_2},$ $(a > 1$ and $R_0 > 1$ when $-1 < x_2 < x_1 < 1).$

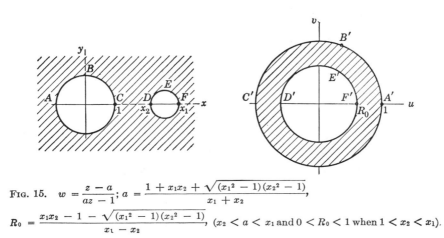

FIG. 15. $w = \dfrac{z - a}{az - 1}; \; a = \dfrac{1 + x_1 x_2 + \sqrt{(x_1{}^2 - 1)(x_2{}^2 - 1)}}{x_1 + x_2},$

$R_0 = \dfrac{x_1 x_2 - 1 - \sqrt{(x_1{}^2 - 1)(x_2{}^2 - 1)}}{x_1 - x_2},$ $(x_2 < a < x_1$ and $0 < R_0 < 1$ when $1 < x_2 < x_1).$

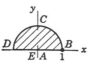
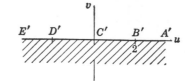

FIG. 16. $w = z + 1/z$.

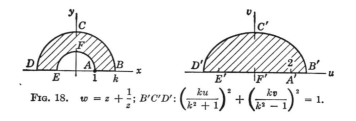

FIG. 17. $w = z + 1/z$.

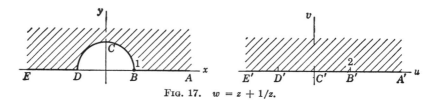

FIG. 18. $w = z + \dfrac{1}{z}$; $B'C'D'$: $\left(\dfrac{ku}{k^2 + 1}\right)^2 + \left(\dfrac{kv}{k^2 - 1}\right)^2 = 1$.

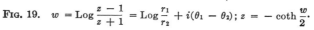
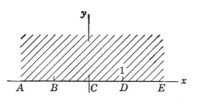
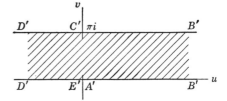

FIG. 19. $w = \operatorname{Log} \dfrac{z - 1}{z + 1} = \operatorname{Log} \dfrac{r_1}{r_2} + i(\theta_1 - \theta_2)$; $z = -\coth \dfrac{w}{2}$.

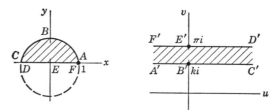

FIG. 20. $w = \operatorname{Log} \dfrac{z - 1}{z + 1}$; ABC: $x^2 + y^2 - 2y \cot k = 1$.

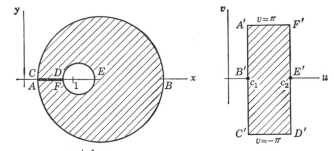

FIG. 21. $w = \operatorname{Log} \dfrac{z+1}{z-1}$; centers of circles at $z = \operatorname{coth} c_n$, radii: $\operatorname{csch} c_n\,(n = 1, 2)$.

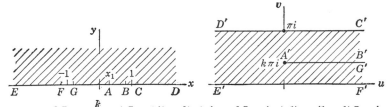

FIG. 22. $w = k \operatorname{Log} \dfrac{k}{1-k} + \operatorname{Log} 2(1-k) + i\pi - k \operatorname{Log}(z+1) - (1-k)\operatorname{Log}(z-1)$,
$x_1 = 2k - 1$.

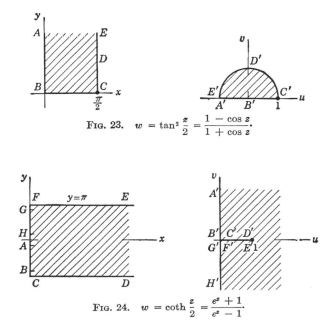

FIG. 23. $w = \tan^2 \dfrac{z}{2} = \dfrac{1 - \cos z}{1 + \cos z}$.

FIG. 24. $w = \operatorname{coth} \dfrac{z}{2} = \dfrac{e^z + 1}{e^z - 1}$.

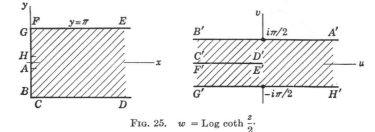

FIG. 25. $w = \text{Log coth } \dfrac{z}{2}$.

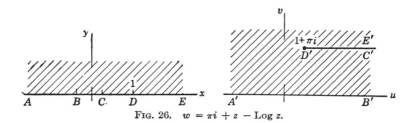

FIG. 26. $w = \pi i + z - \text{Log } z$.

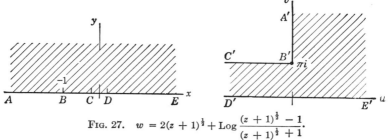

FIG. 27. $w = 2(z + 1)^{\frac{1}{2}} + \text{Log } \dfrac{(z + 1)^{\frac{1}{2}} - 1}{(z + 1)^{\frac{1}{2}} + 1}$.

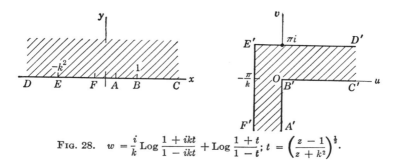

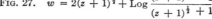

FIG. 28. $w = \dfrac{i}{k} \text{Log } \dfrac{1 + ikt}{1 - ikt} + \text{Log } \dfrac{1 + t}{1 - t}; \; t = \left(\dfrac{z - 1}{z + k^2} \right)^{\frac{1}{2}}$.

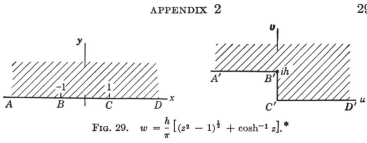

FIG. 29. $w = \dfrac{h}{\pi}\left[(z^2 - 1)^{\frac{1}{2}} + \cosh^{-1} z\right].$*

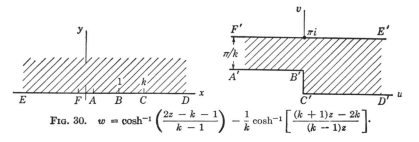

FIG. 30. $w = \cosh^{-1}\left(\dfrac{2z - k - 1}{k - 1}\right) - \dfrac{1}{k}\cosh^{-1}\left[\dfrac{(k + 1)z - 2k}{(k - 1)z}\right].$

* See Exercise 4, Sec. 98.

INDEX